GLOBE FEARON

LITERATURE

- *Purple Level* -

Upper Saddle River, New Jersey
www.globefearon.com

PROGRAM REVIEWERS

Kathy Babigian, Coordinator, Tioga Literacy Center, Fresno, California
Pat Bartholomew, M.A., Reading Specialist, Milton, Ohio
Jennifer Dilks-Mundt, English Teacher, Brant Rock, Massachusetts
Ann Fitzgerald, M.A., Education Director, Southshire Community School,
  North Bennington, Vermont
Pat Miller, M.A., Reading/English/Language Arts Supervisor, Prince Georges County
  Public Schools, Maryland
Artie P. Norton, English Teacher, Suffern, New York
Timothy Rasinski, Professor of Curriculum and Instruction, Kent State University, Kent, Ohio
Cynthia Saska, M.A., Professor of English, University of Texas, San Antonio, Texas
Margaret-Mary Sulentic, Ph.D., Assistant Professor of Literacy, Department of Curriculum
  and Instruction, University of Southern Mississippi, Hattiesburg, Mississippi
Dr. Helen W. Taylor, Director of Programs K-12 Curriculum and Instruction, Portsmouth City
  Public Schools, Virginia

CONSULTANTS

Dr. Virginia Bryg; Josephine Gemake, Ph.D.; Alfred Schifini, Ph.D.; Deborah Walker; Robert
  Wandberg, Ph.D.

Supervising Editor/Team Leader: Karen McCollum
Editors: Ayanna Taylor, Amy Greenberg, Theresa McCarthy
Editorial Developer: Pearson Education Development Group
Marketing Assistant: Kate Krimsky
Production Editor: Travis Bailey
Associate Production Editors: Amy Benefiel, Alia Lesser
Senior Designer: Angel Weyant
Manufacturing Buyer: Mark Cirillo
Cover and Interior Design/Production: Pearson Education Development Group
Photo Research: Pearson Education Development Group

ABOUT THE COVER

The Workers on the Cart, Alberto Magnelli. Musee National d'Art Moderne, Paris, France/
Bridgeman Art Library. Alberto Magnelli was a pioneer in abstract art, the defining style of the
20th century. Abstractionists have challenged themselves to capture the unseen aspects of nature
and the heroic capacities of individuals and society. What does Magnelli's painting of workers on a
cart say about the human spirit?

ISBN 0-130-23562-8

Printed in the United States of America
2 3 4 5 6 7 8 9 10   05 04 03 02 01

1-800-848-9500
www.globefearon.com

Preview

UNIT 1 *Looking at Love*

Writing • Vocabulary • Grammar, Usage, and Mechanics
Speaking and Listening • Critical Thinking • Effective Studying
• Test Preparation

UNIT 2 *The Unknown*

UNIT 3 Suspense

Writing • Vocabulary • Grammar, Usage, and Mechanics
Speaking and Listening • Critical Thinking • Effective Studying
• Test Preparation

UNIT 4 Discoveries

UNIT 5 Heroes

Writing • Vocabulary • Grammar, Usage, and Mechanics
Speaking and Listening • Critical Thinking • Effective Studying
• Test Preparation

UNIT 6 *Generations*

References

HOW TO USE THIS BOOK ▬▬▬▬

Welcome to *Globe Fearon Literature*. As you read this textbook, you will learn about many new worlds. By reading literature you can experience the past and the future, and you can learn about people—how they feel and how they think.

To get the most out of this book, you will need to become an active reader. Active readers think about reading materials before they begin, during, and after they read.

TIPS FOR IMPROVING YOUR READING

Before You Read
- Think about the title of the selection. What does it tell you about the topic? What do you already know about the topic?
- Determine the genre of the selection. For example—if the selection is a poem, ask yourself, "How will this be different from reading an essay or short story?"
- Set a purpose for reading. What do you think you will learn by reading this selection?

As You Read
- Predict what you think will happen next. Then pause occasionally and ask yourself if your predictions were correct.
- Form questions about what you are reading. For example, ask yourself, "What idea is the author trying to convey?"
- When you encounter a word you are unfamiliar with, use the help that Globe Fearon Literature gives you. Difficult words are defined at the bottom of the page they appear on.

After You Read
Consider the following questions:
- Did the selection end the way you anticipated?
- What did you learn from reading this selection?
- How does this selection relate to others you have read?

THE BOOK IS ORGANIZED TO HELP YOU

Your literature book has been organized into units. Each unit is introduced with a piece of fine art and a quote. Look at these pages. What do you think this unit will be about?

The next two pages of the unit give you a preview of what to expect. These two pages will help you set the stage for reading and understanding the selections. You may want to refer back to these pages as you read through the unit.

The "Focus On" feature gives you some tips to help you understand specific genres of literature, such as fiction or poetry You will notice that each Model selection has blue notes in the margin. These are study hints to help you read actively. The notes relate back to the "Focus On" feature. The notes will help you identify key elements of the genre. Later, you can look for similar elements in other selections as you read independently.

Before each selection, you will be introduced to a reading skill, a literary skill, and a writing activity. The reading skill will help you understand what you are reading. The literary skill will call your attention to elements of literature. The writing activity will help you relate the literature to your own life.

There are review questions at the end of each selection. These questions help you think about what you have just read. They will also help you relate this selection to others that you may have read.

Globe Fearon Literature was created for you. Reading literature can be one of the most rewarding experiences you can ever have. There are new worlds to explore and exciting people to meet. It's all here. So, let's begin. . .

Looking at Love

How do I love thee? Let me count the ways.
—Elizabeth Barrett Browning

Birthday, Marc Chagall, 1915. Oil on cardboard, 31³/₄ × 39¹/₄".
Collection, The Museum of Modern Art, New York
Acquired through the Lillie P. Bliss Bequest.

Looking at Love

Why do writers always write about love? Why do singers always sing about love?

It must be because love is a theme always on people's minds.

Do we know, however, what love is? The poet Elizabeth Barrett Browning was able to count the ways she loved someone.

Are we all so lucky? Does everyone find love? What happens when we lose love? Is love for friends, family, and the world a totally different kind of love from what is felt between a boy and a girl?

The selections in this unit are about love and its power over people.

■ LOVE FOUND

What do we mean by "true love"? Are there different kinds of love? "The Locket" and "The Kiss" explore these questions.

"Love," an African American folk poem, describes love as "a lizard" and calls it "the great fall." The poem is simple and direct, yet powerful.

Poet Phyllis Gotlieb knows she loves someone in "First Person Demonstrative," but she is unable to do all the little things people expect from someone in love. Elizabeth Coatsworth reintroduces romance in "What Is Once Loved," while Carole Gregory Clemmons in "Spring" thinks she will be more realistic about "second" love.

"Luckiest Time of All" was the time Mrs. Pickens met Mr. Pickens. "Stepping Out with My Baby" tells about some of the foolish things we do for love.

A classic love story in the English language is William Shakespeare's *The Tragedy of Romeo and Juliet*. An adaptation appears here. Romeo and Juliet are bound by love. Their families are divided by hate. Love is found, but lost in death.

■ LOVE LOST
You can become depressed when you are apart from someone you love or love begins to unravel, as Maya Angelou shows in the poem "Greyday." Mari Evans tries to cope with not being able to communicate with someone you love in "Here—Hold My Hand."

Waring Cuney in "Finis" sees love ending and warns that the next time he will not love "overmuch." In "Housecleaning," Nikki Giovanni would end a relationship in the same way she cleans house. Mari Evans in "Where Have You Gone" feels lonely and hurt.

■ LOVE FOR FRIENDS AND FAMILY
Shakespeare reappears in M.E. Kerr's "Where Are You Now, William Shakespeare?" However, this is not the Shakespeare of *Romeo and Juliet*. The characters are even younger than Romeo and Juliet were. As you read it, ask who the characters really love.

■ LOVE FOR THE WORLD
The last two poems in the unit, "I Dream A World" by Langston Hughes and "Reflections" by Vanessa Howard, talk about love (and hate) between different kinds of people rather than just love between individuals. How do you translate your feelings of love for individuals into love for people of different races and countries?

What is love? Come, discover!

The Letter, Mary Cassatt. Courtesy of the Library of Congress

READING FOCUS

Draw Conclusions An author often uses a character's words or thoughts to reveal something about that character's emotions. You can use what the author tells you, and what you know from your own experience, to draw conclusions about a character's emotions. Drawing conclusions helps you better understand characters and what motivates them.

POINT OF VIEW

Have you ever read a story and wished you knew what the characters were thinking?

If the author tells the story as an outside observer, he or she can reveal different characters' actions and thoughts. If the author assumes a role in the story, he or she can tell the story only from the perspective of that role.

The position from which a story is told is called **point of view**. Telling the story as an outside observer is called **third-person** point of view. If a story is written in third-person point of view, the author uses the pronouns *he*, *she*, and *they* rather than *I*. The storyteller in third-person point of view is an observer of the action but not a participant in it.

Third-person writing can be very informative. The author can choose to tell you about different characters' thoughts and help you to understand their motives.

As you read both "The Locket" and "The Kiss," ask yourself:

1. How do you know the story's point of view?
2. How does the story's point of view contribute to your understanding of the characters?

WRITING CONNECTION

Think of something interesting or amusing that recently happened to you or someone you know. Write three sentences about it using the third-person point of view. Remember to use the pronouns *he*, *she*, and *they*.

The Locket

ADAPTED

by Kate Chopin

PART 1

One night in autumn a few men were gathered about a fire on the slope of a hill. They belonged to a small group of Confederate forces and were waiting for orders to march. Their gray uniforms were old and worn out. One of the men was heating something in a tin cup over the fire. Two were lying down a little distance away, and a fourth was trying to read a letter and had come close to the light. He had unbuttoned a good bit of his flannel shirt.

"What's that you have around your neck, Ned?" asked one of the other men.

Ned—or Edmond—did not reply. He went on reading his letter.

"Is it your sweetheart's picture?"

"It's no girl's picture," said the man at the fire. He had removed his tin cup and was stirring its contents with a small stick. "It's a charm—some kind of lucky piece that's supposed to keep him out of trouble. That's how come Frenchy got promoted and never got a scratch since he's been here. Hey, French! Am I right?" Edmond looked up from his letter.

"What is it?" he asked.

"Isn't that a lucky charm you got around your neck?"

"It must be, Nick," returned Edmond with a smile. "I don't know how I could have gone through this year and a half without it."

The letter he was reading had made Edmond heartsick and homesick. He stretched out on his back and looked straight up at

---

Confederate (kun FED uh raht) during the Civil War, a supporter of
the South

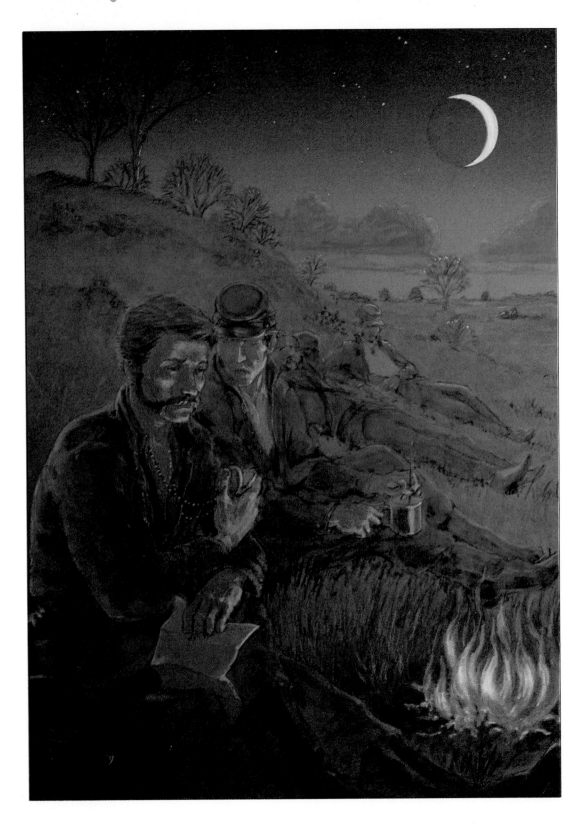

the blinking stars. But he was not thinking of them nor of anything but a certain spring day when a girl was saying good-bye to him. He could see her as she took from her neck the locket that she put around his own. It was an old-fashioned locket bearing pictures of her father and mother with their names and the date of their marriage. It was her most precious earthly possession. Edmond could feel again the folds of the girl's soft white gown. He could picture her as she circled her fair arms about his neck. Her sweet face, pained by the thought of parting, appeared before him as vividly as life. He turned over, burying his face in his arm. There he lay, still and motionless.

The darkness of night with its semblance of peace settled upon the camp. He dreamed that the fair Octavie brought him a letter. He had no chair to offer her and was pained and embarrassed at the condition of his clothing. He was ashamed of the poor food he had to offer her.

He dreamed of a serpent coiling around his throat. When he tried to grasp it, it glided away from his clutch. Then he was awakened by a great deal of noise.

"Get up! You! Frenchy!" Nick was shouting in his face. There was what appeared to be a scramble and a rush rather than any smooth movement. The hillside was alive with clatter and motion. Lights suddenly appeared among the pines. In the east the dawn was unfolding out of the darkness. Its glimmer was still dim in the plain below.

"What's it all about?" wondered a big black bird perched in the top of the tallest tree. He was an old and wise bird, yet he was not wise enough to guess what it was all about. So all day long he kept blinking and wondering.

The noise reached far out over the plain and across the hills. It awoke the little babes that were sleeping in their cradles. The smoke curled up toward the sun and shadowed the plain. The stupid birds thought it was going to rain, but the wise one knew better.

"They are children playing a game," thought he. "I shall know more about it if I watch long enough."

---

semblance (SEHM bluns) outward appearance or show

By night they had all vanished away with their noise and smoke. Then the old bird fluffed his feathers. At last he had understood! With a flap of his great, black wings he shot downward, circling toward the plain.

A man was picking his way across the plain. He was dressed as a priest. His mission was to bring the consolations of religion to any of the men who might still be alive. A young man accompanied him, carrying a bucket of water.

There were no wounded here. They had all been taken away. But the retreat had been hurried, and the vultures and the priest would have to look to the dead.

---

consolations (KAHN suh LAY shunz) the acts of comforting in time of sorrow

There was a soldier—a mere boy—lying with his face to the sky. His hands were clutching the grass on either side. His fingernails were stuffed with earth and bits of grass that he had gathered in his despairing grasp upon life. His musket was gone. He was hatless and his face and clothing were dirty. Around his neck hung a gold chain and locket. The priest, bending over him, removed it from the dead soldier's neck. He had grown used to the terrors of war and could face them without flinching, but its sorrows, somehow, always brought the tears to his old, dim eyes.

The church bells were ringing half a mile away. The priest and the young man knelt and murmured together the evening prayers and a prayer for the dead.

PART 2

Back in Louisiana, where Octavie lived, the peace and beauty of a spring day had fallen upon the earth like a blessing. Along the leafy road, which skirted the narrow stream near her house, rumbled an old-fashioned carriage, much the worse for hard and rough usage over country roads and lanes. The fat, black horses went in a slow, measured trot in spite of the constant urging on the part of the fat coachman. Within the vehicle were seated the fair Octavie and her old friend and neighbor, Judge Pillier. He had come to take her for a morning drive.

Octavie wore a plain black dress. A narrow belt held it at the waist. Its sleeves were gathered into close-fitting wristbands. She had discarded her hoop skirt and appeared not unlike a nun. Beneath the folds of her clothing was the old locket. She never displayed it now. It had returned to her sanctified in her eyes. It seemed to have been made precious as material things sometimes are by being forever identified with a significant moment in one's life.

A hundred times she had read over the letter with which the locket had come back to her. No later than that morning she had again pored over it. As she sat beside the window, smoothing the letter out upon her knee, heavy and spiced odors stole in to her with the songs of birds and the humming of insects in the air.

---

musket (MUHS kut) an old type of firearm, now replaced by the rifle
sanctified (SANK tuh fyd) set apart as holy

She was so young and the world was so beautiful that there came over her a sense of unreality as she read again and again the priest's letter. He told of that autumn day drawing to its close, with the gold and the red fading out of the west, and the night gathering its shadows to cover the faces of the dead. Oh! She could not believe that one of those dead was her own! A spasm of resistance and rebellion seized and swept over her. Why was the spring here with its flowers and its warm breath if he was dead! Why was she here! What further had she to do with life and the living!

Octavie had experienced many such moments of despair, but a blessed resignation had never failed to follow. This feeling of acceptance then fell upon her like a mantle and enveloped her.

"I shall grow old and quiet and sad like poor Aunt Tavie," she murmured to herself as she folded the letter and put it back in the desk. Already she gave herself a modest little air like her Aunt Tavie. She walked with a slow glide, unconsciously imitating Mademoiselle Tavie, whom some youthful sorrow had robbed of earthly joys while leaving her with the illusions of youth.

As she sat in the old carriage beside the father of her dead beloved, Octavie again felt the terrible sense of loss. The soul of her youth clamored for its rights, for its share in the world's glory and joy. She leaned back and drew her veil a little closer about her face. It was an old black veil of her Aunt Tavie's. A whiff of dust from the road had blown in. She wiped her cheeks and her eyes with her soft, white handkerchief, a homemade handkerchief, made from one of her old fine petticoats.

"Will you do me the favor, Octavie," requested the judge in his usual courteous tone, "to remove that veil. It seems out of harmony, somehow, with the beauty and promise of the day."

The young girl obediently yielded to her old companion's wish. She unpinned the black veil from her bonnet, folded it neatly, and laid it upon the seat in front of her.

"Ah! That is better, far better!" he said in a tone expressing great relief. "Never put it on again, dear." Octavie felt a little hurt, as if he wished to keep her from sharing the sorrow that had been

---

resignation (reh zig NAY shun) patient acceptance

placed upon all of them. Again she drew forth the old homemade handkerchief.

They had left the big road and turned into a level plain which used to be an old meadow. There were clumps of thorn trees here and there, gorgeous in their spring beauty. Some cattle were grazing off in the distance in spots where the grass was tall and thick. At the far end of the meadow was the towering lilac hedge that lined the lane leading to Judge Pillier's house. The scent of its heavy blossoms met them like a soft and tender embrace of welcome.

As they neared the house the old gentleman placed an arm around the girl's shoulders. Turning her face up to him he said, "Do you not think that on a day like this, miracles might happen? When the whole earth is full of life, does it not seem to you, Octavie, that heaven might for once relent and give us back our dead?" He spoke very low, softly, and impressively. In his voice was an unusual trembling, and there was excitement in every line of his face. She gazed at him with eyes that were full of pleading and a certain terror of joy.

They had been driving through the lane with the towering hedge on one side and the open meadow on the other. The horses had somewhat quickened their lazy pace. As they turned into the avenue leading to the house, a whole choir of birds suddenly sang a melodious greeting from their leafy hiding places.

There was the old gray house with its sloping roof. Amid the blur of green, and dimly, she saw familiar faces and heard voices as if they came from far across the fields. Suddenly Edmond was holding her. She felt the beating of his heart against her and the agonizing joy of his kisses. The spirit of life and the awakening spring had given back the soul to her youth and told her to rejoice.

It was many hours later that Octavie pulled out the locket and looked at Edmond with a questioning appeal in her glance.

"It was the night before a battle," he said. "In the hurry of the fight, and the falling back the next day, I never missed it till the battle was over. I thought of course I had lost it in the heat of the struggle, but it was stolen."

---

relent (ruh LEHNT) to become gentler or more compassionate

"Stolen," she shuddered. She thought of the dead soldier with his face uplifted to the sky in an agony of prayer.

Edmond said nothing, but he thought of his messmate—the one who had lain far back in the shadow, the one who had said nothing.

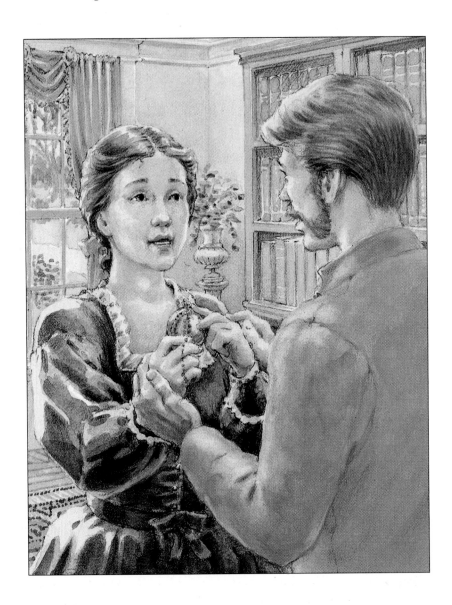

The *Kiss*

ADAPTED

by Kate Chopin

It was still quite light out of doors, but inside, with the curtains drawn and the low fire sending out a dim, uncertain glow, the room was full of deep shadows.

Brantain sat in one of these shadows. It had overtaken him and he did not mind. The darkness gave him the courage to keep his eyes fastened as ardently as he liked upon the girl who sat in the firelight.

She was very good-looking, with the fine, rich coloring that true brunettes often have. She was quite calm, as she gently stroked the satiny coat of the cat that lay curled in her lap. She occasionally sent a slow glance into the shadow where her companion sat. They were talking low, of ordinary things that plainly were not the things that occupied their thoughts.

She knew that he loved her. He was an honest fellow who didn't have enough guile to conceal his feelings, and he had no desire to do so. For the past two weeks he had sought her company eagerly and persistently. She was confidently waiting for him to declare himself and she meant to accept him. The rather unattractive Brantain was enormously rich. Even though she didn't especially like him, she liked and required all the things that his wealth could give her.

During one of the pauses between their talk of the last tea and the next party, the door opened. A young man whom Brantain knew quite well entered. The girl turned her face toward him. A stride or two brought him to her side, and he bent over her chair. Before she could suspect what he would do, for she did not realize that he had not seen her visitor, he pressed a warm kiss upon her lips.

---

ardently (AR dent lee) with great enthusiasm and eagerness
guile (GYL) the use of cunning; slyness

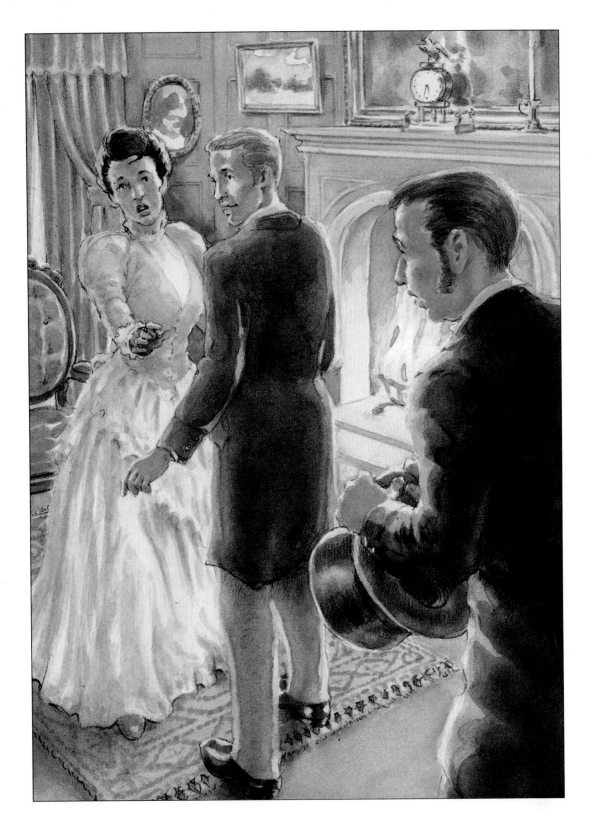

Brantain slowly arose. The girl arose, too, but quickly. The newcomer stood between them, a little amusement and some challenge struggling with the confusion in his face.

"I believe," stammered Brantain, "I see that I have stayed too long. I—I had no idea—that is, I must wish you good-bye." He was holding his hat with both hands, and probably did not see that she was extending her hand to him. Her presence of mind had not completely deserted her, but she could not have trusted herself to speak.

After Brantain had gone, the other man spoke. "Hang me if I saw him sitting there, Nattie! I know it must have been awkward for you. But I hope you'll forgive me this once—this very first break. Why, what's the matter?"

"Don't touch me! Don't come near me," she returned angrily. "What do you mean by entering the house without ringing?"

"I came in with your brother, as I often do," he answered coldly, explaining himself. "We came in the side way. He went upstairs and I came in here hoping to find you. The explanation is simple enough and ought to prove to you that I didn't mean any harm. But do say that you forgive me, Nathalie," he pleaded, softening.

"Forgive you! You don't know what you are talking about. Let me pass. It depends on—a good deal whether I ever forgive you."

At that next party which she and Brantain had been talking about, she approached the wealthy young man with a delicious frankness of manner when she saw him there.

"Will you let me speak to you a moment or two, Mr. Brantain?" she asked with a sweet but perturbed smile. He seemed extremely unhappy. But when she took his arm and walked away with him, seeking a quiet corner, the expression on his face changed. A ray of hope seemed to mingle with his look of almost comical misery. She was apparently very outspoken.

"Perhaps I should not have approached you, Mr. Brantain. But—but, oh, I have been very uncomfortable, almost miserable, since what happened the other afternoon. When I thought how you might have misinterpreted it, and believed things . . ." As she spoke, hope was clearly overcoming the misery in Brantain's round, guileless face. Nathalie continued, "Of course, I know it is

---

stammered (STAM urd) in speaking, repeated the same sound without meaning to

perturbed (pur TURBD) greatly disturbed or alarmed

nothing to you, but for my own sake I do want you to understand that Mr. Harvy is an intimate friend of long standing. Why, we have always been like cousins—like brother and sister, I may say. He is my brother's most intimate associate and often thinks that he is entitled to the same privileges as the family. Oh, I know it is ridiculous, uncalled for, to tell you this—it is undignified, even." She was almost weeping as she spoke. "But it makes so much difference to me what you think of—of me." Her voice had grown very low and agitated. The misery had all but disappeared from Brantain's face.

"Then you do really care what I think, Miss Nathalie? May I call you Miss Nathalie?" They turned into a long, dim corridor that was lined on either side with tall, graceful plants. They walked slowly to the very end of it. When they turned to walk back, Brantain's face was radiant and hers was triumphant.

◆ ◆ ◆ ◆ ◆ ◆ ◆ ◆

Harvy was among the guests at the wedding. He sought Nathalie out in a rare moment when she stood alone.

"Your husband," he said, smiling, "has sent me over to kiss you."

A quick blush suffused her face and round polished throat. "I suppose it's natural for a man to feel and act generously on an occasion of this kind. He tells me he doesn't want his marriage to interrupt that pleasant closeness that has existed between you and me. I don't know what you've been telling him," said Harvy with an insolent smile, "but he has sent me here to kiss you."

She felt like a chess player who, by the clever handling of his pieces, sees the game going his way. Her eyes were bright and tender with a smile as they glanced up into his. Her lips looked hungry for the kiss which they invited.

"But, you know," he went on quietly, "I didn't tell him so—it would have seemed ungrateful—but I can tell you. I've stopped kissing women. It's dangerous."

Well, she had Brantain and his million left. A person can't have everything in this world. It was a little unreasonable of her to expect it.

---

suffused (suh FYOOSD) spread through or over, as with a color, liquid, or light

insolent (IN suh lunt) deliberately rude or insulting

Review the Selection

UNDERSTAND THE SELECTION

Recall

1. Who finds the locket and returns it to Octavie?

2. What is the relationship between Edmond and Judge Pillier?

3. Why does Nathalie want to marry Brantain?

Infer

4. What must the thief of the locket have believed about it?

5. What must the judge know that Octavie does not? How do you know?

6. What choice is Nathalie making when she scolds Harvy?

7. Describe Brantain's feelings when Nathalie tells him about her relationship with Harvy.

Apply

8. How do you feel about the soldier who stole the locket?

9. If you were Brantain, would you have believed Nathalie's explanation of her relationship to Harvy? Why?

10. Who do you think will have a happier marriage, Octavie or Nathalie? Why?

Respond to Literature

These stories suggest that "love" can mean different things to different people. Do you agree with this idea? Explain.

WRITE ABOUT THE SELECTION

Use what you have read to compare and contrast these relationships: Octavie/Edmond and Nathalie/Brantain. How would each character define "love"? Which couple will probably be happier in the future? Come up with your own definition for a successful relationship between two people.

Prewriting   List the qualities you feel are necessary for a good relationship, such as a marriage. Then brainstorm for descriptions of Octavie and Edmond as shown through their thoughts and actions. Write down any details that reveal their emotions, motivations, and hopes. Do the same for Nathalie and Brantain.

Writing   Use your prewriting notes to define a successful relationship. Then write a paragraph about each couple, comparing and contrasting their personal qualities and attitudes toward love and relationships. End with a paragraph which answers the question: which couple will be happier in the future?

Revising   Did you state your own definition of a successful relationship, such as a marriage? Did you make use of your prewriting notes to compare and contrast Octavie's and Nathalie's relationships? Whose relationship, if any, is a success according to your definition? Is this the couple you picked to have a happy future?

Proofreading   Reread what you have written and check for errors. Have you capitalized the first word of every sentence and all proper nouns?

THINK ABOUT POINT OF VIEW

The third-person point of view allows the author to observe all aspects of the story. The author can then choose to tell the reader not only what the characters are doing and saying but also what they are thinking. This helps the reader to understand their motivations.

1. Look at the paragraphs in "The Locket" in which the author tells the thoughts of the bird viewing the battle scene. What does the bird's confusion reveal to you about the scene?

2. The author describes the beauty of spring while also telling of Octavie's sorrowful thoughts. What effect does this contrast have on Octavie?

3. How would this story be different if told from Edmond's point of view?

4. Early in "The Kiss" the author reveals Nathalie's thoughts about Brantain. How does this make you feel about what she later tells him about Harvy?

5. If Nathalie had told this entire story, what might be her final line?

READING FOCUS

Draw Conclusions Do you think Brantain may ever regret marrying Nathalie? Do you think he may discover her reason for marrying him? How might he feel? Use details from the story to explain your conclusion.

DEVELOP YOUR VOCABULARY

Both of these stories use some unfamiliar vocabulary for which we have more common words. Different words that have the same meaning are called **synonyms**.

The definitions of unfamiliar words were given in the stories, but do you understand how these words are used?

Below are several sentences from the stories. Each has at least one unfamiliar word. Rewrite the sentences substituting a more common synonym or phrase for the unfamiliar word. You may have to rearrange the parts of the sentences.

1. The darkness of night with its *semblance* of peace settled upon the camp.

2. When the whole earth is full of life, does it not seem . . . that heaven might for once *relent* and give us back our dead?

3. He was an honest fellow who didn't have enough *guile* to conceal his feelings.

4. A quick blush *suffused* her face and round polished throat.

5. "I don't know what you've been telling him," said Harvy with an *insolent* smile, "but he has sent me here to kiss you."

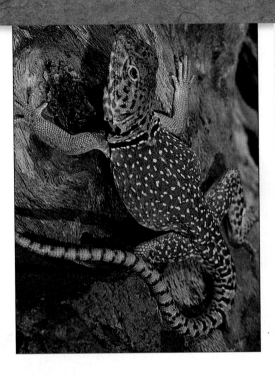

RHYME

Many, but not all, poems are written in rhyme. Why is rhyme a popular technique?

Our brains seem to remember things that are repeated. Rhyme is the repeating of the same sound, so this repetition says to us "Hey, take notice of this and remember!"

The next selection is a **folk poem**, a term that refers to poetry that has unknown origins and an unknown author. It was told among African Americans, and no doubt rhyme helped people remember its message.

The pairing of words by rhyme can help to communicate the feeling and meaning of a poem. An imaginative rhyme can make you smile or nod with immediate understanding.

As you read the folk poem, ask:

1. What are the rhymes, and where do they occur in the poem?
2. Do the rhymes occur regularly?

READING FOCUS

Understand Idioms An idiom is an expression that has a different meaning from the dictionary definition of its words. For example, if you fall for a trick, you know you don't literally fall. You can look at the context to determine another meaning.

Idioms are often used in poetry to express a particularly strong feeling, and they can enhance the overall tone of the poem. Look for idioms as you read the poem. If you are not sure whether or not an expression is an idiom, think of the dictionary definitions of the words in the phrase.

WRITING CONNECTION

Rhymes are all around us, not just in poetry. Suppose that you work for an advertising company. You have just been told to write a rhyme that advertises a product. Choose a product, and write a rhyming advertisement for it.

Love

an African American folk poem

Love is a funny thing
Shaped like a lizard,
Run down your heartstrings
And tickle your gizzard.

You can fall from a mountain,
You can fall from above,
But the great fall is
When you fall in love.

Folk Singer, Charles White. Courtesy Heritage Gallery, Los Angeles. Harry Belafonte Collection

---

gizzard (GIZ-urd) [Colloq.] the stomach; usually a humorous usage

Review the Selection

UNDERSTAND THE SELECTION

Recall

1. Love is compared to an animal in the poem. What animal is it?

2. Two parts of the body are mentioned in the poem. What are they?

3. According to the poem, what is the greatest fall of all?

Infer

4. What is the theme of the poem?

5. Why do you think love is compared to an animal?

6. What is meant by "heartstrings"? Do they really exist?

7. The poem calls love "a funny thing." What is meant by "funny"?

Apply

8. If you had to describe how love felt, what description might you use?

9. How is falling from a mountain or from "above" like falling in love?

10. Why do you think the word "fall" is used to describe what happens when you first love someone?

Respond to Literature

Do you believe people "fall" in love or is it an old-fashioned idea? Have you ever fallen in love? What did it feel like to you?

WRITE ABOUT THE SELECTION

What is love like for you? What can you compare it to?

Maybe it is like a broken-down car that will not start, a stereo set at maximum volume, or an alarm clock that always seems to go off too early. Perhaps you think love is like the flowering plant on your window sill.

What does love look like? How does it affect your attitude toward life? How does it make you feel?

Write your own description of love by comparing it with something real.

Prewriting   In the middle of a piece of paper, write down the object that you want to compare love to. Around it, cluster ideas about its connection to love.

Writing   Use the cluster to write a paragraph comparing love to this object. Make sure you make clear the connection between the object and love.

Revising   Turn your paragraph into poetry. Consider using rhyme to add emphasis or to make imaginative connections between ideas. You may prefer using free verse so that you can form lines and verses in any form. You may want to try writing a concrete poem where the lines form a recognizable shape.

Proofreading   Reread what you have written and check for spelling errors. If you are using rhyming words, a mistake in spelling could confuse the reader.

THINK ABOUT RHYME

What counts as a rhyme? Do you consider *thing* and *strings* a rhyme? Most poets would, although strictly speaking the words do not rhyme. The final *s* on *strings* makes the sounds slightly different.

1. **Poetic license** usually allows rhymes between words that "almost" rhyme. Think of an example.

2. Rhymes often occur at the end of lines, but they also can occur within the same line. Find an example of **internal** rhyme.

3. The best rhymes are those that link interesting words or ideas. What is your favorite rhyme in the poem, and why?

4. Eliminate one of the rhymes in the poem by substituting another word. Reread the poem. How does it sound now?

5. Without looking back, try to recite the poem. Which lines, if any, are easiest to remember?

READING FOCUS

Understand Idioms As you read the poem, you were able to recognize the author's use of idioms. Choose one idiom from the poem. How did the use of that idiom enhance the poem?

DEVELOP YOUR VOCABULARY

A **noun** is a word that names a person, place, idea, or object. A **verb** is a word that expresses an action or state of being. Poets often use both forms of a word in a poem to make a connection between two ideas or feelings.

In the poem you have just read, *fall* is used as both a noun and a verb. Which *fall* is a noun and which is a verb?

In the sentences below, decide whether the italicized word in the sentence pairs is a noun or verb. Find the dictionary definition that fits the meaning of the word in the sentence. Then, use both words in original sentences.

1. **a.** You can *fall* from a mountain.
   b. The great *fall* is love.

2. **a.** She took a *turn* down the street.
   b. I *turn* cartwheels when I see her.

3. **a.** *Love* is a book with blank pages.
   b. We *love* creating new things.

4. **a.** The *shape* of my feelings is square.
   b. I *shape* my life around you.

Focus ON POETRY

*M*any people do not like poetry. Others think poetry is still the world's most powerful form of communication—whether it be a sixteenth-century Shakespearean sonnet or a modern age lyric by Stevie Wonder.

The poet uses language in a very different way from prose writers. To understand a poet's message, you need to learn the elements of poetry.

Character   Character in poetry refers to the speaker. If the poet uses *I*, you usually learn about the poet him- or herself. The poem can be very personal, as in "Finis." However, sometimes the *I* is a speaker very different from the poet.

Often the poet addresses an unidentified "you," as in "Where Have You Gone." This person is an absent character whom we know only through the speaker.

Imagery   Poets often use language to appeal to any or all of your five senses. They use images to help you see, hear, smell, feel, or taste what they are writing about.

The author of "Greyday" uses images from the Christian religion of "a crown of thorns" and "a shirt of hair" to help you feel the heaviness she is describing.

Theme   The idea or meaning of a poem is its theme. The poems "Reflections" and "I Dream A World" both have themes about the world. In the first, the poet expresses the idea that there is only hate, not love, in the world. The author of the second poem might agree with that idea, but he also expresses hope that "love will bless the earth."

Tone   The poet conveys to you an attitude when writing. That attitude is called tone. Tone is a clue to meaning.

Maybe the tone is earnest yet light-hearted, as in "First Person Demonstrative." The tone also can be sad, as in "Finis."

You can determine a poem's tone by simply asking yourself, "How does this poem make me feel?" Do not be afraid to give more than one answer, for often tone creates many feelings.

Rhyme   Rhyme is repetition of the same sound. If it comes at the end of a line, it is called **end rhyme**. If it comes within a single line, it is called **internal rhyme**.

End rhyme is the more common type. "Love," an African American folk poem uses it. Notice the rhyming of *lizard* and *gizzard*, and *above* and *love*.

Figures of Speech   When you use an expression that says one thing to mean something else, you are using a figure of speech. Common figures of speech are metaphor, simile, personification, and hyperbole.

The author of "Spring" talks about a "wishbone," yet she does not mean that she and her "second man" actually will find a wishbone and make wishes. "Wishbone" is a **metaphor** for the hopes that she and her partner will have.

The comparison of one thing to another through the use of *like* or *as* is a **simile**. In "I Dream a World," for example, *joy* is described as being *like a pearl*.

Another line in "I Dream a World" is an example of **personification**, or the giving of human qualities to nonhuman subjects. In this line the poet talks of a world "where wretchedness will hang its head." The poet has given a human quality to an abstract idea in order to express his idea more forcefully.

Another way to express ideas forcefully is to exaggerate by using **hyperbole**. In "First Person Demonstrative," the poet says she would rather "wrench off an arm than hug you." She uses hyperbole to exaggerate her feelings.

As you read the next selections in this unit, look for the elements of the poems. Ask yourself these questions:

1. How do the elements of poetry such as imagery and figures of speech strengthen a poem?
2. Is the theme of a poem always easy to determine? What can I do if a poem confuses me?

First Person Demonstrative

by Phyllis Gotlieb

FOCUS ON POETRY
STUDY HINTS

Can you imagine anyone heaving a brick rather than saying, "I love you?" The speaker is exaggerating her feelings, using hyperbole.

Notice the speaker's appeal to your sense of touch. She uses imagery to describe how she feels.

The speaker fears showing her emotions. She speaks in first person. Her character is frank and open.

The poet is being sarcastic, making fun of usual expressions about feelings. The tone is serious yet mocking.

The "message" is the theme of the poem. The speaker wants to make sure that the reader "gets" her main idea. If you do not, read it again, she says, in a lighthearted yet earnest tone.

I'd rather
heave half a brick than say
I love you, though I do
I'd rather
5 crawl in a hole than call you
darling, though you are
I'd rather
wrench off an arm than hug you though
it's what I long to do
10 I'd rather
gather a posy of poison ivy than
ask if you love me

so if my
hair doesn't stand on end it's because
15 I never tease it
and if my heart isn't in my mouth it's because
it knows its place
and if I
don't take a bite of your ear it's because
20 gristle gripes my guts
and if you
miss the message better get new
glasses and read it twice

---

posy (POH zee) a flower or bouquet
gristle (GRIS ul) tough, elastic white animal tissue
gripe (GRYP) to cause sharp pain in the bowels

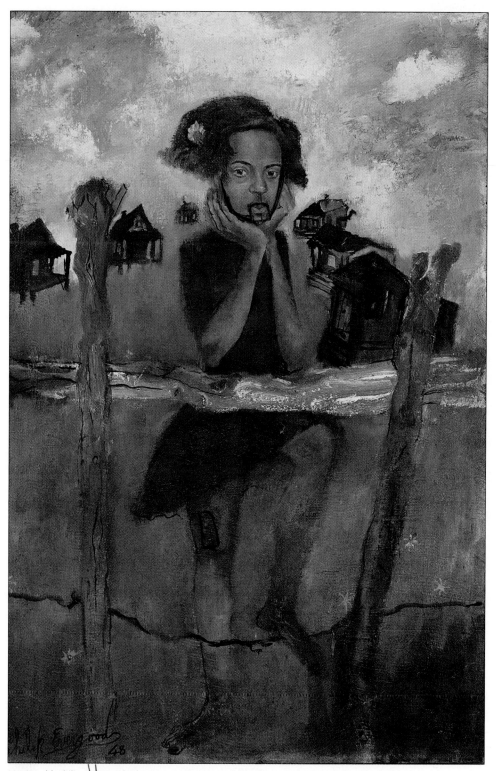

Her World, Philip Evergood. The Metropolitan Museum of Art, Arthur Hoppock Hearn Fund

Review the Selection

UNDERSTAND THE SELECTION

Recall

1. What would the speaker rather do than call someone "darling"?

2. What plant is mentioned in the poem?

3. What instructions does the speaker give at the end of the poem?

Infer

4. Does the speaker love the person to whom she is talking? Explain.

5. Why do you think poison ivy is mentioned in the poem?

6. What connects all the "if" expressions in the second half of the poem?

7. What is the "message" of the poem?

Apply

8. The theme of the poem is repeated a number of times. Point to at least three examples, and explain them.

9. Which of the statements of the theme seems clearest to you?

10. Do you think this poem was written recently, or a long time ago? Why?

Respond to Literature

Do you show your feelings? Maybe you are like the speaker in "First Person Demonstrative." Perhaps you are somewhere in between. Describe your personal style of expressing feelings.

WRITE ABOUT THE SELECTION

Phyllis Gotlieb uses humor in "First Person Demonstrative," even if the theme of the poem is serious. She exaggerates, using hyperbole to make her point. She mocks, poking fun at figurative expressions that are used to describe strong emotions.

Can you use humor to make some point about your feelings? Write a poem to express your feelings in a humorous way. You may choose a feeling other than love.

Prewriting Pick a feeling, or several feelings, you would like to write about. Write the feelings in the middle of the page. How do having these feelings make you feel? In other words, do you become strong when you are angry or afraid, or shy when you care about someone? Cluster ideas around the feeling or feelings. Think humor!

Writing Use the form of "First Person Demonstrative" to write several lines of poetry about your subject. Substitute your ideas for the poet's, if you like. Study how she uses hyperbole, and see if you can do the same.

Revising Have you used imagery? Add an image appealing to one sense, or try to strengthen any images you have.

Proofreading Writing a poem in the first person means you will be using a lot of pronouns. Reread what you have written and make sure you are using all pronouns correctly, and your verb forms agree. Also, be very careful to check the punctuation in your poem.

THINK ABOUT POETRY

Poetry shares some elements with other types of literature. However, because a poet wants to create a strong feeling with only a few words, he or she also uses special language techniques. The main characters in a poem are usually the speaker and the listener. Poets use images to appeal to their readers' senses. Poems, like stories and plays, have themes—ideas—to communicate. Poets convey their attitudes toward their subjects through tone. Rhyme is the repetition of the same sounds at the ends of words. Poets use rhyme at the end or inside lines of their poems. Figures of speech are expressions that compare two or more unlike things.

1. Who is the speaker in "First Person Demonstrative"? Who is the listener?

2. What is your favorite image in this poem? Explain.

3. What is the poem's theme?

4. What is the tone of the poem? How do you know?

5. Give an example of a figure of speech.

DEVELOP YOUR VOCABULARY

Figurative expressions are groups of words that have a special meaning. The meaning is usually different from the meanings of the individual words. Phyllis Gotlieb uses several figurative expressions in "First Person Demonstrative."

Below is a list of the figurative expressions that Gotlieb uses in her poem, and some others. What does each mean?

1. hair standing on end

2. heart in your mouth

3. keep an ear to the ground

4. look down your nose at someone

5. put your foot in your mouth

6. cross your fingers

7. to jawbone someone

8. a lump in your throat

9. catch your eye

10. bite your lip

Now write five sentences that use figurative expressions to make a point.

Learn About

The Equatorial Jungle, Henri Rousseau.
National Gallery of Art, Washington, D.C.

READING FOCUS

Compare and Contrast When you compare and contrast two different pieces of writing, you may find similarities and differences that you did not notice at first. Comparing allows you to see broader themes or similarities in tone, while contrasting may help you to notice differences in smaller details. As you read, try to find as many similarities and differences in the following two poems.

FIGURES OF SPEECH

Poetry allows you to use language in a free and creative way. Figures of speech give you a special kind of freedom. They allow you, the poet, to make connections between things that normally you might not connect.

The connections allow the reader to transfer knowledge of one thing to another. It is as though you, the writer, are carrying a torch lighting new paths for the reader.

Metaphor is one of the most common figures of speech. A **metaphor** shows the connection between two ideas without using the words "as" or "like." An example is "The sun was a golden shield hung in the sky." Other figures of speech are simile, which compares using the words *like* or *as*; personification, which gives human qualities to nonhuman things; and hyperbole, which exaggerates a quality or element.

As you read "What Is Once Loved" and "Spring," ask yourself:

1. What metaphors are used?
2. What is the purpose of the metaphors?

WRITING CONNECTION

People use figures of speech all the time, both in writing and speaking. Create your own metaphor.

What Is Once Loved

by Elizabeth Coatsworth

What is once loved
You will find
Is always yours
From that day.
Take it home
In your mind
And nothing ever
Can take it away.

Spring

by Carole Gregory Clemmons

the second man I love,
we'll find the wishbone
and make our wishes,
I won't even try for the strongest end,
because this time when the bone breaks
either way I'll be in

Review the Selection

UNDERSTAND THE SELECTION

Recall

1. What "is always yours" in "What Is Once Loved"?

2. Where should you keep what "is always yours"?

3. Who will be at the other end of Carole Gregory Clemmons's "wishbone"?

Infer

4. Do you think Elizabeth Coatsworth is talking about lost love or an existing love in "What Is Once Loved"?

5. Explain the phrase "home in your mind" in "What Is Once Loved."

6. What does a wishbone have to do with love in the poem "Spring"?

7. Explain why the speaker says she will not "try for the strongest end" in "Spring".

Apply

8. Does *what* in "What Is Once Loved" refer to people, things, or both?

9. Why do you think Carole Gregory Clemmons chose the title "Spring"?

10. Explain the last line "either way I'll be in" in the poem "Spring."

Respond to Literature
Can you *always* carry in your mind "what is once loved," or is that an exaggeration of the power of memory?

WRITE ABOUT THE SELECTION

What is it like to carry something "in your mind"? It is an odd expression. You can never carry a "thing" in your mind, just abstract thoughts.

Poets try to make abstract thoughts, particularly feelings, become real. You will do the same. How can you turn a feeling into something real? Try using a metaphor; it might help.

Prewriting Brainstorm to find a feeling to describe. Choose one of your ideas, and jot down a few notes about it. Think about what you associate it with: perhaps a specific color, a special place, a wonderful song, or a valued possession. Write about experiences with the feeling, give examples, and compare it to other things.

Writing Use your notes to describe the feeling. Try to write in poetry form, but use prose if you can not.

Revising Have you used a metaphor to describe the feeling? Try to add one if you have not. Make your ideas clear by using specific words and vivid phrases. Eliminate any dull, boring, or overused phrasing.

Proofreading Reread what you have written and check for mistakes in verb-subject agreement. Singular nouns take singular verbs, and plural nouns take plural verbs. Be careful with punctuation at the end of lines if you wrote a poem. You can use punctuation more creatively in poetry, but do not confuse your readers.

THINK ABOUT FIGURES OF SPEECH

Carole Gregory Clemmons used a metaphor to relate love to a wishbone in "Spring." She also could have used a **simile**, which is distinguished from a metaphor by the use of the words *like* or *as*: "Love is *like* a wishbone."

Phyllis Gotlieb used hyperbole, a figure of speech, again and again in her poem "First Person Demonstrative."

A fourth common figure of speech is **personification**. Human qualities are given to a nonhuman subject in the following example: *The broom stared at my empty hands.*

1. What human qualities are given to the broom in the example above?

2. How can personification be used to describe a car or something a car does?

3. Use a simile to express the kind of love Phyllis Gotlieb describes in "First Person Demonstrative. "

4. Do you think hyperbole is used in "What Is Once Loved"? Think back to your answer to the discussion question in "Review the Selection."

5. Use a metaphor to describe weather.

READING FOCUS

Compare and Contrast As you read "What Is Once Loved" and "Spring," you were able to look for similarities and differences between the two poems. In what ways are the poems similar? In what ways are they different?

DEVELOP YOUR VOCABULARY

A **contraction** is a shortened form of two words. One or more letters have been omitted, and these are replaced by an apostrophe (').

> *Examples:* **he** + **is** = **he's**
> **they** + **will** = **they'll**

Only one contraction requires a spelling change:

> **will** + **not** = **won't**

Write the two words that have been joined, or contracted, to form the italicized contractions.

1. *We'll* find the wishbone.

2. I *won't* even try for the strongest end.

3. Either way *I'll* be in.

4. *I'd* rather heave a brick than say I love you.

5. If my hair *doesn't* stand on end *it's* because I never tease it.

6. If I *don't* take a bite of your ear *it's* because gristle gripes my guts.

Write an original paragraph or poem that uses five contractions.

Learn About

Reading Focus

Identify the Author's Purpose Writers have many reasons for putting words on paper, including a need to express themselves. Most text, though, is written either to describe, entertain, inform, or persuade, or for a combination of these. You can understand the author's purpose by looking at the word choice, tone, and—of course—subject matter. As you read, think about what the author's purpose may be. Jot down details in the selection that reveal the author's purpose.

DIALECT

Dialect is a way of speaking that is different from standard English, or the language spoken in the United States. Dialect is the form of the language that is used among a certain group or only in a certain place. Dialects may vary from region to region of a country. For example, people from Maine may use words or pronunciations not used by natives of Texas. Some fiction writers use dialect to create colorful speech. This technique helps give life and personality to the characters in a story. As you read "Luckiest Time of All," notice the southern dialect spoken by Mrs. Elzie F. Pickens. Try to "hear" her talking as you read.

Ask yourself:

1. How does Mrs. Pickens' dialect make her a more realistic and interesting character?
2. What does the use of dialect tell you about the setting?
3. How would the story be different if Mrs. Pickens spoke standard English?

WRITING CONNECTION

Think of someone you know who speaks in a dialect or in some other unique way. Write a paragraph in the "voice" of that person. Then write how the dialect adds a dimension or uniqueness.

Luckiest Time of All
from The Lucky Stone

by Lucille Clifton

Mrs. Elzie F. Pickens was rocking slowly on the porch one after-noon when her Great-granddaughter, Tee, brought her a big bunch of dogwood blooms, and that was the beginning of the story.

"Ahhh, now that dogwood reminds me of the day I met your Great-granddaddy, Mr. Pickens, Sweet Tee.

"It was just this time, spring of the year, and me and my best friend Ovella Wilson, who is now gone, was goin to join the Silas Greene. Usta be a kinda show went all through the South, called it the Silas Greene show. Somethin like the circus. Me and Ovella wanted to join that thing and see the world. Nothin wrong at home or nothin, we just wanted to travel and see new things and have high times. Didn't say nothin to nobody but one another. Just up and decided to do it.

"Well, this day we plaited our hair and put a dress and some things in a croksack and started out to the show. Spring day like this.

"We got there after a good little walk and it was the world, Baby, such music and wonders as we had never had seen! They had everything there, or seemed like.

"Me and Ovella thought we'd walk around for a while and see the show before goin to the office to sign up and join.

"While we was viewin it all we come up on this dancin dog. Cutest one thing in the world next to you, Sweet Tee, dippin and movin and head bowin to that music. Had a little ruffly skirt on itself and up on two back legs twistin and movin to the music. Dancin dancin dancin till people started throwin pennies out of they pockets.

"Me and Ovella was caught up too and laughin so. She took a penny out of her pocket and threw it to the ground where that dog was dancin, and I took two pennies and threw-em both.

"The music was faster and faster and that dog was turnin and turnin. Ovella reached in her sack and threw out a little pin she had won from never being late at Sunday school. And me, laughin and all excited, reached in my bag and threw out my lucky stone!

---

plaited (PLAT ihd) braided
croksack, variation of *croker sack* (KRO kur sak) a bag of rough cloth
   or burlap

"Well, I knew right off what I had done. Soon as it left my hand it seemed like I reached back out for it to take it back. But the stone was gone from my hand and Lord, it hit that dancin dog right on his nose!

"Well, he lit out after me, poor thing. He lit out after me and I flew! Round and round the Silas Greene we run, through every place me and Ovella had walked before, but now that dancin dog was a runnin dog and all the people was laughin at the new show, which was us!

"I felt myself slowin down after a while and I thought I would turn around a little bit to see how much gain that cute little dog was makin on me. When I did I got such a surprise! Right behind me was the dancin dog and right behind him was the finest fast runnin hero in the bottoms of Virginia.

"And that was Mr. Pickens when he was still a boy! He had a length of twine in his hand and he was twirlin it around in the air just like the cowboy at the Silas Greene and grinnin fit to bust.

"While I was watchin how the sun shined on him and made him look like an angel come to help a poor sinner girl, why, he twirled that twine one extra fancy twirl and looped it right around one hind leg of that dancin dog and brought him low.

"I stopped then and walked slow and shy to where he had

---

bottoms (BAH tumz) low-lying land along a river
twine (TWYN) a thin rope with several strands

picked up that poor dog to see if he was hurt, cradlin him and talkin to him soft and sweet. That showed me how kind and gentle he was, and when we walked back to the dancin dog's place in the show he let the dog loose and helped me to find my stone. I told him how shiny black it was and how it had the letter *A* scratched on one side. We searched and searched and at last he spied it!

"Ovella and me lost heart for shows then and we walked home. And a good little way, the one who was gonna be your Great-granddaddy was walkin on behind. Seein us safe. Us walkin kind of slow. Him seein us safe. Yes." Mrs. Pickens' voice trailed off softly and Tee noticed she had a little smile on her face.

"Grandmama, that stone almost got you bit by a dog that time. It wasn't so lucky that time, was it?"

Tee's Great-grandmother shook her head and laughed out loud.

"That was the luckiest time of all, Tee Baby. It got me acquainted with Mr. Amos Pickens, and if that ain't luck, what could it be! Yes, it was luckier for me than for anybody, I think. Least mostly, I think it."

Tee laughed with her Great-grandmother though she didn't exactly know why.

"I hope I have that kind of good stone luck one day," she said.

"Maybe you will someday," her Great-grandmother said.

And they rocked a little longer and smiled together.

---

acquainted (uh KWAYN tid) known to one another

AUTHOR BIOGRAPHY
Lucille Clifton (1936–   )

When (Thelma) Lucille Clifton was a little girl growing up in Depew, New York, she already understood the importance of literature. That was because of her parents, neither of whom had finished elementary school. However, her father often told his four children stories, especially about his ancestors. Her mother wrote poetry filled with feeling, which she read to her children. Lucille Clifton has said, "From Mama I knew one could write as a way to express oneself."

Clifton is best known for her poetry and her children's books. She says her writing is often inspired by her own six children: Sidney, Fredrica, Channing, Gillian, Graham, and Alexia.

Clifton's work is centered on the African American family. She is concerned about the destruction of its youth. She believes that husbands and fathers are necessary family members. Her characters often portray strong and loving women. She says, "I am not interested if anyone knows whether or not I am familiar with big words. I am interested in trying to render big ideas in a simple way."

Review the Selection

UNDERSTAND THE SELECTION

Recall

1. Who does Elzie tell her story to?

2. Why do Elzie and Ovella want to join the Silas Greene show?

3. What does Amos look like in the sunshine?

Infer

4. Why might Ovella have thrown her Sunday-school pin to the dog rather than money?

5. Why does Elzie call Amos a "fast run-nin hero"?

6. Why might Elzie's lucky stone have the letter A scratched on it?

7. Why do Ovella and Elzie "lose heart" for the show and go home?

Apply

8. What words might Amos use to describe Elzie? Why?

9. Name some objects that you or other people think are lucky.

10. What type of marriage do you think the Pickenses have? How does it compare to your ideas about what marriage should be?

Respond to Literature

Does Elzie's first impression of Amos Pickens last through the years? Do you think love like this can happen in real life?

WRITE ABOUT THE SELECTION

How do you think Amos Pickens would tell the story of meeting his future wife at the Silas Greene show? Would he be as impressed with her as she was with him? Pretend to be a writer assigned to interview Amos Pickens about love at first sight. Write a brief magazine article about the interview with Amos.

Prewriting   Re-read the part of the story that tells what happens when Elzie first sees Amos. Think about how the same incident might seem to Amos. Brainstorm to make a quick list of questions to ask Amos, including what he observed about her actions and her personal qualities.

Writing   Use the questions from your brainstorming list to write answers from Amos's point of view. Try using some dialect in your writing, since Amos might speak the same way Elzie does. Then write several paragraphs about the Pickens's relationship. Use quotes from Amos in the article.

Revising   Look again at the original story to re-check your facts. Can you use more descriptive words or details to make your paragraphs more interesting? Did you use the pronouns *I* and *me* to speak as Amos? If you have used dialect, try reading aloud or to a partner to make sure it sounds realistic.

Proofreading   Read through your paragraphs and check for errors. If you have misspelled words on purpose for the dialect, make sure you have spelled them as you want them to sound.

THINK ABOUT DIALECT

Dialect is a regional way of speaking that is different from standard English in vocabulary, grammar, and pronunciation. In "Luckiest Time of All" Elzie F. Pickens, who is an elderly woman of rural Virginia, speaks in dialect.

1. Find several words used by Mrs. Pickens that might be unfamiliar to someone from a different region of the country.

2. Words may also be pronounced differently in dialect. Point out several examples in this story.

3. Mrs. Pickens's great-granddaughter doesn't speak the same dialect. Why might this be so?

4. How does the use of dialect bring the events of the story and the character of Mrs. Pickens to life?

READING FOCUS

Identify the Author's Purpose As you read "Luckiest Time of All," you thought about the author's purpose in writing the story. What did you conclude is the author's purpose? List three details from the story that support your conclusion.

DEVELOP YOUR VOCABULARY

Antonyms are words with the opposite or nearly opposite meaning. *Rich* and *poor*, are antonyms. So are *before* and *after*. In the first sentence of "Luckiest Time of All," Mrs. Pickens was rocking slowly. An antonym for *slowly* is *quickly*. Replacing *slowly* with *quickly* would give the phrase an opposite meaning.

Think of a word that is the antonym of the bold word in each sentence below. Then choose one sentence with the antonym as a story starter. Write a short story, keeping in mind that the events and outcome should be different from the selection.

1. Usta be a kinda show went all through the **South**, called it the Silas Greene show.

2. The music was **faster** and **faster** and that dog was turnin and turnin.

3. And a good little way, the one who was gonna be your Great-granddaddy was walkin on **behind**.

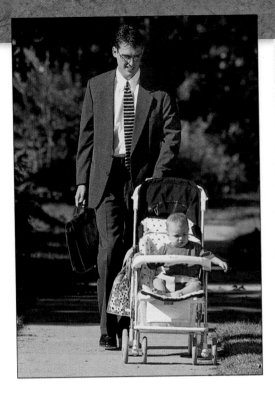

POINT OF VIEW

Point of View is the position from which a story is told. If a story is being told by a character in the story, this is called *first-person point of view*. The character refers to himself or herself as *I* or *me*, and can only tell what he or she experiences, thinks, or knows.

In *third-person point of view*, the narrator is someone outside the story who observes and tells what happens. Sometimes the third-person storyteller is *omniscient*, or all-knowing. The narrator knows everything about the characters—even what they think and feel. In a *limited* third-person point of view, the storyteller knows only the thoughts and feelings of one character.

As you read the next selection, ask yourself these questions:

1. What is the narrator's point of view?
2. How would the story be different if told from a different viewpoint?

WRITING CONNECTION

Write two paragraphs that describe your experiences at school so far today. Write one paragraph using first-person point of view and the other using third-person omniscient point-of-view.

READING FOCUS

Distinguish Fact From Opinion A **fact** is a statement that can be proven to be true. An **opinion** is a judgment that cannot be proven true or false. For example, in "Luckiest Time of All," it was a fact that the dancing animal was a dog, but it was an opinion that the dog was cute. Cuteness cannot be proven because it depends on each person's idea of what is cute and what isn't. Before you read this selection, make two columns on a sheet of paper, one for facts and one for opinions. As you read, jot down the facts and opinions you notice.

Stepping Out with My Baby

by Paul Reiser

Finally we arrive at the mailbox—an exhausting block and a half from home. Dizzy with the victory of arriving at our destination in more or less one piece, I reach into my pocket, retrieve the now sweaty envelopes, and am about to toss them into the mailbox when I hear a voice. It's my wife's voice, echoing in my head.

"Talk to him."

"Hmm?" I say automatically, totally accepting that my wife might in fact be physically standing next to me, just for a follow-up evaluation on my performance.

"Talk to him. Explain to him what you're doing." The voice in my head suggests.

Sometimes I forget that part- talking to my child. Actually *being* with him. When I'm in charge of the kid, I tend to either stare at him like he's a television or drift totally into a world of my own, running through my list of things-I-have-to-do-later-when-I'm-not-taking-care-of-the-kid. Or take the job so seriously I become blinded by the severity of the responsibility, and panic. What I

---

exhausting (eg ZAW sting) very tiring
destination (des tuh NAY shun) a place to which one is going
automatically (aw tuh MAT ihk lee) happening in a regular way
   without planning
severity (suh VAIR uh tee) great strictness or harshness

seem to miss is the middle ground- the part where you share, teach, learn, play-the part you can actually enjoy.

"Right. Talk to him. I'll do that. Thanks." I say to myself, and the voice of the Nice Lady in My Head leaves me alone again.

"So." I say to my buckled-up Beautiful Boy. "This is a mailbox."

And in response, he takes a hearty bite out of his little red corduroy clown's terry-cloth head.

"See? Daddy's going to put these letters into the mailbox. See? . . . What else can I tell you . . . The mailbox is blue."

When in doubt, mention the color. They can't get enough of colors, these kids.

"It's a blue mailbox."

Another ferocious bite-and-tug almost removes the corduroy clown's left ear. Clearly the boy is not that interested- I'll just mail the letters.

"Explain to him how it works."

"I tried."

"Try again."

"All right, all right. Quit yelling."

Fortunately, no one sees or hears this violent exchange in my head. (See what I mean? They think I am the guy-with-this-kid, and in fact I'm not only hearing voices but barking back at them.)

"We put the letters in the mailbox, and then the mailman comes and gets them."

Talking to your baby is a lot like being on a first date; you feel like you're either saying too little or too much.

"The postal system was invented by Benjamin Franklin. In Philadelphia. He also invented bifocals."

Probably too much.

"The mailman takes the letters and puts them in a big bag and then he takes them to where they're going. See, this one goes to Aunt Ellen, who sent you that itchy sweater you hate, and this one goes to the Electric Company so they don't shut off our electricity and force us out of our home."

A little too heavy.

"Forget that. That will never happen."

Then, remembering that Demonstrating is always better than

---

ferocious (fuh ROH shus) very fierce or savage
bifocals (BY foh kulz) eyeglasses with parts to correct both near vision and far vision

Explaining. I unbuckle him, scoop him up, and illustrate my letter-mailing technique.

"What you want to do is: Pull down the handle, open the mailbox's mouth, and then you *flick* the letters in. You want to get that nice flicking motion in your wrist . . . And then you pull the mouth open-and-closed a few times, to make sure the letters went down. A lot of people will tell you that doesn't do anything. They're wrong. You *must* check. Otherwise the mailbox will chew up your letter and stick it in a corner where no one can find it for years and years and years."

My son smiles. I pull the handles up and down again. He seems to enjoy the squeaky noise. Who said mailboxes aren't a dynamite activity for youngsters? As we prepare for our return voyage, I wonder if I left anything out.

"Now, you may notice, it says here they pick up at eleven A.M., but between you and me it says the same thing on every mailbox in town at the same time, so I say just throw it in whenever you feel like it-it makes no difference. But you know what? You probably won't be mailing things by yourself for a while, so forget that. The main thing for you to remember, I would say, is: The box is blue. It's a big shiny blue box with a squeaky blue mouth."

As I buckle him back in, my son gives me one of those magnificent, otherworldly smiles, and looks at me as if to say, "Dad, I don't know what you're talking about, but you seem like a very nice man."

---

illustrate (IL uh strayt) to make clear by giving an example
technique (tek NEEK) a way of doing something

Review the Selection

UNDERSTAND THE SELECTION

Recall

1. How far from home is the mailbox?

2. What happens to the father when he takes the parenting job too seriously?

3. What does the father do with the mailbox that the baby seems to like?

Infer

4. Who is "the Nice Lady" in the father's head?

5. Why are the envelopes sweaty when the father takes them from his pocket?

6. Do you think the father has other children? Explain your answer.

7. Why does the father think of the block-and-a-half walk as a "voyage"?

Apply

8. Do you think explaining or demonstrating is a better way to teach? Explain.

9. What responsibility have you been given that made you nervous at first?

10. What have you taught a baby or younger child to do? How did you do it?

Respond to Literature

What do you think will happen the next time Paul Reiser takes his son for a walk? Will he still be as anxious? Will he still talk the same way to the baby?

WRITE ABOUT THE SELECTION

Paul Reiser tried to show and tell his son in a clear and simple way how to operate a mailbox. Write a numbered list, in order, of the steps needed to operate another simple machine or appliance, such as a toaster, a blender, a washing machine, or a TV set. Keep your directions as brief and clear as possible.

Prewriting   First, decide what object you are going to write about. Choose something with only a few necessary steps for operation. Then, visualize step-by-step what you do to make it work. Think through it again and jot down the steps.

Writing   Give your instruction list a title, such as *How to Operate a Toaster*. Write down your steps in the order you would do them. Make sure each step describes only one action. Make sure you describe the entire process from beginning to end.

Revising   Carefully read through your instructions, picturing yourself doing each step. Are your instructions clear? Have you left out any steps in the process? Could any of the steps be explained more briefly?

Proofreading   Make sure that every step of your instructions is written in a complete sentence, which begins with a capital letter and ends with a period.

THINK ABOUT POINT OF VIEW

You can determine the point of view in a story by looking at the pronouns the narrator uses. *I* and *me* are always used by a first-person narrator, who is a character in the story. The third-person narrator is not a character in the story and therefore uses *he, she, they, it, them, him, her.*

1. Describe the point of view of "Stepping Out With My Baby."

2. If Paul Reiser's baby son could tell the story of the trip to the mailbox, what point of view would the story have?

3. What do you call nonfiction writing by a person telling about his or her real life? Which point of view is most likely to be used in this type of writing?

4. If a bystander observed and described what happened at the mailbox, what would be the point of view?

5. Rewrite a paragraph of the story so that it is told from the third-person omniscient viewpoint.

READING FOCUS

Distinguish Fact from Opinion As you read "Stepping Out With My Baby," you listed some of the facts and opinions you found. On a separate paper, write two paragraphs. Provide the facts in the first paragraph and the opinions in the second.

DEVELOP YOUR VOCABULARY

A **root word** is a word, or a part of a word, that is used to form other words. Often finding the root word can help you figure out the meaning of the entire word.

An example is *physically*. You might not know what it means, but you might know what the root word, *physical*, means. *Physical* means "of or about the body"; *physically* is an adverb that tells that someone reacts with his or her body.

Write the root of each of the following words. Check definitions in a dictionary if you are not sure. Then figure out the meaning of the entire word, and use each word in a sentence.

1. destination
2. automatically
3. evaluation
4. responsibility
5. fortunately
6. exchange
7. bifocals
8. activity
9. beautiful
10. unbuckle

Learn About

FIGURES OF SPEECH

Figures of speech are expressions that follow a particular form. Two important figures of speech are similes and metaphors. Similes and metaphors are comparisons. They point out similarities between things that ordinarily do not seem similar. **Similes** use *like* or *as* to point out a comparison—*eyes like stars*—while **metaphors** compare without special words—*her eyes are stars*.

Figures of speech add punch to a poem or literary passage; they make literature more powerful and effective.

William Shakespeare is considered by many the greatest English-language writer who ever lived. What makes him stand out among writers is his creative use of language. Among other things, Shakespeare includes many figures of speech in his plays and poems.

As you read the adaptation of *Romeo and Juliet*, ask yourself:

1. How are similes and metaphors used?
2. How do figures of speech enrich the play?

WRITING CONNECTION

Use a simile or metaphor to describe your feelings about reading Shakespeare. Try writing several different ones, and then choose your favorite.

READING FOCUS

Recognize Imagery An author uses imagery to create a vivid picture in the reader's mind. Imagery uses words that will appeal to the reader's sense of sight, smell, taste, hearing, or touch. By appealing to your senses, the author brings details in a story to life and allows you to experience them the way the characters in the story do. Look for imagery as you read this play, and try to recognize which of your senses it appeals to.

from

The Tragedy of
ROMEO and JULIET

ADAPTED   *by William Shakespeare*

*T*he *Tragedy of Romeo and Juliet* opens with a chorus providing background that serves as an introduction to the play.

The story takes place in Verona, Italy in the 1500s. Two socially prominent families, the Capulets and the Montagues, have had a long-running feud, and lately new violence has broken out.

The chorus provides some foreshadowing. "A pair of star-crossed lovers," from the opposing families, will lose their lives because of the feud. The only hopeful note is that through their deaths, the families' conflict will end.

The lovers are, of course, Romeo and Juliet. Romeo is the son of Montague; Juliet, the daughter of Capulet. We meet Romeo first—not during the fight that opens the play, but afterwards. He has been off by himself, and he is depressed. He loves a woman, Rosaline, who, unfortunately, does not seem to love him.

A friend, Benvolio, tells him that Rosaline is not so pretty. He promises to show him some much prettier women if he will go to a banquet that evening. He must go in disguise, though, for the banquet is hosted by Capulet.

We meet Juliet as she is preparing for the banquet. Her father is hosting it partly as a way to introduce his daughter to Verona society. She is 14, and her parents think that it is time for her to marry. They hope to match her with Paris, a handsome young count. Paris has already declared his love for her. Juliet promises to consider him.

We join the action at the banquet, Act I, Scene 5. Use this list of characters to help you identify the players.

CHARACTERS

THREE SERVING MEN	FRIAR LAWRENCE
CAPULET	PARIS
SECOND CAPULET	PARIS' PAGE
ROMEO	BALTHASAR, *Romeo's man*
TYBALT	THREE WATCHMEN
JULIET	A PRINCE, *with* ATTENDANTS
NURSE	LADY CAPULET
BENVOLIO	MONTAGUE
MERCUTIO	

ACT I, SCENE 5

A hall in CAPULET'S *house.*

[*Enter* CAPULET, *his* WIFE, JULIET, TYBALT, NURSE, *and all the* GUESTS *and* GENTLEWOMEN *to the* MASKERS.]

CAPULET: Welcome, gentlemen! Ladies that have their toes
　　　Unplagued with corns will walk a bout[1] with you.
　　　Ah, my mistresses, which of you all
　　　Will now deny to dance? She that makes dainty.[2]
　　　She I'll swear hath[3] corns. Am I come near ye[4] now?
　　　Welcome, gentlemen! I have seen the day
　　　That I have worn a visor and could tell
　　　A whispering tale in a fair lady's ear.
　　　Such as would please. 'Tis gone, 'tis gone, 'tis gone.
　　　You are welcome, gentlemen! Come, musicians, play.

[*Music plays, and they dance.*]

　　　A hall,[5] a hall! Give room! And foot it, girls.
　　　More light, you knaves,[6] and turn the tables up,
　　　And quench the fire; the room is grown too hot.
　　　Ah, sirrah, this unlooked-for sport comes well.
　　　Nay,[7] sit; nay, sit, good cousin Capulet;
　　　For you and I are past our dancing days.
　　　How long is't now since last yourself and I
　　　Were in a mask?

SECOND CAPULET: By'r[8] Lady, thirty years.

CAPULET: What, man? 'Tis not so much, 'tis not so much:
　　　'Tis since the nuptial of Lucentio.
　　　Come Pentecost[9] as quickly as it will,
　　　Some five-and-twenty years, and then we masked.

SECOND CAPULET: 'Tis more, 'tis more. His son is elder, sir;
　　　His son is thirty.

---

nuptial (NUP shul) wedding
[1]**walk a bout:** dance a turn
[2]**makes dainty:** hesitates
[3]**hath:** (*archaic*) has
[4]**ye:** (*archaic*) you
[5]**a hall:** clear the hall for dancing
[6]**knave:** (*archaic*) serving boy or male servant; also sometimes a dishonest, deceitful person; a rogue
[7]**nay:** (*archaic*) no
[8]**by'r:** contraction of "by your"
[9]**Pentecost:** Christian holiday fifty days after Easter, marking the descent of the Holy Spirit upon Christ's apostles

CAPULET: Will you tell me that?

    His son was but a ward two years ago.

ROMEO [*to a* SERVINGMAN]: What lady's that which doth
      enrich the hand

    Of yonder knight?

SERVINGMAN: I know not, sir.

ROMEO: O, she doth teach the torches to burn bright!

    It seems she hangs upon the cheek of night

    As a rich jewel in an Ethiop's[10] ear—

    Beauty too rich for use, for earth too dear!

    So shows a snowy dove trooping with crows

    As yonder lady o'er[11] her fellows shows.

    The measure done, I'll watch her place of stand

    And, touching hers, make blessed my rude hand.

    Did my heart love till now? Forswear[12] it, sight!

    For I ne'er[13] saw true beauty till this night.

TYBALT: This, by his voice, should be a Montague.

    Fetch me my rapier, boy. What! Dares the slave

    Come hither, covered with an antic face,[14]

    To fleer[15] and scorn at our solemnity?

    Now, by the stock and honor of my kin,

    To strike him dead I hold it not a sin.

CAPULET: Why, how now, kinsman? Wherefore[16] storm you so?

TYBALT: Uncle, this is a Montague, our foe,

    A villain, that is hither come in spite

    To scorn at our solemnity this night.

CAPULET: Young Romeo is it?

TYBALT: 'Tis he, that villain Romeo.

CAPULET: Content thee, gentle coz,[17] let him alone.

---

ward (WAWRD) a minor, or someone under the age of 18 or 21
rude (ROOD) crude or rough; also, impolite
rapier (RAY pee ur) sword
hither (H*ITH* ur) to, toward, or here
[10]**Ethiop:** old term for a Black person; short for Ethiopian
[11]**o'er:** shortened form of "over"
[12]**forswear:** (*archaic*) deny
[13]**ne'er:** shortened form of "never"
[14]**antic face:** (*archaic*) strange or funny; an "antic face" is a mask
[15]**fleer:** (*archaic*) sneer or mock
[16]**wherefore:** (*archaic*) why
[17]**coz:** usually "cousin" but used here as a term of address for any relative.
    Capulet is Tybalt's uncle.

A bears him like a portly gentleman,[18]
And, to say truth, Verona brags of him
To be a virtuous and well-governed youth.
I would not for the wealth of all this town
Here in my house do him disparagement.
Therefore be patient; take no note of him.
It is my will, the which if thou respect,
Show a fair presence and put off these frowns,
An ill-beseeming[19] semblance for a feast.

[Meanwhile, Romeo and Juliet meet.]

ROMEO: If I profane with my unworthiest hand
    This holy shrine, the gentle sin is this:
    My lips, two blushing pilgrims, ready stand
    To smooth that rough touch with a tender kiss.
JULIET: Good pilgrim, you do wrong your hand too much,
    Which mannerly devotion shows in this;
    For saints have hands that pilgrims' hands do touch,
    And palm to palm is holy palmers' kiss.
ROMEO: Have not saints lips, and holy palmers too?
JULIET: Ay, pilgrim, lips that they must use in prayer.
ROMEO: O, then, dear saint, let lips do what hands do!
    They pray; grant thou, lest faith turn to despair.
JULIET: Saints do not move,[20] though grant for prayers' sake.
ROMEO: Then move not while my prayer's effect I take.
    Thus from my lips, by thine my sin is purged.   *[Kisses her.]*
JULIET: Then have my lips the sin that they have took.
ROMEO: Sin from my lips? O trespass sweetly urged![21]
    Give me my sin again.   *[Kisses her.]*

---

portly (PAWRT lee) heavy, but dignified
virtuous (VUR choo us) honorable
disparagement (dih SPAR ij munt) discredit, insult
semblance (SEM bluns) appearance
profane (proh FAYN) show disrespect for holy things
shrine (SHRYN) place of worship or devotion
palmers (PAHM urz) pilgrims
lest (LEST) for fear that
purge (PURJ) get rid of
[18]**A . . . gentleman:** He behaves like a dignified gentleman.
[19]**ill-beseeming:** (*archaic*) inappropriate
[20]**move:** initiate involvement in earthly affairs
[21]**O . . . urged!:** Romeo is saying, in substance, that he is happy. Juliet calls
  his kiss a sin, for now he can take it back—by another kiss.

JULIET: You kiss by th' book.

NURSE: Madam, your mother craves a word with you.

ROMEO: What is her mother?

NURSE: Marry, bachelor,
> Her mother is the lady of the house,
> And a good lady, and a wise and virtuous.
> I nursed her daughter that you talked withal[22]
> I tell you, he that can lay hold of her
> Shall have the chinks.[23]

ROMEO: Is she a Capulet?
> O dear account! My life is my foe's debt.[24]

BENVOLIO: Away, be gone; the sport is at the best.

ROMEO: Ay,[25] so I fear; the more is my unrest.

CAPULET: Nay, gentlemen, prepare not to be gone;
> We have a trifling foolish banquet towards.[26]
> Is it e'en[27] so?[28] Why then, I thank you all.

---

[22]**withal:** (*archaic*) with

[23]**chinks:** (*archaic*) money

[24]**My life . . . debt:** Since Juliet is a Capulet, Romeo's life is at the mercy of the enemies of his family

[25]**ay:** (*archaic*) yes

[26]**towards:** being prepared

[27]**e'en:** even

[28]**Is . . . so?:** Is it the case that you really must leave?

I thank you, honest gentlemen. Good night.
More torches here! Come on then; let's to bed.
Ah, sirrah,[29] by my fay,[30] it waxes late:
I'll to my rest.   [*Exit all but* JULIET *and* NURSE.]
JULIET: Come hither, nurse. What is yond[31] gentleman?
NURSE: The son and heir of old Tiberio.
JULIET: What's he that now is going out of door?
NURSE: Marry, that, I think, be young Petruchio.
JULIET: What's he that follows here, that would not dance?
NURSE: I know not.
JULIET: Go ask his name—if he is married,
My grave is like to be my wedding bed.
NURSE: His name is Romeo, and a Montague,
The only son of your great enemy.
JULIET: My only love, sprung from my only hate!
Too early seen unknown, and known too late!
Prodigious birth of love it is to me
That I must love a loathèd enemy.
NURSE: What's this? What's this?
JULIET: A rhyme I learnt even now.
Of one I danced withal.   [*One calls within, "Juliet."*]
NURSE: Anon,[32] anon!
Come, let's away; the strangers all are gone.   [*Exit.*]

ACT II

The second act begins again with the chorus. It tells us that
Romeo has replaced his love for Rosaline with love for Juliet, and
that Juliet is "alike bewitched." It reminds us of the conflict
between the families, but notes that "passion lends them [Romeo
and Juliet] power."

Benvolio and another of Romeo's friends, Mercutio, discuss
Romeo's new state of mind. They, and Romeo, have snuck into
Capulet's orchard. Then comes one of the most famous love scenes
in literature, the "balcony meeting" between Romeo and Juliet.

---

prodigious (pruh DIJ us) monstrous
loathe (LOH*TH*) detest, hate
[29]**sirrah:** old form of address, usually said to show anger
[30]**fay:** faith
[31]**yond:** yonder; at a distance
[32]**anon:** (*archaic*) immediately, at once; also, very soon

SCENE 2

CAPULET'S *orchard.*

ROMEO [*coming forward*]: He jests at scars that never felt a wound.
    [*Enter* JULIET *at a window.*]

    But soft! What light through yonder window breaks?
    It is the East, and Juliet is the sun!
    Arise, fair sun, and kill the envious moon.
    Who is already sick and pale with grief
    That thou her maid art[33] far more fair than she.
    Be not her maid, since she is envious.
    Her vestal livery is but sick and green,
    And none but fools do wear it. Cast it off.
    It is my lady! O, it is my love!
    O, that she knew she were!
    She speaks, yet she says nothing. What of that?
    Her eye discourses; I will answer it.
    I am too bold; 'tis not to me she speaks:
    Two of the fairest stars in all the heaven,
    Having some business, do entreat her eyes
    To twinkle in their spheres[34] till they return.
    What if her eyes were there, they in her head?
    The brightness of her cheek would shame those stars
    As daylight doth a lamp; her eyes in heaven
    Would through the airy region stream so bright
    That birds would sing and think it were not night.
    See how she leans her cheek upon that hand,
    O, that I were a glove upon that hand,
    That I might touch that cheek!
JULIET: Ay me!
ROMEO: She speaks.
    O, speak again, bright angel, for thou art
    As glorious to this night, being o'er my head,
    As is a wingèd messenger of heaven

---

vestal (VES tul) virtuous, pure
livery (LIV uh ree) clothing worn by servants
discourses (dis KAWRS iz) utters, talks, communicates
entreat (en TREET) beg, ask earnestly
[33]**art:** (*archaic*) is
[34]**spheres:** orbits

Unto the white-upturnèd wond'ring eyes
Of mortals that fall back to gaze on him
When he bestrides the lazy puffing clouds
And sails upon the bosom of the air.

JULIET: O Romeo, Romeo! Wherefore art thou Romeo?[35]
Deny thy father and refuse thy name:
Or, if thou wilt[36] not, be but sworn my love,
And I'll no longer be a Capulet.

ROMEO: [*Aside*] Shall I hear more, or shall I speak at this?

JULIET: 'Tis but thy name that is my enemy.
Thou art thyself, though not[37] a Montague.
What's Montague? It is nor hand, nor foot,
Nor arm, nor face. O, be some other name
Belonging to a man.
What's in a name? That which we call a rose
By any other word would smell as sweet.
So Romeo would, were he not Romeo called.
Retain that dear perfection which he owes[38]
Without that title. Romeo, doff thy name:
And for thy name, which is no part of thee,
Take all myself.

ROMEO: I take thee at thy word.
Call me but love, and I'll be new baptized:
Henceforth I never will be Romeo.

JULIET: What man art thou, thus bescreened in night,
So stumblest on my counsel?[39]

ROMEO: By a name
I know not how to tell thee who I am.
My name, dear saint, is hateful to myself
Because it is an enemy to thee.
Had I it written, I would tear the word.

JULIET: My ears have yet not drunk a hundred words

---

bestride (bih STRYD) sit or mount
bosom (BUUZ um) breast
retain (rih TAYN) hold or keep
doff (DOF) take off or discard
bescreened (bih SKREEND) hidden
[35]**Wherefore . . . Romeo?:** Why are you Romeo, a Montague?
[36]**wilt:** (*archaic*) will
[37]**though not:** even if you were not
[38]**owes:** owns, possesses
[39]**counsel:** here, secret thoughts or plans

Of thy tongue's uttering, yet I know the sound.
Art thou not Romeo, and a Montague?

ROMEO: Neither, fair maid, if either thee dislike.

JULIET: How camest thou hither, tell me, and wherefore?
The orchard walls are high and hard to climb,
And the place death, considering who thou art,
If any of my kinsmen find thee here.

ROMEO: With love's light wings did I o'erperch[40] these walls;
For stony limits cannot hold love out,
And what love can do, that dares love attempt.
Therefore thy kinsmen are no stop to me.

JULIET: If they do see thee, they will murder thee.

ROMEO: Alack[41] there lies more peril in thine eye
Than twenty of their swords! Look thou but sweet,
And I am proof[42] against their enmity.

JULIET: I would not for the world they saw thee here.

ROMEO: I have night's cloak to hide me from their eyes;
And but[43] thou love me, let them find me here.
My life were better ended by their hate
Than death proroguèd, wanting of thy love.

JULIET: By whose direction found'st thou out this place?

ROMEO: By love, that first did prompt me to inquire.
He lent me counsel, and I lent him eyes.
I am no pilot; yet, wert thou as far
As that vast shore washed with the farthest sea,
I should adventure[44] for such merchandise.

JULIET: Thou knowest the mask of night is on my face;
Else would a maiden blush bepaint my cheek
For that which thou hast heard me speak tonight.
Fain[45] would I dwell on form—fain, fain deny
What I have spoke; but farewell compliment![46]
Dost thou love me? I know thou wilt say "Ay";

---

enmity (EN muh tee) hate
prorogued (proh ROHGD) postponed
[40]**o'erperch:** shortened form of "overperch," meaning "fly over"
[41]**alack:** exclamation of surprise or disappointment
[42]**proof:** here, protected with armor
[43]**and but:** unless
[44]**adventure:** here, risk as a voyage
[45]**fain:** (*archaic*) with eagerness, gladly
[46]**compliment:** here, etiquette

And I will take thy word. Yet, if thou swear'st,
Thou mayst prove false. At lovers' perjuries,
They say Jove[47] laughs. O gentle Romeo,
If thou dost love, pronounce it faithfully.
Or if thou thinkest I am too quickly won,
I'll frown and be perverse and say thee nay,
So thou wilt woo; but else, not for the world.
In truth, fair Montague, I am too fond,
And therefore thou mayst think my havior[48] light:
But trust me, gentleman, I'll prove more true
Than those that have more cunning to be strange.[49]
I should have been more strange, I must confess,
But that thou overheard'st, ere[50] I was ware,
My truelove passion. Therefore pardon me,
And not impute this yielding to light love,
Which the dark night hath so discovered.

ROMEO: Lady, by yonder blessed moon I vow,
That tips with silver all these fruit-tree tops—

JULIET: O, swear not by the moon, th' inconstant moon,
That monthly changes in her circle orb,
Lest that thy love prove likewise variable.

ROMEO: What shall I swear by?

JULIET: Do not swear at all;
Or if thou wilt, swear by thy gracious self,
Which is the god of my idolatry,
And I'll believe thee.

ROMEO: If my heart's dear love—

JULIET: Well, do not swear. Although I joy in thee,
I have no joy of this contract[51] tonight.
It is too rash, too unadvised, too sudden;
Too like the lightning, which doth cease to be
Ere one can say it lightens. Sweet, good night!
This bud of love, by summer's ripening breath,

---

perverse (pur VURS) here, stubbornly difficult or contrary
impute (im PYOOT) charge to or blame
[47]**Jove:** supreme god in Roman mythology: also called "Jupiter"
[48]**havior:** behavior
[49]**strange:** distant and cold
[50]**ere:** before
[51]**contract:** betrothal

May prove a beauteous flow'r when next we meet.
Good night, good night! As sweet repose and rest
Come to thy heart as that within my breast!

ROMEO: O, wilt thou leave me so unsatisfied?

JULIET: What satisfaction canst thou have tonight?

ROMEO: Th' exchange of thy love's faithful vow for mine.

JULIET: I gave thee mine before thou didst request it;
    And yet I would it were to give again.

ROMEO: Wouldst thou withdraw it? For what purpose, love?

JULIET: But to be frank[52] and give it thee again.
    And yet I wish but for the thing I have.
    My bounty[53] is as boundless as the sea,
    My love as deep; the more I give to thee,
    The more I have, for both are infinite,
    I hear some noise within. Dear love, adieu!

                    [NURSE *calls within.*]

---

repose (rih POHZ) rest, or peace of mind
adieu (uh DYOO) French for "goodbye"
[52]**frank:** here, generous
[53]**bounty:** what I have to give

Anon, good nurse! Sweet Montague, be true.
Stay but a little, I will come again.   [*Exit.*]
ROMEO: O blessed, blessed night! I am afeard,
Being in night, all this is but a dream
Too flattering-sweet to be substantial.

[*Enter* JULIET *again.*]

JULIET: Three words, dear Romeo, and good night indeed.
If that thy bent of love be honorable,
Thy purpose marriage, send me word tomorrow
By one that I'll procure to come to thee,
Where and what time thou wilt perform the rite;
And all my fortunes at thy foot I'll lay
And follow thee my lord throughout the world.
NURSE [*within*]: Madam!
JULIET: I come anon.—But if thou meanest not well,
I do beseech thee—
NURSE [*within*]: Madam!
JULIET: By and by[54] I come.—
To cease thy strife[55] and leave me to my grief.
Tomorrow will I send.
ROMEO: So thrive my soul—
JULIET: A thousand times good night!   [*Exit.*]
ROMEO: A thousand times the worse, to want thy light!
Love goes toward love as schoolboys from their books;
But love from love, toward school with heavy looks.
[*Enter* JULIET *again.*]
JULIET: Hist![56] Romeo, hist! O for a falc'ner's[57] voice
To lure this tassel[58] gentle back again!
Bondage[59] is hoarse and may not speak aloud,

---

substantial (sub STAN chul) real
bent (BENT) purpose or inclination
procure (proh KYUUR) obtain, arrange
beseech (bih SEECH) ask earnestly
[54]**By and by:** at once
[55]**strife:** (*archaic*) strong efforts
[56]**hist:** exclamation said to draw attention, like "listen" or "quiet"
[57]**falc'ner:** falconer, or someone who keeps and trains the hawklike
  birds known as falcons
[58]**tassel:** a male falcon, properly called a "tiercel"
[59]**bondage:** slavery, or being subjected to someone else. Juliet means
  the nearness of her family makes it hard to talk.

Else would I tear the cave where Echo[60] lies
And make her airy tongue more hoarse than mine
With repetition of "My Romeo!"

ROMEO: It is my soul that calls upon my name.
How silver-sweet sound lovers' tongues by night,
Like softest music to attending ears!

JULIET: Romeo!

ROMEO: My sweet?

JULIET: What o'clock tomorrow
Shall I send to thee?

ROMEO: By the hour of nine.

JULIET: I will not fail. 'Tis twenty year till then.
I have forgot why I did call thee back.

ROMEO: Let me stand here till thou remember it.

JULIET: I shall forget, to have thee still stand there,
Rememb'ring how I love thy company.

ROMEO: And I'll stay, to have thee still forget,
Forgetting any other home but this.

JULIET: 'Tis almost morning. I would have thee gone—
And yet no farther than a wanton's bird,
That lets it hop a little from his hand,
Like a poor prisoner in his twisted gyves,[61]
And with a silken thread plucks it back again,
So loving-jealous of his liberty.

ROMEO: I would I were thy bird.

JULIET: Sweet, so would I.
Yet I should kill thee with much cherishing.
Good night, good night! Parting is such sweet sorrow
That I shall say good night till it be morrow.   [*Exit.*]

ROMEO: Sleep dwell upon thine eyes, peace in thy breast!
Would I were sleep and peace, so sweet to rest!
Hence will I to my ghostly friar's[62] close cell,
His help to crave and my dear hap[63] to tell.   [*Exit.*]

---

wanton (WAHN tun) spoiled child
cell (SEL) small room
[60]**Echo:** in Greek mythology, a nymph whose love for Narcissus made her
   waste away until nothing was left of her but her voice
[61]**gyves:** chains or fetters
[62]**ghostly friar's:** spiritual father's
[63]**dear hap:** good luck or fortune

Romeo goes to see Friar Lawrence, a Catholic priest. The friar, who knows Romeo well, consents to marry Juliet and him. Friar Lawrence hopes the marriage will end the feud between the Capulets and Montagues.

The marriage takes place, secretly, in Friar Lawrence's cell, or room.

ACT III

Act III brings another confrontation between the Capulets and Montagues. Tybalt and Mercutio fight. Romeo tries to stop them, but only hinders Mercutio, his friend. Tybalt stabs Mercutio. He dies. Romeo, distraught that he had not defended his friend, kills Tybalt.

Romeo is banished from the city for the murder. Juliet hears of the fight, and is overcome with grief: Tybalt, a cousin, has been killed by Romeo, her husband. And now Romeo is exiled.

Both Romeo and Juliet feel banishment from each other is the worst of the tragedies, however. With the help of Friar Lawrence, they spend their wedding night together, and plan for Romeo to leave for the city of Mantua. There, he will wait until tempers cool, Friar Lawrence can arrange a pardon, and the wedding is made public.

The situation, however, is complicated by Juliet's father. He announces that she is to marry Paris in three days. Juliet begs her parents to delay the wedding, but they will not. They order her to obey their wishes.

ACT IV

In Act IV Juliet flees to Friar Lawrence for guidance. She sees no way out of the situation.

Friar Lawrence, though, comes up with a plan. Juliet will take a potion that will make her appear dead. Her body will be taken to the Capulet family tomb. Romeo will be summoned from Mantua and will wait at the tomb while the potion wears off. Reunited, the two lovers can then flee together to Mantua.

ACT V

The plan goes awry, however. In Act V, the letter that Friar Lawrence sends to Romeo informing him of the plan does not reach Romeo in Mantua. Instead, Balthasar, Romeo's old servant, arrives hurriedly in Mantua and tells him he has seen Juliet's body being taken to the Capulet vault for burial. Romeo, thinking her dead, leaves immediately for Verona. He takes with him a bottle of poison. If Juliet is dead, he, too, does not wish to live. The stage is set for the dramatic climax.

SCENE 3

A churchyard: in it a monument belonging to the CAPULETS.

[*Enter* PARIS *and his* PAGE *with flowers and sweet water.*]

PARIS: Give me thy torch, boy. Hence, and stand aloof.
　　　Yet put it out, for I would not be seen.

---

aloof (uh LOOF) at a distance, apart

Under yond yew trees lay thee all along,[64]
Holding thy ear close to the hollow ground.
So shall no foot upon the churchyard tread
(Being loose, unfirm, with digging up of graves)
But thou shalt hear it. Whistle then to me,
As signal that thou hearest something approach.
Give me those flowers. Do as I bid thee, go.

PAGE [*aside*]: I am almost afraid to stand alone
Here in the churchyard; yet I will adventure.[65]   [*Retires.*]

PARIS: Sweet flower, with flowers thy bridal bed I strew
(O woe! thy canopy is dust and stones)
Which with sweet[66] water nightly I will dew;
Or, wanting that, with tears distilled by moans.
The obsequies that I for thee will keep
Nightly shall be to strew thy grave and weep.

[BOY *whistles.*]

The boy gives warning something doth approach.
What cursèd foot wanders this way tonight
To cross[67] my obsequies and true love's rite?
What, with a torch? Muffle me, night, awhile.   [*Retires.*]

[*Enter* ROMEO, *and* BALTHASAR *with a torch, a mattock,
and a crow*[68] *of iron.*]

ROMEO: Give me that mattock and the wrenching iron.
Hold, take this letter. Early in the morning
See thou deliver it to my lord and father.
Give me the light. Upon thy life I charge thee,
Whate'er thou hearest or seest, stand all aloof
And do not interrupt me in my course.
Why I descend into this bed of death
Is partly to behold my lady's face.
But chiefly to take thence[69] from her dead finger

---

yew (YOO) a kind of evergreen shrub or small tree
obsequies (OB sih kweez) funeral rites or ceremonies
mattock (MAT uk) a tool like a pickax for loosening soil
[64]**lay . . . along:** lie down flat
[65]**adventure:** chance it
[66]**sweet:** perfumed
[67]**cross:** interrupt
[68]**crow:** here, crowbar
[69]**thence:** (*archaic*) from that place

A precious ring—a ring that I must use
In dear employment.[70] Therefore hence, be gone.
But if thou, jealous,[71] dost return to pry
In what I farther shall intend to do,
By heaven, I will tear thee joint by joint
And strew this hungry churchyard with thy limbs.
The time and my intents are savage-wild,
More fierce and more inexorable far
Than empty[72] tigers or the roaring sea.

BALTHASAR: I will be gone, sir, and not trouble ye.

ROMEO: So shalt thou show me friendship. Take thou that.
Live, and be prosperous; and farewell, good fellow.

BALTHASAR [*aside*]: For all this same, I'll hide me hereabout.
His looks I fear, and his intents I doubt.   [*Retires.*]

ROMEO: Thou detestable maw, thou womb of death,
Gorged with the dearest morsel of the earth,
Thus I enforce thy rotten jaws to open.
And in despite[73] I'll cram thee with more food.

[ROMEO *opens the tomb.*]

PARIS: This is that banished haughty Montague
That murd'red my love's cousin—with which grief
It is supposed the fair creature died
And here is come to do some villainous shame
To the dead bodies. I will apprehend him.
Stop thy unhallowèd toil, vile Montague!
Can vengeance be pursued further than death?
Condemnèd villain, I do apprehend thee.
Obey, and go with me; for thou must die.

---

inexorable (in EKS uh ruh bul) unable to change or control
detestable (dih TES tuh bul) hateful
maw (MAW) stomach
womb (WOOM) stomach or uterus; any place that holds or generates
    something else
morsel (MAWR sul) a small piece or bit
haughty (HAWT ee) proud, showing disdain for others
apprehend (ap rih HEND) catch, seize, or arrest
unhallowed (un HAL ohd) unholy
vengeance (VEN juns) revenge
[70]**dear employment:** important business
[71]**jealous:** here, curious; that is, jealous of one's privacy
[72]**empty:** hungry
[73]**in despite:** to spite

ROMEO: I must indeed: and therefore came I hither.
    Good gentle youth, tempt not a desp'rate man.
    Fly hence and leave me. Think upon these gone;
    Let them affright thee. I beseech thee, youth,
    Put not another sin upon my head
    By urging me to fury. O, be gone!
    By heaven, I love thee better than myself,
    For I come hither armed against myself.
    Stay not, be gone. Live, and hereafter say
    A madman's mercy bid thee run away.
PARIS: I do defy thy conjurations.
    And apprehend thee for a felon here.
ROMEO: Wilt thou provoke me? Then have at thee, boy!

    [*They fight.*]

PAGE: O Lord, they fight! I will go call the watch.

    [*Exit.* PARIS *falls.*]

PARIS: O, I am slain! If thou be merciful,
    Open the tomb, lay me with Juliet.   [*Dies.*]
ROMEO: In faith, I will. Let me peruse this face.
    Mercutio's kinsman, noble Count Paris!
    What said my man when my betossèd[74] soul
    Did not attend[75] him as we rode? I think
    He told me Paris should have married Juliet.
    Said he not so, or did I dream it so?
    Or am I mad, hearing him talk of Juliet.
    To think it was so? O, give me thy hand,
    One writ[76] with me in sour misfortune's book!
    I'll bury thee in a triumphant grave.
    A grave? O, no, a lanthorn,[77] slaught'red youth,
    For here lies Juliet, and her beauty makes

---

conjuration (kon juh RAY shun) threatening appeal
felon (FEL un) criminal
provoke (pruh VOHK) excite, irritate, or anger to action
slain (SLAYN) from "slay," to kill
peruse (puh ROOZ) look at or read
[74]**betossed:** upset
[75]**attend:** give attention to
[76]**writ:** (*archaic*) wrote or written
[77]**lanthorn:** structure with windows at the top of a room to admit light;
    sometimes also used instead of "lantern"

This vault a feasting presence[78] full of light.
Death, lie thou there, by a dead man interred.

[*Lays him in the tomb.*]

How oft when men are at the point of death
Have they been merry! Which their keepers call
A lightning before death. O, how may I
Call this a lightning? O my love, my wife!
Death, that hath sucked the honey of thy breath,
Hath had no power yet upon thy beauty.
Thou art not conquered. Beauty's ensign yet
Is crimson in thy lips and in thy cheeks,
And death's pale flag is not advanced there.
Tybalt, liest thou there in thy bloody sheet?
O, what more favor can I do to thee
Than with that hand that cut thy youth in twain[79]
To sunder his that was thine enemy?

---

interred (in TURD) buried
keepers (KEEP urz) jailers
ensign (EN sun) flag or banner
sunder (SUN dur) break apart or split
[78]**feasting presence:** chamber fit for celebration
[79]**twain:** (*archaic*) two

Forgive me, cousin! Ah, dear Juliet.
Why art thou yet so fair? Shall I believe
That unsubstantial Death is amorous,
And that the lean abhorrèd monster keeps
Thee here in dark to be his paramour?
For fear of that I still will stay with thee
And never from this pallet of dim night
Depart again. Here, here will I remain
With worms that are thy chambermaids. O, here
Will I set up my everlasting rest
And shake the yoke of inauspicious stars
From this world-wearied flesh. Eyes, look your last!
Arms, take your last embrace! And, lips, O you
The doors of breath, seal with a righteous kiss
A dateless[80] bargain to engrossing death!
Come, bitter conduct;[81] come, unsavory guide!
Thou desperate pilot,[82] now at once run on
The dashing rocks thy seasick weary bark!
Here's to my love! [*Drinks*] O true apothecary!
Thy drugs are quick. Thus with a kiss I die.   [*Falls.*]

[*Enter* FRIAR LAWRENCE, *with lanthorn, crow, and spade.*]

FRIAR: Saint Francis be my speed![83] How oft tonight
  Have my old feet stumbled[84] at graves! Who's there?
BALTHASAR: Here's one, a friend, and one that knows you well.
FRIAR: Bliss be upon you! Tell me, good my friend,
  What torch is yond that vainly lends his light

---

amorous (AM uh rus) full of love
abhorred (ab HAWRD) hated, dreaded
paramour (PAR uh muur) lover
pallet (PAL it) bed
inauspicious (in aw SPISH us) unlucky, forecasting misfortune
righteous (RY chus) morally right, virtuous
engrossing (en GROHS ing) taking all one's attention
unsavory (un SAY vuh ree) unpleasant
bark (BAHRK) a small sailing boat
apothecary (uh POTH uh ker ee) someone who prepares and
  dispenses drugs
[80]**dateless:** eternal
[81]**conduct:** here, guide (referring to the poison)
[82]**pilot:** captain (Romeo himself)
[83]**speed:** help
[84]**stumbled:** stumbling was thought to be a bad omen

To grubs and eyeless skulls? As I discern,
It burneth in the Capels' monument.

BALTHASAR: It doth so, holy sir; and there's my master,
One that you love.

FRIAR: Who is it?

BALTHASAR: Romeo.

FRIAR: How long hath he been there?

BALTHASAR: Full half an hour.

FRIAR: Go with me to the vault.

BALTHASAR: I dare not, sir.
My master knows not but I am gone hence,
And fearfully did menace me with death
If I did stay to look on his intents.

FRIAR: Stay then; I'll go alone. Fear comes upon me.
O, much I fear some ill unthrifty[85] thing.

BALTHASAR: As I did sleep under this yew tree here.
I dreamt my master and another fought,
And that my master slew him.

FRIAR: Romeo!
Alack, alack, what blood is this which stains
The stony entrance of this sepulcher?
What mean these masterless[86] and gory swords
To lie discolored by this place of peace?   [*Enters the tomb.*]

Romeo! O, pale! Who else? What, Paris too?
And steeped in blood? Ah, what an unkind[87] hour
Is guilty of this lamentable chance!
The lady stirs.   [JULIET *rises.*]

JULIET: O comfortable[88] friar! Where is my lord?
I do remember well where I should be,
And there I am. Where is my Romeo?

---

grubs (GRUBZ) young wormlike stage of some insects
discern (dih SURN) make out or recognize
sepulcher (SEP ul kur) small chamber used as a tomb
gory (GAWR ee) bloody
lamentable (LAM un tuh bul) distressing, sorrowful
[85]**unthrifty:** (*archaic*) unfortunate
[86]**masterless:** discarded
[87]**unkind:** unnatural
[88]**comfortable:** (*archaic*) comfort-giving

FRIAR: I hear some noise. Lady, come from that nest
    Of death, contagion, and unnatural sleep.
    A greater power than we can contradict
    Hath thwarted our intents. Come, come away.
    Thy husband in thy bosom there lies dead;
    And Paris too. Come, I'll dispose of thee
    Among a sisterhood of holy nuns.
    Stay not to question, for the watch is coming.
    Come, go, good Juliet. I dare no longer stay.
JULIET: Go, get thee hence,[89] for I will not away.   *[Exit* FRIAR.]
    What's here? A cup, closed in my truelove's hand?
    Poison, I see, hath been his timeless[90] end.
    O churl! Drunk all, and left no friendly drop
    To help me after? I will kiss thy lips.
    Haply[91] some poison yet doth hang on them
    To make me die with a restorative.   *[Kisses him.]*
    Thy lips are warm!
CHIEF WATCHMAN *[within]*: Lead, boy. Which way?
JULIET: Yea, noise? Then I'll be brief. O happy[92] dagger!

    [Snatches ROMEO'S *dagger.]*

    This is thy sheath: there rust, and let me die.

    [She stabs herself and falls.]

    [Enter PARIS' BOY *and* WATCH.]

BOY: This is the place. There, where the torch doth burn.
CHIEF WATCHMAN: The ground is bloody. Search about the
    churchyard.
    Go, some of you: whoe'er you find attach.[93]

    [Exit some of the WATCH.]

---

contagion (kun TAY jun) spreading disease
thwarted (THWAWRT id) blocked or stopped
churl (CHURL) selfish, mean, rude person
restorative (rih STAWR uh tiv) something that brings back consciousness
    or health generally; a medicine
[89]**hence:** (*archaic*) away from this place
[90]**timeless:** here, too soon
[91]**haply:** perhaps
[92]**happy:** (*archaic*) convenient
[93]**attach:** here, arrest

Pitiful sight! Here lies the County slain:
And Juliet bleeding, warm, and newly dead,
Who here hath lain this two days burièd.
Go, tell the Prince; run to the Capulets;
Raise up the Montagues: some others search.

[*Exit others of the* WATCH.]

We see the ground whereon these woes do lie,
But the true ground[94] of all these piteous woes
We cannot without circumstance[95] descry.

[*Enter some of the* WATCH, *with* ROMEO'S MAN, BALTHASAR.]

SECOND WATCHMAN: Here's Romeo's man. We found him in the
  churchyard.
CHIEF WATCHMAN: Hold him in safety till the Prince come hither.

[*Enter* FRIAR LAWRENCE *and another* WATCHMAN.]

THIRD WATCHMAN: Here is a friar that trembles, sighs, and weeps.
  We took this mattock and this spade from him
  As he was coming from this churchyard's side.
CHIEF WATCHMAN: A great suspicion! Stay[96] the friar too.

[*Enter the* PRINCE *and* ATTENDANTS.]

PRINCE: What misadventure is so early up,
  That calls our person from our morning rest?

[*Enter* CAPULET *and his* WIFE *with others.*]

CAPULET: What should it be, that is so shrieked abroad?
LADY CAPULET: O, the people in the street cry "Romeo,"
  Some "Juliet," and some "Paris": and all run
  With open outcry toward our monument.
PRINCE: What fear is this which startles in your ears?

---

woes (WOHZ) misery, sorrows
descry (dih SKRY) discover, see clearly
[94]**ground:** cause
[95]**circumstance:** here, details
[96]**stay:** here, keep or hold

CHIEF WATCHMAN: Sovereign, here lies the County Paris lain;
    And Romeo dead; and Juliet, dead before,
    Warm and new killed.
PRINCE: Search, seek, and know how this foul murder comes.
CHIEF WATCHMAN: Here is a friar, and slaughtered Romeo's man.
    With instruments upon them fit to open
    These dead men's tombs.
CAPULET: O heavens! O wife, look how our daughter bleeds!
    This dagger hath mista'en, for, lo, his house[97]
    Is empty on the back of Montague.
    And it missheathèd in my daughter's bosom!
LADY CAPULET: O me, this sight of death is as a bell
    That warns my old age to a sepulcher.

[*Enter* MONTAGUE *and others.*]

PRINCE: Come, Montague; for thou art early up
    To see thy son and heir more early down.
MONTAGUE: Alas, my liege, my wife is dead tonight!
    Grief of my son's exile hath stopped her breath.
    What further woe conspires against mine age?
PRINCE: Look, and thou shalt see.
MONTAGUE: O thou untaught! What manners is in this,
    To press before thy father to a grave?
PRINCE: Seal up the mouth of outrage[98] for a while,
    Till we can clear these ambiguities
    And know their spring, their head, their true descent;
    And then will I be general of your woes[99]
    And lead you even to death. Meantime forbear,
    And let mischance be slave to patience.[100]
    Bring forth the parties of suspicion.

---

liege (LEEJ) lord
conspire (kun SPYR) plan and act together secretly
ambiguities (am buh GYOO uh teez) things that are not clear
forbear (fawr BAIR) keep under control, endure
mischance (mis CHANS) misfortune
[97]**house:** sheath
[98]**mouth of outrage:** violent cries
[99]**general . . . woes:** leader in your sorrowing
[100]**let . . . patience:** be patient in the face of misfortune

FRIAR: I am the greatest, able to do least,
    Yet most suspected, as the time and place
    Doth make against me, of this direful murder;
    And here I stand, both to impeach and purge
    Myself condemnèd and myself excused.
PRINCE: Then say at once what thou dost know in this.
FRIAR: I will be brief, for my short date of breath[101]
    Is not so long as is a tedious tale.
    Romeo, there dead, was husband to that Juliet;
    And she, there dead, that's Romeo's faithful wife.
    I married them; and their stol'n marriage day
    Was Tybalt's doomsday, whose untimely death
    Banished the new-made bridegroom from this city;
    For whom, and not for Tybalt, Juliet pined.
    You, to remove that siege of grief from her,
    Betrothed and would have married her perforce
    To County Paris. Then comes she to me
    And with wild looks bid me devise some mean
    To rid her from this second marriage,
    Or in my cell there would she kill herself.
    Then gave I her (so tutored by my art)
    A sleeping potion: which so took effect
    As I intended, for it wrought on her
    The form of death. Meantime I writ to Romeo
    That he should hither come as[102] this dire night
    To help to take her from her borrowed grave,
    Being the time the potion's force should cease,
    But he which bore my letter, Friar John,
    Was stayed by accident, and yesternight
    Returned my letter back. Then all alone
    At the prefixèd hour of her waking
    Came I to take her from her kindred's vault:

---

direful (DYR ful) terrible, dreadful
impeach (im PEECH) accuse
bridegroom (BRYD groom) groom
potion (POH shun) a drink with special powers, such as medicine or poison
wrought (RAWT) formed or brought about
[101]date of breath: term of life
[102]as: here, on

Meaning to keep her closely[103] at my cell
Till I conveniently could send to Romeo.
But when I came, some minute ere the time
Of her awakening, here untimely lay
The noble Paris and true Romeo dead.
She wakes; and I entreated her come forth
And bear this work of heaven with patience;
But then a noise did scare me from the tomb,
And she, too desperate, would not go with me,
But, as it seems, did violence on herself.
All this I know, and to the marriage
Her nurse is privy; and if aught[104] in this
Miscarried by my fault, let my old life
Be sacrificed some hour before his time
Unto the rigor of severest law.

CAPULET: O brother Montague, give me thy hand.
This is my daughter's jointure,[105] for no more
Can I demand.

MONTAGUE: But I can give thee more;
For I will raise her statue in pure gold,
That whiles Verona by that name is known,
There shall no figure at such rate[106] be set
As that of true and faithful Juliet.

CAPULET: As rich shall Romeo's by his lady's lie—
Poor sacrifices of our enmity!

PRINCE: A glooming[107] peace this morning with it brings.
The sun for sorrow will not show his head.
Go hence, to have more talk of these sad things;
Some shall be pardoned, and some punishèd;
For never was a story of more woe
Than this of Juliet and her Romeo.

[*Exit all.*]

---

untimely (un TYM lee) coming before the expected time
privy (PRIV ee) secretly informed
miscarried (mis KAR eed) went wrong
rigor (RIG ur) strictness
[103]**closely:** here, hidden
[104]**aught:** (*archaic*) anything whatever
[105]**jointure:** marriage gift
[106]**rate:** value
[107]**glooming:** cloudy, gloomy

AUTHOR BIOGRAPHY
William Shakespeare (1564–1616)

William Shakespeare is considered by many to be the greatest playwright, and perhaps the greatest author, of all time. His works show a talent for characterization and poetic expression that have never been equaled.

Shakespeare was born in Stratford-upon-Avon in 1564. Little is known about his early life, except that he was the son of a businessman and probably attended the local grammar school. In 1582 he married Anne Hathaway, and they had three children.

Shakespeare was an actor as well as a playwright, and was a member of a group of actors called Lord Chamberlain's Men. Shakespeare was part owner of the company's theater, the Globe, and he wrote his plays exclusively for this company at the rate of about two a year.

The characters in Shakespeare's plays are the first "modern" dramatic characters—with both strengths and weaknesses. Shakespeare skillfully conveys a sense of his characters' psychological identities, and this is part of the reason why these characters have endured so vividly for so many years.

In the course of his life, Shakespeare wrote over 30 plays and hundreds of sonnets and other poems. Because Shakespeare wrote his plays for performance, he was indifferent about their publication. Many of the plays that were published shortly after his death were reconstructed from memory by actors.

Review the Selection

UNDERSTAND THE SELECTION

Recall

1. Who threatens Romeo at the banquet?

2. Where are Romeo and Juliet married?

3. What is the first question Juliet asks when she awakes in the tomb?

Infer

4. How could Romeo change his love so quickly from Rosaline to Juliet?

5. Explain "That which we call a rose by any other word would smell as sweet."

6. Why does Friar Lawrence suggest Juliet go to a convent of nuns?

7. Chance plays an important part in this story. Give one example.

Apply

8. The Capulets and Montagues fight not for a good reason, but because they are enemies. Give a modern-day example of such conflict.

9. Whom should the prince pardon, and whom should he punish? Why?

10. Why is *Romeo and Juliet* one of the most famous love stories in literature?

Respond to Literature

The story of Romeo and Juliet has been retold many times and sometimes adapted and modernized. Why?

WRITE ABOUT THE SELECTION

During Shakespeare's time, educated people wrote many letters. If you could write a letter of advice to any of the characters in *Romeo and Juliet*, to whom would you write—Romeo, Mercutio, or Juliet? How about giving advice to Tybalt, the friar, or Juliet's nurse? Choose one character with which to correspond and compose a letter.

Prewriting   As you choose the character, you will be thinking of things you would like to say to him or her. Write them down in clusters around the character's name. If at first you cannot decide on one character, choose several, make clusters, and then pick the one you think will give you the chance to write the most interesting letter.

Writing   Use the cluster to write your letter. Make sure the comments and help you offer are clear. Since you are writing a letter, you need to use the second-person pronouns—*you, yourself*.

Revising   You may write in poetry or prose. Whichever form you use, have you thought of trying to make the letter sound "old"? That is, can you make it sound as though it were written by a contemporary of the person to whom you are writing?

Proofreading   Reread what you have written and check for mistakes. Pay particular attention to **homophones**, or words that sound alike but are spelled differently. The person reading your letter might think that you are trying to make a joke instead of simply having misspelled something!

THINK ABOUT FIGURES OF SPEECH

Let us examine one specific case of Shakespeare's imaginative use of language—**simile**, which uses the words *like* or *as* to compare two different things. Figures of speech like similes add richness to literature. Romeo speaks these lines when he must leave Juliet at the end of the balcony scene:

"Love goes toward love as schoolboys
    from their books;
But love from love, toward school with
    heavy looks."

1. What figure of speech is used?

2. What is being compared?

3. Explain the meaning of the first part of the comparison.

4. Explain the meaning of the second part of the comparison.

5. What adds to the effectiveness of the comparison?

READING FOCUS

Recognize Imagery As you read *Romeo and Juliet* you were able to see how the author used imagery to make the characters, setting, and action of the play come alive. Shakespeare was skilled at creating vivid images by appealing to your senses. What senses in particular did this play appeal to? Provide examples from the play to support your answer.

DEVELOP YOUR VOCABULARY

Shakespeare uses many words that are uncommon today. Sometimes the meaning he intended has dropped out of use, or sometimes the word itself is no longer used.

The words *thou* and *thee* are good examples. They are pronouns, and in Shakespeare's time were used instead of the word *you* to address friends and other close acquaintances. *Thou* is the nominative case, *thee* the objective case, and *thy* or *thine* the possessive case.

The dictionary can help you learn about old word usages. Sometimes it will note that a word, or a particular definition of a word, is **archaic** (abbreviated *arch.*). This means the word, or definition, is rarely used today.

Look up the following words in a dictionary. Write down the definition that fits with Shakespeare's time, and then use the word in a sentence.

1. knave
2. sirrah (or "sirah")
3. doth
4. hither
5. perforce
6. choler

Summer Millinery, Charles W. Hawthorne, 1866.
(American, 1872–1930) Oil on board, 58½ × 46¾ in.
Chrysler Museum of Art, Norfolk, VA
Gift of Walter P. Chrysler, Jr. 71.659

READING FOCUS

Paraphrase Poetry When you paraphrase you restate the speaker's experiences and feelings in your own words. Restating the lines or stanzas of a poem will help you to clarify their meaning. As you read the next three poems, practice paraphrasing the lines of each one.

IMAGERY

An image is a mental "sensation." You are provided with information that creates a picture that you can see, hear, smell, feel, or taste in your mind. You form this picture with your imagination. The use of language that stimulates these mental pictures is called **imagery**.

Imagery appeals to the senses and helps you experience what a writer is describing. For example, a visual image allows you to "see"; an aural image allows you to "hear." When you read, you are not really seeing or hearing these things, but you can imagine that you are. You experience, in your imagination, what the writer creates.

Poets use all kinds of objects and activities to create images in their poems. In fact, if an image is unexpected or unique, it is usually very effective.

Look for answers to the following questions as you read the poems:
1. Why is imagery a powerful tool?
2. How is imagery used effectively?

WRITING CONNECTION

Using imagery, describe something in your classroom. Try to think of an image that gives a vivid sense of what you are describing.

Greyday

by Maya Angelou

The day hangs heavy
loose and grey
when you're away.

A crown of thorns
a shirt of hair
is what I wear.

No one knows
my lonely heart
when we're apart.

Here—Hold My Hand

by Mari Evans

Here
hold my hand
let me touch you
there is
5   nothing
we can
say . . . your
soul
eludes me
10   when I reach
out
your eyes
resent
my need to know
15   you
here
hold my hand
since
there is nothing
20   we can
say

---

eludes (ih LOODS) avoids or escapes
resent (rih ZENT) to feel or show anger

FINIS

by Waring Cuney

Now that our love has drifted
To a quiet close,
Leaving the empty ache
That always follows when beauty goes;
5   Now that you and I,
Who stood tiptoe on earth
To touch our fingers to the sky,
Have turned away
To allow our little love to die—
10   Go, dear, seek again the magic touch.
But if you are wise,
As I shall be wise,
You will not again
Love overmuch.

AUTHOR BIOGRAPHY
Maya Angelou (1928–   )

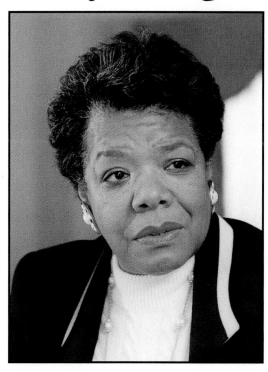

When the American choreographer Alvin Ailey was a college student at San Francisco State, he took time away from the books to form a nightclub dance act with a young woman named Marguerite Johnson. Little did the two dancers know that in a few decades, both would be famous—Ailey as the founder of the Alvin Ailey Dance Company and Marguerite Johnson as the celebrated author Maya Angelou.

Twelve years after her partnership with Ailey, Angelou was in Cairo, Egypt as associate editor of the *Arab Observer*. A year later she went to Ghana, where she became a writer for the *Ghanaian Times* and an assistant administrator at the University of Ghana. In 1966 she returned to the states as a lecturer at the University of California.

Maya Angelou is best known for her autobiography, *I Know Why the Caged Bird Sings*, which was written in 1970. The book tells the moving and often humorous story of her childhood in segregated Arkansas. The book was made into a play for television in 1977.

In addition to her careers as a dancer and a writer, Angelou has worked as a movie and stage actress. She has written plays, books of poetry, and screenplays, and has also composed music.

Review the Selection

UNDERSTAND THE SELECTION

Recall

1. When does the day seem grey to the speaker in "Greyday"?

2. Why does the speaker of "Here—Hold My Hand" want to hold hands?

3. How has love ended in "Finis?"

Infer

4. Why did Maya Angelou choose the title "Greyday" for her poem?

5. Explain the images of a "crown of thorns" and "a shirt of hair".

6. Do you think that the two people in "Here—Hold My Hand" can look at each other honestly? Why or why not?

7. Why does the speaker of "Finis" tell his partner not to "love over-much" again?

Apply

8. What is suggested to you by the lines "Who stood tiptoe on earth to touch our fingers to the sky" in "Finis"?

9. What is the character in "Here—Hold My Hand" feeling?

10. Is the character in "Finis" the same as in "Here—Hold My Hand"? Explain.

Respond to Literature

Is it better to love and then lose that love, rather than never to love at all? Why?

WRITE ABOUT THE SELECTION

Maya Angelou loses love only temporarily in "Greyday," while Mari Evans and Waring Cuney lose their loved ones completely in their poems.

All three poets are trying to capture the feeling of losing love, however. Each does it in his or her unique way, based on feelings.

How do you best express your feelings when writing about something? Do you use the first person? Do you think of images that describe your feelings? Express an important feeling with images.

Prewriting Concentrate on one feeling. Write the feeling at the top left corner of a piece of paper. Now, make a Z from there. Along the line, fill in words or draw pictures that describe your feeling.

Writing Combine your thoughts into a single paragraph or a few lines of poetry. "Translate" any pictures into words, using imagery if you can. Appeal to several different senses, not just sight. Can you make your readers hear, taste, smell, or feel?

Revising Are your words communicating your feeling? Think of changing or adding words that "sharpen" your description. Make every word count!

Proofreading Reread your description and check for unnecessary repetition. Also, check that your punctuation is consistent throughout; for example, Maya Angelou uses only a final period at the end of each verse.

THINK ABOUT IMAGERY

Imagery is one device an author uses to appeal to the senses. Images can be strengthened by appealing to the same sense in different ways or by appealing to a different sense at the same time. Maya Angelou describes the day as hanging "heavy loose and grey." "Heavy" and "loose" appeal to your sense of touch. "Grey" appeals to your sense of sight.

1. Think of an image that describes the hand in "Here—Hold My Hand." To which sense will you appeal?

2. Try to add an image to the description you have just thought of. Appeal to the same or a different sense.

3. None of the three poems has imagery appealing to the senses of hearing, smell, or taste. Why is this so?

4. Is any one sense best for imagery?

5. Think of an image appealing to the sense of hearing, smell, or taste that describes something mentioned in one of the poems.

READING FOCUS

Paraphrase Poetry Paraphrase one of the poems you just read. Then tell how restating the poem in your own words helped to make the meaning clearer.

DEVELOP YOUR VOCABULARY

Context, or the words or phrases surrounding a word, can be an important help in understanding words you do not know. Even when you do know a word, context can help to understand added meaning behind a word.

Look at the word *elude* in "Here—Hold My Hand": "your soul *eludes* me when I reach out." The theme of the poem is falling out of love. The two people cannot communicate anymore. You might guess that *elude* relates to not being able or not wanting to reach something. It does. *Elude* means "to avoid or escape."

Use context to help you write the meaning of the italicized words in the following lines. When you have finished, use a dictionary to check your meanings.

1. "Your eyes *resent* my need to know you. "

2. "The sweetest joy, the wildest *woe* is love. "

3. "Many waters cannot *quench* love, neither can the floods drown it."

Learn About

Portrait of Langston Hughes, Winold Reiss.
National Portrait Gallery, Gift of W. Tjark Reiss

READING FOCUS

Compare and Contrast Comparing and contrasting two different poems helps you to focus on both the smaller details and the larger themes or messages of the poems. Poems can be very different in tone or theme and still have many characteristics in common. Compare and contrast these two poems to help you to see what makes the poems similar and different.

TONE IN POETRY

Writers often have strong opinions about what they are writing. These opinions usually show in the attitude a writer expresses towards his or her subject. This attitude is usually expressed in the **tone** of a selection.

The tone can be lighthearted and mocking. It can be serious and depressing. It can be several things at once.

Poems that have strong tones tell you something about the poet's attitude. The speaker in the poem can say things in a certain way that reveals the poet's opinions about the theme.

Look for answers to the following questions as you read the poems:

1. What is the tone of each of the poems?
2. What creates the tone?

WRITING CONNECTION

Think of a recent conversation you have had with somebody. How did you reveal your opinions, other than by direct comments? Did you use certain words that sounded angry, disappointed, proud, or expressed some other feeling? Did you talk about something else in order to describe your thoughts? Write a few lines of what you said. What kind of tone do the lines have? Why?

Housecleaning

by Nikki Giovanni

    i always liked housecleaning
    even as a child
    i dug straightening
    the cabinets
5   putting new paper on
    the shelves
    washing the refrigerator
    inside out
    and unfortunately this habit has
10 carried over and i find
    i must remove you
    from my life

Anna Washington Derry, Laura Wheeler Waring.
National Museum of American Art, Smithsonian
Institution, Gift of the Harmon Foundation

Where Have You Gone

by Mari Evans

    Where have you gone

    with your confident
    walk with
    your crooked smile

5   why did you leave
    me
    when you took your
    laughter
    and departed

10 are you aware that
    with you
    went the sun

    all light
    and what few stars
15 there were?

    where have you gone
    with your confident
    walk your
    crooked smile the
20 rent money
    in one pocket and
    my heart
    in another . . .

Review the Selection

UNDERSTAND THE SELECTION

Recall

1. When did the housecleaner begin to love cleaning?

2. What does she call housecleaning?

3. What "things" were in the friend's pocket when he left?

Infer

4. What does washing the refrigerator "inside out" mean?

5. What does "unfortunately" mean in the next line of "Housecleaning"?

6. What does "crooked smile" tell about the person who walked out?

7. Why does the speaker of "Where Have You Gone" say "what few stars there were" when she describes life?

Apply

8. What did you think the tone of "Where Have You Gone" would be? Did your idea change?

9. How does the speaker in "Where Have You Gone" feel after the friend left?

10. Why must the housecleaner remove someone from her life?

Respond to Literature

If you could meet either speaker from these two poems, which one would you choose to meet? Explain your answer.

WRITE ABOUT THE SELECTION

Why do you think the "you" in the poem "Where Have You Gone" left the speaker? Do you think the person is a good-for-nothing who cheated the speaker? Do you think the speaker did not mention something about how the relationship ended, and that the speaker is as much to blame as the partner for their falling out of love?

Write a "reply" to the speaker of the poem. Present your ideas about why the relationship broke up.

Prewriting   What happened to end the relationship? Answer that question and write it in the middle of a piece of paper. Cluster reasons for the ending and the partner's feelings around it in boxes.

Writing   Read over your cluster and add any new ideas. Decide what reasons you will use in your response. Assemble your information into a few lines of poetry. See if you can keep the same style as Mari Evans. Write in the first person.

Revising   Pay attention to tone. Is your attitude toward the ending of the relationship clear? Are you happy, sad, relieved, or happy-go-lucky? Does your poem reflect this?

Proofreading   If you have kept the same style as Mari Evans, you will have no punctuation or capital letters. However, what words would be capitalized and what punctuation would there be in "normal" writing? Make notes in the margin to indicate the correct style.

THINK ABOUT TONE

Tone is the overall attitude a writer brings to his or her work. Tone gives you a clue about what a writer feels about the subject and theme.

1. Read the opening of "Where Have You Gone" without "crooked" before "smile." Does the tone seem different?

2. How do the lines "the rent money in one pocket and my heart in another" make you feel? Do they tell anything about the speaker?

3. "Where Have You Gone" ends with an **ellipsis**, three periods in a row. Does this add to the tone of the poem? How?

4. Tone is often best created when you do not say directly how you feel. Does the speaker in "Housecleaning" say directly how she feels? How do you think she feels?

5. What do you think people mean by the expression "the tone of your voice"?

READING FOCUS

Compare and Contrast Tell how the tone and themes of the two poems are alike or different. How did comparing and contrasting the two poems help you to better understand each one?

DEVELOP YOUR VOCABULARY

Words used informally to mean something other than their usual, accepted definitions are called **slang**.

An example is *dug* in "Housecleaning": "I dug straightening the cabinets."

The usual definition of *dug* is "made a hole." This definition does not fit in the context of the poem, however. The poet means the slang definition of *dug*, which is "liked."

Dictionaries usually give definitions for slang. When you look up the word, the slang definition is usually given following the notation "slang." Make sure that you look under root words (under *dig* for *dug*, for example).

What are the slang definitions of the italicized words in these sentences? Check them in a dictionary.

1. The lead drummer plays *cool*.

2. She *aced* the test with ease.

3. His one-man show *bombed*.

4. Jimmy *beat* the robbery charge.

5. Hey, let's *rap* about this first.

6. "*Split!* Cat's here!" said the mice.

The Breakfast Room, Pierre Bonnard Collection,
The Museum of Modern Art, New York.
Given anonymously.

READING FOCUS

Analyze Details Authors supply details to provide information about the characters, setting, tone or plot of a piece of writing. Analyzing the details in a story will help you to understand the author's attitude toward the subject matter. Look carefully at how the author describes characters and events. Does the author seem to be having fun? Does the author express sorrow or anger?

TONE IN NONFICTION

Like a poet writing a poem, when a writer tells a story what he or she thinks about the subject is very important. If a writer thinks the subject is funny, his or her attitude will probably be humorous. If a writer thinks the subject is serious, the attitude will be earnest.

A writer often sends "messages" to you, the reader, hinting how he or she feels about the subject. How those messages are expressed is also very important, for it reveals the writer's attitude toward you.

These attitudes—toward the subject and toward you—make up **tone**. Tone is all the unstated understandings between the writer and you about what the writer is trying to do.

As you read "Where Are You Now, William Shakespeare?", ask yourself:

1. What is the author's attitude toward the subject?
2. What is the author's attitude toward the reader?

WRITING CONNECTION

Write a short paragraph on something you feel strongly about. Exchange papers with a partner. Read your partner's paragraph, and determine its tone. Discuss with your partner your evaluation.

Where Are You Now, William Shakespeare?

by M. E. Kerr

My very first boyfriend was named William Shakespeare. This was his real name, and he lived over on Highland Hill, about a block from my house.

I often went to his house to get him, or I met him down in the empty lot on Alden Avenue, or over at Hoopes Park, where we caught sunfish and brought them from the pond in bottles of murky water with polliwogs.

Marijane is ten [my father wrote in his journal]. *She plays with boys and looks like one.*

This was true.

My arms and knees were full of scabs from falls out of trees and off my bicycle. I was happiest wearing the pants my brother'd grown out of, the vest to one of my father's business suits over one of my brother's old shirts, Indian moccasins, and a cap. Everything I said came out of the side of my mouth, and I strolled around with my fists inside my trouser pockets.

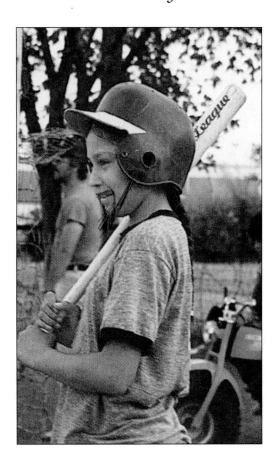

murky (MUR kee) clouded; unclear
journal (JUR nul) daily record; diary
stroll (STROHL) walk in a leisurely way

This did not faze Billy Shakespeare, whose eyes lit up when he saw me coming, and who readily agreed that when we married we'd name our first son Ellis, after my father, and not William after him.

"Because William Shakespeare is a funny name," I'd say.

"It isn't funny. It's just that there's a famous writer with the same name," he'd say.

"Do you agree to Ellis Shakespeare then?"

"Sure, if it's all right with your father."

"He'll be pleased," I'd tell Billy.

Around this time, I was always trying to think of ways to please my father. (The simplest way would have been to wear a dress and a big hair ribbon, stay out of trees, stop talking out of the side of my mouth, and act like a girl . . . but I couldn't have endured such misery even for him.)

Billy Shakespeare accepted the fact early in our relationship, that my father was my hero. He protested only slightly when I insisted that the reason my father wasn't President of the United States was that my father didn't want to be.

That was what my father told me, when I'd ask him why he wasn't President. I'd look at him across the table at dinner, and think, he knows more than anybody knows, he's handsome, and he gets things done—so he ought to be President. If he was, I'd think, there'd be no problems in the world.

Sometimes I'd ask him: "Daddy, why aren't you President of the United States?"

His answer was always the same.

"I wouldn't want that job for anything. We couldn't take a walk without Secret Service men following us. Do you think we could go up to the lake for a swim by ourselves? No. There'd be Secret Service men tagging along. It'd ruin our lives. It'd end our privacy. Would you want that?"

Billy Shakespeare would say, "He's not President because nobody elected him President."

"He won't let anyone elect him," I'd answer. "He doesn't want Secret Service men around all the time."

"I'm not sure he could *get* elected," Billy would venture.

"He could get elected," I'd tell Billy. "He doesn't want to! We like our privacy."

"Okay." Billy'd give in a little. "But he never tried getting elected, so he really doesn't know if he could."

I'd wave that idea away with my dirty hands. "Don't worry. He'd be elected in a minute if he wanted to be. You don't know *him*."

Billy Shakespeare's other rivals for my attention were movie stars. I'd write Clark Gable and Henry Fonda and Errol Flynn, and they'd send back glossy photos of themselves and sometimes letters, too.

---

faze (FAYZ) confuse; weaken
endure (en DUUR) put up with
venture (VEN chur) proceed onward; risk
rival (RY vul) one who wants the same thing as another person

These photographs and letters were thumbtacked to the fiberboard walls of a playhouse my father had built for me in our backyard.

When I did play with a girl, the game was always the same: getting dinner ready for our husbands. I had an old set of dishes back in the playhouse, and my girl friend and I played setting the table for dinner. During this game, Billy Shakespeare was forgotten. When my husband came through the playhouse door, he would be one of the movie stars pinned to the wall.

I played this game with Dorothy Spencer, who lived behind our house.

She was a tall redhead who looked like a girl, and who always had it in her head to fix meat loaf with mashed potatoes for a movie star named Spencer Tracy.

I changed around a lot—the menu as well as the movie star—but Dorothy stuck to meat loaf with mashed for Spencer.

I'd be saying, "Well, Clark is a little late tonight and the turkey is going to be overdone," or "Gee, Henry isn't here yet and the ham is going to be dried up." But Dorothy would persist with "Spencer's going to love this meat loaf when he gets here. I'll wait until I hear his footsteps to mash the potatoes."

Billy Shakespeare was jealous of this game and tried his best to ruin it

The Letter, Pierre Bonnard. National Gallery of Art, Washington, D.C., Chester Dale Collection

with reality.

He'd say, "What are two famous movie stars doing living in the same house?"

He'd say, "How come famous movie stars only have a one-room house with no kitchen?"

But Dorothy Spencer and I went on happily playing house, until the movie *Brother Rat* came to town.

That was when we both fell in love with the movie star Ronald Reagan.

Suddenly we were both setting the table for the same movie star—different menus, but the same husband.

---

fiberboard (FY bur bawrd) building material made from compressed wood chips
persist (pur SIST) say over and over; keep on going
reality (ree AL uh tee) actual fact

"You've always stuck to meat loaf and mashed for Spencer!" I said angrily. "Now you want my Ronald!"

"He's not *your* Ronald," she said.

"It's my playhouse, though," I reminded her.

"But I won't play if I can't have Ronald," she said.

"We both can't have Ronald!" I insisted.

We took the argument to her mother, who told us to pretend Ronald Reagan was twins. Then we could both have him.

"He isn't twins, though," Dorothy said.

"And if he is," I put in, "I want the real Ronald, and not his twin."

Our game came to a halt, but our rivalry did not. Both of us had written to Ronald Reagan and were waiting for his reply.

"No matter what he writes her," I told Billy Shakespeare, "my letter from him will be better."

"You might not even get a letter," Billy said. "She might not get one either. "

"She might not get one," I said, "but I will."

"You don't know that," Billy said.

"Do you want to know why I know I'll get one?" I asked him.

I made him cross his heart and hope to die if he told anyone what I'd done.

Billy was a skinny little kid with big eyes that always got bigger when I was about to confess to him something I'd done.

"Crossmyheartandhopetodie, "he said very fast. "What'd you do?"

"You know that Ronald Reagan isn't like any of the others," I said.

"Because Dorothy Spencer likes him, too."

"That's got nothing to do with it!" I said. "He's just different. I never felt this way about another movie star."

"Why?"

"*Why?* I don't know why! That's the way love is."

"Love?" Billy said.

"Yes. What did you think made me write him that I was a crippled child, and had to go to see him in a wheelchair?"

"Oh migosh!" Billy exclaimed. "Oh migosh!"

"I had to get his attention somehow."

"Oh migosh!"

"Just shut up about it!" I warned him. "If word gets out I'll know it's you."

Dorothy Spencer was the first to hear from Ronald Reagan. She didn't get a letter, but she got a signed photograph.

"Since I heard from him first," she said, "he's my husband."

"Not in my playhouse!" I said.

"He wrote me back first," she said.

"Just wait," I said.

"I don't have to wait," she said. "I'm setting the table for him in my own house."

"It's not even your house, it's your father's," I said. "At least when he's married to me, we'll have our own house."

---

rivalry (RY vul ree) competition; trying to get the same thing as another

"He's married to me now," she said.

"We'll see about that," I said.

I was beginning to get a panicky feeling as time passed and no mail came from Ronald Reagan. You'd think he'd write back to a crippled child first . . . . Meanwhile Dorothy was fixing him meat loaf and mashed at her place.

I had pictures of him cut out of movie magazines scotch-taped to my bedroom walls. I went to sleep thinking about him, wondering why he didn't care enough to answer me.

The letter and photograph from Ronald Reagan arrived on a Saturday.

I saw the Hollywood postmark and let out a whoop, thereby attracting my father's attention.

"What's all the excitement?"

I was getting the photograph out of the envelope. "I got a picture from Ronald Reagan!"

"Who's he?"

"Some movie star," my mother said.

By that time I had the photograph out. My heart began to beat nervously as I read the inscription at the bottom. "To a brave little girl, in admiration, Ronald Reagan."

"What does it say?" my father said.

"Nothing, it's just signed," I said, but he already saw what it said as he stood behind me looking down at it.

"Why are you a brave little girl?" he asked.

"How do I know?" I said.

"There's a letter on the floor," said my mother.

"That's my letter," I said, grabbing it. "Why are you considered a brave little girl?" my father said again. "Why does *he* admire *you*?"

I held the letter to my chest. "Those are just things they say," I said.

"They say you're *brave*?" my father said.

"Brave or honest or any dumb thing," I said weakly.

"Read the letter, Marijane," said my father.

I read the letter to myself,

Dear Marijane,

Thank you for your letter.

Remember that a handicap can be a challenge.

Always stay as cheerful as you are now.

Yours truly,
Ronald Reagan

"What does it say?" my mother asked. "Just the usual," I said. "They never say much."

"Let me see it, brave little girl," my father said.

"It's to me."

"Marijane . . ." and he had his hand out.

After my father read the letter, and got the truth out of me concerning my correspondence with Ronald Reagan, he told me what I was to do.

What I was to do was to sit down immediately and write Ronald Reagan, telling him I had lied. I was to add that I thanked God for my good health. I was to return both the letter and the photograph.

---

correspondence (kawr uh SPON duns) exchange of letters

No Saturday in my entire life had ever been so dark.

My father stood over me while I wrote the letter in tears, convinced that Ronald Reagan would hate me all his life for my deception. I watched through blurred eyes while my father took my letter, Ronald Reagan's letter, and the signed photograph, put them into a manila envelope, addressed it, sealed it, and put it in his briefcase to take to the post office.

For weeks and weeks after that, I dreaded the arrival of our postman. I was convinced a letter'd come beginning,

> Dear Marijane,
> How very disappointed I am in you. . . .

"I don't think he'll write back," Billy Shakespeare told me. "I don't think he'll want anything more to do with you."

That ended getting dinner for movie stars in my playhouse.

I told Dorothy Spencer that I'd outgrown all that.

Three years after I wrote Ronald Reagan that letter, I slumped way down in my seat in humiliation as I watched him lose a leg in the movie *King's Row*. . . . I was sure he thought of the little liar from upstate New York who'd pretended she was crippled.

Many, many years later, the man I always thought should be President of the United States was dead, and Ronald Reagan was President of the United States.

I didn't vote for him.

I heard Dorothy Spencer got married, and I envision her making meat loaf and mashed for her husband.

The only remaining question is,
Where are you now,
William Shakespeare?

---

deception (dih SEP shun) trick; act of deceiving

Review the Selection

UNDERSTAND THE SELECTION

Recall

1. Who did Marijane and Billy plan to name their first child after?

2. What meal did Dorothy Spencer always like to serve Spencer Tracy?

3. Why did Marijane slump in her seat when she saw the film *King's Row*?

Infer

4. Describe Marijane.

5. Why did Marijane write Ronald Reagan that she was crippled?

6. Why do you think Marijane and Dorothy always played the same "game" with their actor husbands?

7. What was Billy Shakespeare's reaction to the dinner game Marijane and Dorothy played?

Apply

8. Would you have reacted in the same way to Marijane's letter to Ronald Reagan as her father did? Explain.

9. Do you think Marijane's father would have made a good president?

10. Why do you think Marijane did not vote for Ronald Reagan as president?

Respond to Literature

Were you in love with anyone when you were ten years old? Who and why?

WRITE ABOUT THE SELECTION

Where do you think Marijane's friend, William Shakespeare, is now? Marijane decides to find out. She asks old high school friends what has become of him, she writes some letters to addresses she has been given, and one day a letter with the return address marked "William Shakespeare" arrives. What do you think the letter says?

Assume that you are William Shakespeare. What would you say to an old friend who wonders what you are doing?

Prewriting What are you, William Shakespeare, doing now? Are you married? Do you have a family? What is your job? How do you now feel about the relationship you and Marijane had many years before? Make some notes, and organize your ideas into paragraphs using an informal outline.

Writing Write your letter to Marijane, using the informal outline. Write as much as you want. Remember, you have not seen or talked to Marijane in years.

Revising What is the tone of your letter? Is it consistent with how you imagine William Shakespeare to be now? Make any changes to make clear your attitude toward him and the reader. Remember letters include inside addresses, dates, salutations, and closings. Add them if you do not have them.

Proofreading Reread your letter and check for errors. Make sure transitions from one paragraph to the next are clear. A good letter is well-organized.

THINK ABOUT TONE

A writer sets the tone of a story in many ways. The **tone** can be set through the choice of individual words, the use of certain phrases, detailed descriptions, or by including or omitting specific things.

1. The title of this selection sounds like a trick. Yet M.E. Kerr says in the first paragraph no trick is involved. How does she do this? What does this say about her attitude toward the reader?

2. M.E. Kerr offers a detailed description in the fifth paragraph of herself at age ten. What is the tone?

3. M.E. Kerr gives her father's reason why he did not want to be president. What is the effect of this information?

4. The first time Marijane tells about Dorothy's meal she calls it "meat loaf with mashed potatoes." After that she calls it "meat loaf with mashed." How does that change make you feel?

5. How does the use of the phrase "Crossmyheartandhopetodie" affect tone?

READING FOCUS

Analyze Details While reading this story you were able to analyze details about the characters, tone, or plot. Based on those details, what do you think the overall tone of the story is? What is the author's attitude toward the subject matter of the story?

DEVELOP YOUR VOCABULARY

Homophones are words that sound alike but have different spellings and different meanings.

Examples: son-sun   days-daze
flour-flower

In each sentence below is at least one word that has a homophone. Find the word, and give its homophone.

1. We would name our first son Ellis.

2. This did not faze Billy Shakespeare.

3. This was his real name.

4. Is it all right with your father?

5. She wanted to please my father.

6. I wanted a Ronald Reagan photograph.

7. We had been playing house.

8. Dorothy served Spencer meat loaf.

9. She also gave him mashed potatoes.

10. They were in love.

11. We loved these little games.

12. My hair never had a ribbon.

THEME

Did you ever get to the end of a poem and ask, "What does it mean?" You reread the poem, maybe two or three times. You look up definitions for all the unfamiliar words. You examine each line to understand its meaning, but still you are in doubt.

Now you sit back and try to get the "bigger" picture. You are searching for the "theme" of the poem. The **theme** of a poem is its main idea or meaning.

Perhaps the theme is about the difficulty in expressing love, as in "First Person Demonstrative," or it may be about the ending of a relationship, as in "Finis." Theme can be anything the poet chooses.

The poems you have read so far in this unit have been about love between individual people. The last two poems are a bit different.

As you read them, look for answers to the following questions:

1. How are they different from the other poems in this unit?
2. What is the theme of each of the two poems?

WRITING CONNECTION

Songs are often lyric poetry. Write the lyrics of a song you like; then, in a sentence or two, explain the theme.

READING FOCUS

Recognize Simile and Personification
A simile makes a comparison between two different things, using the words *like* or *as*. Personification gives human characteristics to non-human objects or ideas. For example, in "I Dream a World," the author describes a world where "wretchedness will hang its head." As you read, look at the way similes and personification strengthen the poems and the authors' messages.

I Dream a World

by Langston Hughes

I dream a world where man
No other man will scorn,
Where love will bless the earth
And peace its paths adorn.
5   I dream a world where all
Will know sweet freedom's way,
Where greed no longer saps the soul
Nor avarice blights our day.
A world I dream where black or white,
10   Whatever race you be,
Will *share* the bounties of the earth
And every man is free,
Where wretchedness will hang its head,
And joy, like a pearl,
15   Attend the needs of all mankind.
Of such I dream—
Our world!

Reflections

by Vanessa Howard

If the world looked in a looking glass,
It'd see back hate, it'd see back war and it'd see
    back sorrow,
It'd see back fear.
If the world looked in a looking glass, it'd run
    away with shame, and hide.

---

adorn (uh DAWRN) to beautify or embellish
greed (GREED) a great desire for wealth or material things
avarice (AV uh ris) greed
blights (BLYTS) destroys, disappoints, frustrates

Review the Selection

UNDERSTAND THE SELECTION

Recall

1. Who does the speaker of "I Dream A World" hope will one day share the earth's bounties?

2. The speaker of "I Dream A World" compares the "joy" he is dreaming about to something. What is it?

3. Name at least two things the speaker in "Reflections" feels the world would see in a looking glass.

Infer

4. Speakers in other poems in this unit have addressed a "you." These two poems do not. Why?

5. What is the theme of "I Dream A World"?

6. Why is the title of Vanessa Howard's poem "Reflections"?

7. What is the theme of "Reflections"?

Apply

8. How are the themes similar?

9. How are these themes different?

10. What do you think the poets are like? What kind of lives do they have?

Respond to Literature

Explain which of these poems more accurately presents your view of the world and the love in it.

WRITE ABOUT THE SELECTION

Vanessa Howard uses personification when she describes the world looking in a mirror. The world cannot "look" into a mirror. It also cannot "run" or "hide." Only people can do that.

The mirror is a way for the poet to talk about what she feels exists in the world. Since a mirror reflects only what is there, the technique adds a touch of reality to her opinions.

What do you think the world would see if it looked in a mirror? Vanessa Howard thinks it would see hate, war, sorrow, and fear. Do you agree?

Write what you think would be in the mirror if the world looked at itself.

Prewriting Draw a frame around a blank sheet of paper. Suppose that it is a mirror. Write some words or phrases in the mirror describing what the world would see.

Writing Turn your words and phrases into a poem. You can use the same style Vanessa Howard did, or you can try something different.

Revising What is the theme of your poem? Is it clear? Add any words or phrases that will help to make the meaning clear. Eliminate any words or phrases that are confusing.

Proofreading Have you used any contractions in your poem? Check to make sure that you have spelled them correctly. Be sure to be consistent with your capitalization and punctuation.

THINK ABOUT THEME

There are many clues you can look for when you are searching for theme.

1. Does the poet use negative or positive words? **Negative words** make you feel hopeless and sad. **Positive words** make you feel hopeful and happy. Look at "I Dream A World" and "Reflections." Make a list of key words, and mark them with a + or −.

2. What is the tone of each poem? What is each poet's attitude toward his and her respective subject?

3. Is there any form of humor (such as hyperbole or irony) in either of the poems? Are the poets speaking "straight," or are they hiding meaning?

4. Look at the titles of the poems. Explain how "I Dream A World" and "Reflections" relate to the themes.

5. Use your feelings as a guide to finding the theme. How do you feel when you read these two poems?

READING FOCUS

Recognize Simile and Personification
Provide an example of simile and personification in the two poems. Tell how these figures of speech enhance the poems.

DEVELOP YOUR VOCABULARY

Synonyms are words having the same or nearly the same meaning. Langston Hughes uses *greed* in one line of his poem, and *avarice* in the next. Both mean "a great desire for wealth or material things." They are synonyms.

Synonyms are very useful if you are trying to rhyme. You can choose a synonym that rhymes with another word, rather than one that does not.

Use a dictionary to find synonyms for the following words as they are used in "I Dream A World." Then use each in a sentence.

1. scorn
2. bless
3. adorn
4. sap
5. blight
6. bounties
7. wretchedness
8. attend

WRITING APPLICATIONS

Write About Theme

You have just been hired by a record company to write songs. Your first assignment is to write a love song.

You panic. What can you write about? Then you remember that you once read a series of stories and poems on love in English class. Themes come back to you: love lost; love found; love for friends, family, the world.

You have not been told whether the music has already been written for the song. You could write the words for a tune you already know or for a tune not yet composed.

Prewriting   Think back on the stories and poems. Which "message" did you like the best? Choose one poem or story, and think about the feelings presented in it. Write them down, quickly, with some ideas on how to describe the feelings. Decide on point of view for the song.

Writing   Assemble your material as a song. Think about other love songs you know. What makes their lyrics effective? Think of each verse as a paragraph.

Revising   Make sure that your song has stuck to the feeling that you want to describe. The theme should be clear.

Proofreading   Check that you have used commas and semicolons to make your ideas easy to understand.

Write About Genre

This unit has helped you see the elements of poetry, or how a poem is put together. You now should be better able to analyze poetry, to state what you like and do not like, and give reasons for your opinion.

Choose two poems in the unit, one that you did like and one that you did not. You will figure out why you formed these opinions by looking at the elements involved in each poem.

Prewriting   Review the work you did for the "Think About . . . " sections in this unit. Then make a chart with the name of the selections you have chosen at the top and the elements of poetry down the side: character, imagery, theme, tone, rhyme, and figures of speech. Reread each poem. Write down character, theme, and tone. Look for other elements in each poem: imagery, rhyme, and figures of speech. Note if they are present.

Writing   Look at your chart and determine how one element or the other makes you like or dislike a poem. Were you disappointed by the theme? Was there a lot of good imagery? Was the tone appealing? Write why that was important to you.

Revising   Make sure each paragraph has a topic sentence that expresses the paragraph's main idea.

Proofreading   Reread your writing for errors in spelling, punctuation, and mechanics. Neatly insert any changes.

Vocabulary

Suffixes are often used to turn nouns into adjectives. Notice in this sentence how the suffix *-ful* is added to the noun *success* to form the adjective *successful*: Henry Curran was big, busy, and successful.

If you know how a particular suffix is used, you can often figure out the meaning of the new word.

-ful	= having the quality of
-ic	= characteristic of
-less	= without
-able	= able to or having
-ard	= possessing something to excess
-ish	= characteristic of or tending toward something

Try to define each italicized adjective by examining the root noun and suffix. Remember that spellings sometimes change slightly when a suffix is added. Check your definition in a dictionary. Then write your own sentence using each word.

1. She spoke in an *apologetic* voice.

2. "I do not care if he is *armless*," he said.

3. She had a *sorrowful* look.

4. My time is *valuable*.

5. A *haggard* look was on her face.

6. "He is sixteen, but he is *smallish*," she said.

7. My dog looks *pathetic* after her bath.

Grammar, Usage, and Mechanics

Verbs must always agree with their subjects. Singular subjects take singular verbs, and plural subjects take plural verbs.

You must be careful to match a verb with its subject and not other words in the sentence.

You must remember that "there" is never the subject of a sentence. The verb of a sentence beginning with "there" matches the subject, which comes after the verb.

Here are some examples of correct verb-subject agreement:

Examples: All snowflakes are six-sided. The question on verbs is a good one. There are the buses.

Correct the verb-subject agreement errors in these sentences.

1. It are always one or the other with you innocent victims.

2. Why, I never were in Springfield in my life!

3. Her father own the bank.

4. There is lots of nickel-plated shoehorns in there.

5. Underneath the pigeonholes were a row of three brass-knobbed, little drawers.

6. My hand and shirt cuff was streaked with old dust.

UNIT 1 Review

When you select a poem to read aloud, it should be one that you especially like. If you like it, you will be able to read it in such a way that your audience will like it, too.

Reading poems aloud is much different than reading other types of literature aloud. Most poems have so much emotion that they require certain procedures so the reader and the audience enjoy the poem.

Practice the following steps before you read the poem of your choice.

1. Read the poem to yourself.

2. Read the poem again. Determine the subjects of the verbs and the antecedents of the pronouns. This will help you understand what the poem is about.

3. Pay attention to words that you may not be familiar with. Check their definitions and pronunciations to ensure understanding of the poem.

4. Read the poem aloud softly and slowly so you hear the sounds of the words. This will help the meaning of the poem to set in.

5. Now read the poem once again. This time pay particular attention to the punctuation. Remember, most poetry is written in sentences just as prose is. The way a poem is punctuated tells you how it should be read. Pause when necessary!

6. Practice reading the poem in front of a mirror. Decide when to look at your audience. You want to maintain some eye contact not just out of courtesy, but also because looking forward will help project your voice.

7. Ask a friend or a family member to listen to you read the poem. If someone is not available, use a tape recorder so you can listen to your delivery. Concentrate on reading the poem just loud enough and just slow enough for your audience to enjoy. Think about improvements as you listen to yourself. Then read the poem again if you decide on any changes.

Once you have prepared yourself for this assignment, choose a poem or part of a poem from this unit. Follow the procedures above so you can successfully read your poem to a group or your entire class. Limit your reading to approximately two minutes. There is no need to be nervous if you are prepared adequately. Enjoy yourself!

CRITICAL THINKING

Reasoning   Inductive and deductive reasoning are used to make conclusions based on evidence.

In **inductive reasoning**, you begin with evidence and arrive at a conclusion. Here is an example of inductive reasoning: The desk lamp in your room goes out. You replace the bulb with a new one. The lamp still does not work. You try another new bulb. Still no luck. Something is wrong with the lamp, you conclude.

In **deductive reasoning**, you reason the other way: You begin with a conclusion that is generally accepted as true. You consider the evidence of a situation, and make a conclusion based on whether the evidence fits the conclusion with which you started. Here is an example: Animals with six legs are insects. You see an animal with six legs. You conclude, therefore, that the animal is an insect.

You must be careful to reason correctly. Incorrect inductive reasoning leads to hasty generalization, and incorrect deductive reasoning leads to unsound conclusions. A hasty generalization is a statement made about a whole group on the basis of a few examples. For example: *teenagers are poor drivers and cause most accidents.* Unsound conclusions result when facts and evidence are not true. For example: *John is qualified to be class president because he has run for other offices.*

Look back at the selections in this unit, and find one example each of inductive and deductive reasoning. Explain the reasoning process.

EFFECTIVE STUDYING

Studying Poetry   It is sometimes helpful to step back from what you are reading to get the bigger picture.

When you study a poem, read it straight through once without stopping. This first quick read will give you an idea about character, tone, and theme. It will also put things in context, which could give you clues to parts of the poem you do not understand.

Then go back and read the poem again. Stop whenever you do not understand a word or phrase, and find its meaning. Look for imagery, figures of speech, and rhyme. Take the poem apart, but think how all the elements fit together.

Then step back and get the bigger picture. Read the poem again, straight through. The poet's message now should be loud and clear.

Choose one poem from this book. Use these techniques and write a paragraph analyzing it.

Test Preparation

When answering test questions about a poem, be sure to read the poem several times before answering the questions. Use the strategies listed above.

The Unknown

We are such stuff
As dreams are made on.
—William Shakespeare

The Sleeping Gypsy, 1897, Henri Rousseau. Oil on canvas, 51" × 6'7". Collection, The Museum of Modern Art, New York. Gift of Mrs. Simon Guggenheim

The Unknown

Have you ever had the feeling there are "things" out there that you know nothing about?

The conflict between what is known and what is unknown is a common theme in literature. William Shakespeare suggests that you yourself might be nothing more than dreams. Are you then part of the unknown?

Throughout time, writers have created stories and poems about the unknown. As you read a few of them in this unit, try to keep an open mind about the existence of mysterious, unexplainable things.

■ MATTERS OF LIFE AND DEATH

One part of the unknown that may always remain a mystery is death. Yet writers have tried for centuries to understand death and make it "come alive."

In the first two selections, "Appointment in Baghdad," a folktale that originated long ago in the Middle East, and "Appointment at Noon," Death is an actual person who comes to claim victims whose time on earth has run out. The same theme appears in the poem "Incident in a Rose Garden."

Can people come back from the dead? In the story "Boy in the Shadows," Irene and Ernest Platt wonder about their hired hand; how can his thinness, his listlessness, and his odd manner be explained?

Modern city life abounds with all sorts of fears. What if you were to overhear a phone conversation concerning a murder? In "Sorry, Wrong Number," a woman is faced with just that situation and she tries to do something to prevent the crime. What steps would you take if you were aware of a similar situation?

■ MYSTERIES WITHIN

When you were young, did you have imaginary playmates that you thought were real?

Small Simon is sure that an imaginary companion he calls "Mr. Beelzy" really exists in "Thus I Refute Beelzy." His father, Big Simon, tries to convince him otherwise. Big Simon's logic has no effect on the boy, and the story has a mysterious conclusion.

E. E. Cummings shows his remarkable skill in using language creatively as he conjures images of ghosts, witches, goblins, and toads in the poem "hist, whist." "Overheard on a Saltmarsh" describes a tussle between mysterious night creatures over green glass beads stolen from the moon.

In "The Judge's House," a student finds himself in a frightening situation. Looking for a quiet place to study, he rents an old house that used to belong to a judge. He ignores warnings that the house is haunted and is later threatened by the ghost of the judge. Why do you think some people choose to ignore warnings about potential dangers?

"The Listeners" and "Eldorado" tell of travelers who are searching. They seem to be chasing dreams.

■ COULD IT BE REAL?

In a world of technology you might feel that unknown or unexplainable things are not worth thinking about.

But what do you do when sincere, trustworthy observers provide evidence that suggests you are wrong?

"The Loch Ness Monster" and "The Great Amherst Mystery" take a reasonable, logical approach toward explaining the unexplainable and solving certain mysteries. Both stories suggest that while it's good to be skeptical, you should keep an open mind.

Learn About

FORESHADOWING

Hints or clues about what will happen in a story are called **foreshadowing**. You can take these hints or clues and make a prediction about how the story will develop. Through this technique, the author prepares you for the action ahead.

Good foreshadowing provides just enough information to give you a general idea of what will happen, but not enough to give away the ending.

As you read "Appointment in Baghdad," ask yourself these questions:

1. Does the author use foreshadowing?
2. How can foreshadowing be used to predict what will happen at the end of the story?

READING FOCUS

Draw Conclusions An author does not always state directly why certain events in a story take place, or why characters do certain things.

Often readers must draw their own conclusions. To do this, use clues that the author gives about events and characters and what you already know. Try to draw conclusions as you read by asking questions about why certain events take place and why characters behave as they do.

WRITING CONNECTION

Foreshadowing is often used in jokes. Through foreshadowing, the joke teller gives you clues as to what the "punch line" will be. You make a prediction, but usually it is wrong. When the punch line is finally told, surprise turns to humor. Think of a joke that uses foreshadowing and write it down as a dialogue.

Appointment in Baghdad

traditional version
retold by Edith Wharton

The Race Track (Death on a Pale Horse), Albert Pinkham Ryder. c. 1886–1908. (American, 1847–1917) Oil on canvas, 70.5 × 90 cm. ©The Cleveland Museum of Art, 2000. Purchase from the J. H. Wade Fund, 1928.8

One morning the Sultan was resting in his palace in Damascus.[1] Suddenly the door flew open, and in rushed a young man, out of breath and wild with excitement. The Sultan sat up alarmed, for the young man was his most skillful assistant.

"I must have your best horse!" the youth cried out. "There is little time! I must fly at once to Baghdad!"[2]

The Sultan asked why the young man was in such a rush.

"Because," came the hurried reply, "just now, as I was walking in the palace garden, I saw Death standing there. And when Death saw me, he raised his arms in a frightening motion. Oh, it was horrible! I must escape at once!"

The Sultan quickly arranged for the youth to have his fastest horse. And no sooner had the young man thundered out through the palace gate, than the Sultan himself went into the garden. Death was still there.

The Sultan was angry. "What do you mean?" he demanded. "What do you mean by raising your arms and frightening my young friend?"

"Your Majesty," Death said calmly, "I did not mean to frighten him. You see, I raised my arms only in surprise. I was astonished to see him here in your garden, for I have an appointment with him tonight in Baghdad."

---

[1] **Damascus:** an important Middle Eastern city, now capital of Syria
[2] **Baghdad:** an important city in the old Middle East, now capital of Iraq

Review the Selection

UNDERSTAND THE SELECTION

Recall

1. Where does the story take place?

2. Who is the young man who rushes in asking to borrow a horse?

3. Why did Death raise his arms when he encountered the young man?

Infer

4. Why did Death's actions frighten the young man?

5. Why did the young man want a horse?

6. Describe what happens when the Sultan goes out to the palace garden.

7. What is the significance of the word "Appointment" in the title?

Apply

8. Suppose that you are the young man and you have seen Death in the palace garden. How would you react?

9. The Sultan seems to be a brave man to go out to the palace garden and confront Death. Is this part of the story hard for you to believe?

10. What is the point of this story?

Respond to Literature

Is there such a thing as fate? Are all of our actions predetermined, and we are like players on a stage acting out parts? Explain your answers.

WRITE ABOUT THE SELECTION

What do you think the young man thought when he saw Death in the palace garden? Many thoughts must have raced through his mind when he encountered the figure.

Suppose that you are the young man. Write what happened and what you thought when you were walking in the garden and first saw Death.

Prewriting Draw a quick sketch of the garden to help you visualize the scene before describing it in words. Place the young man in the scene, and mark where he sees Death. Then write a few words next to the man to describe his thoughts just before he met Death, at the moment he met Death, and immediately after their encounter. Finally, try to draw a picture of Death.

Writing Use your picture and notes to write one or several paragraphs to describe what happened in the garden. Remember to use first-person point of view so that your description fits into the rest of the story.

Revising Try to write in the same style as Edith Wharton, using short sentences and simple, direct language. Consider adding specific details and vivid words to make your paragraph really come alive.

Proofreading As you reread what you have written, check carefully that references to the character Death begin with a capital letter. If you have included direct conversation, make sure you have followed the rules of punctuation.

THINK ABOUT FORESHADOWING

What makes "Appointment in Baghdad" such a good short story? It is short—even for a short story—but that is not all. Let us look again at expectations of what will happen, what really happens, and fore-shadowing. The writer's skillful use of foreshadowing—hints or clues that sug-gest what might happen—lead you to expect a certain outcome.

1. After the young man rides off on the horse, what do you expect will happen?

2. How was that expectation formed?

3. How does the story end?

4. Look back at the story again. Are there hints about what will happen?

5. Do you feel the writer has played a trick on you with the ending to the story? Explain your answer.

READING FOCUS

Draw Conclusions As you read the story, you were able to draw conclusions about certain events and why they occurred. Name one such event and the conclusion you drew from it.

DEVELOP YOUR VOCABULARY

The comparative and superlative forms of almost all one-syllable adjectives are formed by adding *er* and *est*.

Some two-syllable adjectives are formed in the same way, but others are formed, (like all adjectives of more than two syllables) by adding *more* and *most*.

fast	faster	fastest
skillful	more skillful	most skillful

Some adjective forms are irregular:

good	better	best

If you are in doubt about adjective forms, check the dictionary.

Give the forms for these adjectives:

1. fresh
2. many
3. plain
4. beautiful
5. dear

6. pretty
7. friendly
8. thin
9. humble
10. contented

Focus ON FICTION

*S*hort stories are a very popular form of fiction. Why?

Short stories are so concentrated that they can have a lot of impact in just a few pages. The conciseness of a short story also provides the chance for a clear examination of the four basic elements of fiction. These are plot, characters, setting, and theme.

Plot   Plot is usually the most obvious element of a short story. Many people think of it first when they talk about a story: the telling of one event after another to form a series of actions leading to a conclusion.

The plot is usually introduced through **exposition**, or written interpretation, by the author. Exposition provides background information for the actions that will take place in the story.

As the action unfolds, a complication arises. The **complication** is like a question demanding an answer. It keeps the story moving, as you wonder what will happen next. Sometimes the answer ends the story, or it can lead to another question.

As the plot develops, the action rises. **Rising action** leads to a crisis with a climax at the end, or near the end, of the story. **Climax** is the peak of the action.

If the story continues beyond the climax, the action falls. The plot develops further, but only to resolve a final question. The **falling action** ends in **resolution**.

When you read a story quickly, you are probably unaware of all those plot developments. Try to keep them in mind as you read the next selections, especially "Thus I Refute Beelzy," when you'll be studying plot developments in detail.

Characters   The characters are the people in a short story. They act, or are acted upon, as the plot develops.

You learn about characters in two ways. First, the writer might tell you directly whether a certain character is clever, mean, bold or shy. The writer is creating **traits** that describe the character.

Second, the writer can tell you indirectly about a character by describing what the character says or how the character acts. This information portrays the character, too, but you must use some imagination to fit the pieces into the overall description.

Usually a writer uses both methods. In "Appointment in Baghdad," you learn that one character is a young man. That is **direct information**. You also learn that he rushes into the Sultan's palace "out of breath and wild with excitement." That is **indirect information**, giving you clues to his general state of mind and how he reacts in certain situations.

Setting   A third element of a short story is setting. You can probably guess that setting includes where a story takes place, but it also includes when a story happens. Additionally, it can include natural events, such as a blizzard or a hurricane.

The short stories in this unit have a variety of settings. "Of Missing Persons" takes place in modern-day New York, while "Appointment in Baghdad" takes place in the Middle East long ago.

Theme   Theme is the fourth element of a short story.

A writer usually has a reason for telling us a story. He or she chooses a subject, and then develops plot, setting, and characters. What the writer wants you to learn from the story is the theme. It is the story's idea or message.

"Appointment in Baghdad" has a single, clear theme: Death cannot be avoided.

Sometimes a short story has more than one theme. Sometimes there is no theme of real importance, or the theme is not clear.

As you read the selections in this unit, look for the elements of the short stories. Ask yourself these questions:
   1. Which elements are the easiest to identify and understand? Which are the hardest?
   2. Are elements more important in some stories than in others?

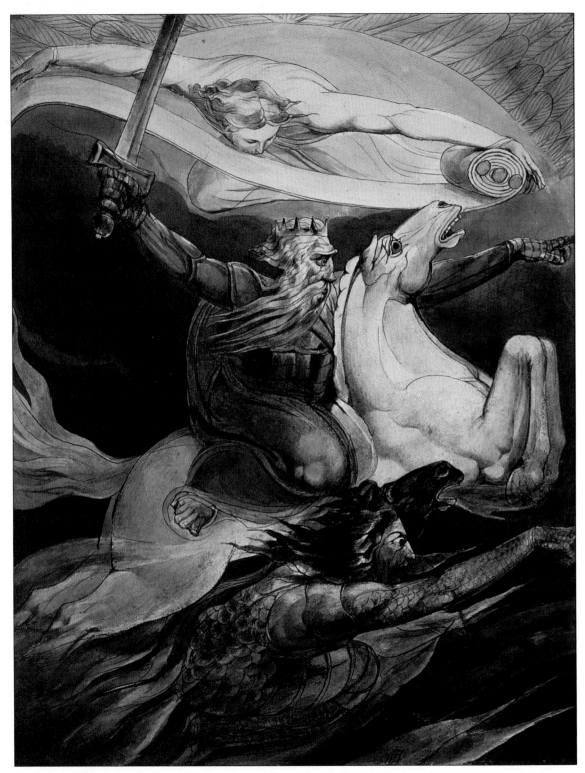

Death on a Pale Horse, William Blake. Fitzwilliam Museum, University of Cambridge/Bridgeman Art Library

APPOINTMENT AT NOON

by Eric Frank Russell

Henry Curran was big, busy, and successful. He had no patience with people who weren't successful. He had the build of a fighter and the soul of a tiger. His time was worth a thousand bucks an hour. He knew of nobody who was worth more.

And crime did not pay? "Bah!" said Henry Curran.

The law of the jungle paid off. Henry Curran had learned that nice people are soft people, and that smiles are made to be slapped.

Entering his large office with the fast, heavy step of a big man in fighting shape, Henry threw his hat onto a hook. He glanced at the wall clock. He noted that it was ten minutes to twelve.

Seating himself in the large chair behind his desk, he kept his eyes on the door. His wait lasted about ten seconds. Frowning at the thought of it, Curran reached over and pushed a red button on his big desk.

"What's wrong with you?" he snapped when Miss Reed came in. "You get worse every day. Old age creeping over you or something?"

She paused. She was tall, neat, and steady. She faced him across the desk, her eyes showing a touch of fear. Curran hired to work for him only people he knew too much about.

"I'm sorry, Mr. Curran, I was—"

"Never mind the excuse. Be faster—or else! Speed's what I like. SPEED—SEE?"

"Yes, Mr. Curran."

"Has Lolordo phoned in yet?"

"No, Mr. Curran."

"He should be through by now if everything went all right." He looked at the clock again, tapping angrily on his desk. "If he's made a mess of it and the mouthpiece comes on, tell him to forget about Lolordo. He's in no position to talk, anyway. A little time in jail will teach him not to be stupid."

"Yes, Mr. Curran. There's an old—"

This is the plot complication.

"Shut up till I've finished. If Michaelson calls up and says the *Firefly* got through, phone Voss and tell him without delay! And I mean without delay! That's important!" He thought for a moment. Then he finished, "There's that meeting downtown at twelve-twenty. God knows how long it will go on. If they want trouble, they can have it! If anyone asks, you don't know where I am. You don't expect me back before four."

"But, Mr. Curran—"

"You heard what I said. Nobody sees me before four."

"There's a man already here," she got out in an apologetic voice. "He said you have an appointment with him at two minutes to twelve."

"And you fell for a joke like that?" He studied her with a cutting smile.

The third character, the uninvited guest, is described indirectly. Despite this description, he is pretty mysterious. This mystery creates tension. Further hints about him heighten the mystery.

"I can only repeat what he said. He seemed quite sincere."

"That's a change," snapped Curran. "Sincerity in *my* office? He's got the wrong address. Go tell him to spread himself across the tracks. "

"I said you were out and didn't know when you would return. He took a seat and said he'd wait because you would be back at ten to twelve."

Without knowing it, both suddenly stared at the clock. Curran lifted an arm and looked at his wristwatch to check the instrument on the wall.

---

mouthpiece (MOUTH pees) slang for criminal lawyer
apologetic (uh POL uh JET ik) filled with apology; suggesting that one is sorry
sincerity (sin SER uh tee) honesty; quality of being sincere

"That's what the scientific bigbrains would call precognition. I call it a lucky guess. One minute either way would have made him wrong. That guy ought to bet money on the horses." He made a gesture of dismissal. "Push him out—or do I have to get the boys to do it for you?"

"That wouldn't be necessary. He is old and blind."

"I don't care if he's armless and legless—that's *his* tough luck. Give him the rush."

Obediently she left. A few moments later she was back. She had the sorrowful look of a person whose job forced her to face Curran's anger.

The action continues to rise. Note how time has become very important to the story.

"I'm terribly sorry, Mr. Curran. He insists that he has a date with you for two minutes to twelve. He is to see you about a personal matter of great importance."

Curran scowled at the wall. The clock said four minutes to twelve. He spoke with purpose.

"I know no blind man and I don't forget appointments. Throw him down the stairs."

She hesitated, standing there wide-eyed. "I'm wondering whether—"

"Out with it!"

"Whether he's been sent to you by someone else, someone who'd rather he couldn't tell who you were by sight."

He thought it over and said, "Could be. You use your brains once in a while. What's his name?"

"He won't say."

"Nor state his business?"

"No."

"H'm! I'll give him two minutes. If he's trying to get money for some church or something he'll go out through the window. Tell him my time is valuable and show him in."

The visitor now confronts Henry Curran. What can you infer about the old man from the description?

She went away and brought back the visitor. She gave him a chair. The door closed quietly behind her. The clock said three minutes before the hour.

Curran sat back and looked at his guest, finding him tall, thin, and white-haired. The old man's clothes were black, a deep,

---

precognition (pree kog NISH un) knowledge of future events
scowled (SKOULD) frowned and looked angry

somber black. They set off the bright, blue, unseeing eyes staring from his colorless face.

Those strange eyes were the old man's most noticeable feature. They were odd, as if somehow they could look *into* the things they could not look at. And they were sorry—sorry for what they saw.

For the first time in his life, Henry Curran felt a little alarmed. He said, "What can I do for you?"

"Nothing," replied the other. "Nothing at all."

His voice was like an organ. It was low, no more than a whisper, and with its sounding a queer coldness came over the room. He sat there unmoving and staring at whatever a blind man can see. The coldness increased, became bitter. Curran shivered despite himself. He frowned and got a hold on himself.

The theme emerges in the visitor's rejoinder to Henry Curran's sharp comment.

"Don't take up my time," advised Curran. "State your business or get out."

"People don't take up time. Time takes up people."

This is the climax. Henry Curran even asks the two questions we want answered.

"Just what do you mean? Who are you?"

"You know who I am. Every man is a shining sun to himself, until he is dimmed by his dark companion."

"You're not funny," said Curran, freezing.

"I am never funny."

The tiger light blazed in Curran's eyes as he stood up. He placed a thick, firm finger near his desk button.

"Enough of this nonsense! What d'you want?"

Suddenly holding out a lengthless, dimensionless arm, the man whispered sadly, "You!"

And Death took him.

At exactly two minutes to twelve.

---

somber (SOM bur) gloomy and dark; very sad
dimensionless (duh MEN shun les) without dimensions, or size that can be measured in length, height, or width

Incident in a Rose Garden

by Donald Justice

GARDENER:
Sir, I encountered Death
Just now among our roses.
Thin as a scythe he stood there.

Notice how this poem shares elements with the short story. The title and the first two lines establish the setting.

5
I knew him by his pictures.
He had his black coat on,
Black gloves, a broad black hat.

The poem has characters, like a short story.

I think he would have spoken,
Seeing his mouth stood open.
Big it was, with white teeth.

10
As soon as he beckoned, I ran.
I ran until I found you.
Sir, I am quitting my job.

The plot has developed from the very first line of the poem. Now the plot complication appears.

15
I want to see my sons
Once more before I die.
I want to see California.

MASTER:
Sir, you must be that stranger
Who threatened my gardener.
This is my property, sir.
I welcome only friends here.

20   DEATH:
Sir, I knew your father.
And we were friends at the end.

As for your gardener,
I did not threaten him.
Old men mistake my gestures.

25
I only meant to ask him
To show me to his master.
I take it you are he?

The theme emerges in the climax. What is the theme?

---

scythe (SYTH) a long, curved blade fixed at an angle to a long, bent handle and used to cut down grass or grain

Review the Selection

UNDERSTAND THE SELECTION

Recall

1. When did Henry Curran enter his office?

2. Before the visitor enters Curran's office, what does Curran think about him?

3. What color were Death's clothes?

Infer

4. What was Curran's profession?

5. Describe Miss Reed.

6. Why is the visitor in "Appointment at Noon" old and blind?

7. Why did Death not speak to the gardener in "Incident in a Rose Garden"?

Apply

8. Discuss the difference in titles between "Appointment in Baghdad" and "Appointment at Noon."

9. Did "Appointment at Noon" turn out the way you expected? Was there any foreshadowing to help you?

10. Why do you think both "Appointment in Baghdad" and "Incident in a Rose Garden" include gardens for settings?

Respond to Literature

"Appointment in Baghdad," "Appointment at Noon," and "Incident in a Rose Garden" show Death as being uninterested in the ages of his "victims." Why?

WRITE ABOUT THE SELECTION

If you had to describe Death as a person, what would you say? Is Death a man or a woman? Does it look like a person? Do only certain parts look like a person? Can Death talk? Can it hear, feel, smell, and touch? What does it wear? Does it carry anything?

Assume that you are writing a story and Death is a character. Write a description of Death.

Prewriting Using clusters, answer the questions above. Add any other information that helps to provide an accurate description of what you think Death looks like. Make a sketch or illustration of the character Death if that will stimulate your imagination.

Writing Use the information in the clusters and your drawing to write your description. You may introduce another character if you want to use conversation to build the description, but Death must remain the central figure.

Revising You want your readers to have as clear a picture as possible of how you imagine Death to be. Can you add any similes to make the description more vivid? Think about using sensory details: description that appeals to the senses of sight, sound, smell, feeling, or taste.

Proofreading Reread what you have written and check that all sentences end with a punctuation mark. Check also that Death as a character always begins with a capital D.

THINK ABOUT FICTION

Were you surprised that the poem "Incident in a Rose Garden" was similar to "Appointment at Baghdad"? Were you surprised that a poem could seem like a short story because it shares the same elements?

1. List all of the similar elements of fiction in "Incident in a Rose Garden" and "Appointment at Baghdad."

2. List the differences between the two.

3. Point to things that are missing in the poem as compared to the story.

4. Why do you think some elements are missing in the poem as compared to the story?

5. Which of these three selections is your favorite? Why?

DEVELOP YOUR VOCABULARY

Many times suffixes are added to adjectives to make them nouns:

patient + -ence = patience

If you know the suffix and the root word you can figure out the meaning.

-ence = act, quality, or result of
-ity = state, character, condition of
-ness = state or quality of being
-tude = state or quality of being

Define each italicized noun by determining the root adjective and suffix. Check your definition in a dictionary. Then write your own sentence using each word.

1. "*Sincerity* in my office?" he snapped.

2. Did he state his *business*?

3. A queer *coldness* came over the room.

4. Her *certitude* was a real advantage.

5. "*Capability* is the thing!" he said.

CHARACTER

Stories are about characters who may not be real but are probably drawn from real life. A character is often modeled after a real human being with all the good and bad traits that people can have. A story usually revolves around the problems the main character or characters have.

Writers can develop characters directly by telling you what they look like or what they are thinking. Characters also can be developed indirectly through their actions or their speech. Good characters make you care about their problems.

As you read "Boy in the Shadows," ask yourself these questions:

1. How might dialogue between characters reveal their traits?
2. Where do actions reveal character?

WRITING CONNECTION

Suppose you are on vacation. You meet someone who is interesting, and you want to write about him or her in a letter to a friend. Describe the person through an event in which the character traits of that person are revealed.

READING FOCUS

Make Predictions You can often predict the outcome of a story by paying attention to the clues that the author provides. Clues can also help you determine character's motives, the story's theme, and how conflicts might be resolved. As you read, watch for clues about characters and events that will help you to predict the story's outcome.

Boy in the Shadows

by Margaret Ronan

Is it true that love is stronger than death? That the human spirit can survive the grave? Perhaps the answer can be found in the strange experience of Irene and Ernest Platt.

The Platts had always lived in cities, but when Ernest retired, they decided they wanted to spend the rest of their lives in the country. They bought a small house tucked away on the lower slopes of the Ozarks.[1] Irene at once planted a vegetable garden. With what she could grow, and a trip once a week to the supermarket in the nearest town, they should have all the food they needed.

Food was the first thing she thought of when she saw the boy. She had been working in the garden when she became aware that someone was watching her. She raised her eyes, and there, standing at the edge of the field, was the boy—a thin, hollow-eyed boy wearing faded jeans and no shoes.

Irene raised her hand and waved, but the boy did not wave back. Perhaps he doesn't have the strength to wave, she thought to herself. He was very thin, and his ribs showed plainly.

The boy stood there a few more minutes. Then, as if he had seen all he wanted to, he turned and slipped away—vanishing among the thicket of trees at the edge of the field.

Two days later he was back. With him was a haggard-looking woman of about 40. When she saw Irene, she came straight up to the fence. The boy lagged slightly behind, head hanging listlessly.

"Are you the lady who bought this place?" the woman asked.

"I'm Mrs. Platt," replied Irene. "What can I do for you?"

"I've come about what we can do for you, Ma'am," replied the woman firmly. "This here's my son, Jayse. He's a good worker and a lot stronger than he looks. He'll work for you, do your garden and your chores, for two dollars a day."

---

thicket (THIK it) bushes or small trees growing close together
haggard (HAG urd) thin and worn from too much worry or pain
listlessly (LIST lis lee) in a tired, inactive way
[1]**Ozarks:** mountains that run through Arkansas and Missouri, Oklahoma, and Illinois

Irene was about to say that she didn't need any help, that she enjoyed doing her own chores. But the sight of Jayse's thin, dangling arms and hollow-cheeked face stopped her.

"He's very young—and he doesn't look strong," she began, but the woman held up a work-scarred hand to stop her.

"He's 16," she said, "but he's small-ish and looks younger. And he's a lot stronger than he looks, like I said. You won't have no cause for complaint. Jayse's a good worker."

"All right," said Irene. Two dollars a day wasn't much, and having Jayse on her own ground would give her a chance to feed him properly. "All right. That will be fine. Jayse can come at ten every morning and go home at five. I'll give him his dinner at noon." She turned to the boy. "Will that be all right with you, Jayse?"

Jayse didn't answer. Irene wondered if he had even heard her, for he kept his head down, never raising his eyes. His mother beckoned Irene to one side and spoke in a low voice. "No, Ma'am. I don't want Jayse traveling back and forth. We live a fair distance from here. He can sleep in that little shed there. And don't you be worrying about feeding him. I'll come every day and bring his food. He's got a finicky stomach. I know just what he can eat and I'll fix it for him. When I come, you can give me his two dollars."

"But what about Jayse?" Irene asked. "If he's working for the money, shouldn't I pay it to him?"

The woman shook her head. "You don't understand. I need that money to feed my other children. Jayse's pa is dead, and now the boy is the only one who can go out to work. He wants to do it to help us out. You won't be sorry you took him on. He's a good worker, is Jayse. He never gets tired, never complains. You'll see."

"Well, all right, but I don't think he should sleep in the shed. I could fix up a room in the house."

"No, Ma'am. Jayse wouldn't care for that. He's a poor sleeper and he wouldn't want to think he might disturb you. The shed will be fine."

So Jayse came to work for the Platts. Irene soon found that the claims his mother had made were true. Jayse never complained and never seemed to get tired. No matter how early Irene and Ernest got up in the morning, the boy was already at work, feeding the chickens, tending the garden. Gradually, Irene let him take over some of the cleaning chores in the house, and once she showed him what she wanted done, she never had to remind him to do it.

"He's a wonder," she told Ernest, "but he's not like a boy at all. He's like . . . like a machine. Do you know he's never said a word to me. He never even looks at me, only at the ground."

Ernest grunted. "All I know is that the kid gives me the creeps. Maybe he can't talk. And if you ask me, he's not all there mentally."

Irene shook her head. "No, he isn't

---

finicky (FIN ik ee) fussy; very hard to please
creeps (KREEPS) feeling of fear or horror

stupid. It's more as though he's walking around in his sleep."

"Well, the price is right," said Ernest. "In fact, it's wrong—two dollars a day is ridiculous for the work he's doing. Let's raise it to four. I'm not crazy about having Jayse around, but let's see if a raise gets some reaction from him."

Why should it? Irene wondered. Jayse never touched the money he earned. Every day, shortly before noon, he would stop what he was doing. Then he would stand, eyes lowered, head turned slightly to one side as though listening. A few minutes later his mother would appear from the wooded thicket, carrying his dinner in a covered tin plate. She would wait until Irene handed her Jayse's daily wages, then lead him to the shed and sit with him while he ate.

"Why won't she let me feed him?" Irene asked furiously. "I've seen the stuff she brings him—it's some kind of mush. That's not decent food for a boy who works as hard as he does. I think he's even thinner than he was when he first came here."

Ernest had to agree. The bones of Jayse's face were more prominent. When the boy bent over the hoe in the garden, his knobby spine was plainly outlined under his thin T-shirt.

Irene decided to try again. "I want to give Jayse a hot meal every day," she told his mother. "Otherwise I can't let him go on working here the way he does. He's getting thinner all the time. I'm afraid he'll get sick."

There was a frightened glitter in the woman's eyes. "You don't understand, Mrs. Platt. Jayse's like his father. He can't eat the food you and I can eat. He can't take salt—his system can't handle it. Please, Ma'am, let things be. Don't say you won't let him stay. He's the only one the kids and I can depend on. Without what he earns here, his brothers and sisters will starve."

Irene gave in. "All right, he can stay. I must admit he's a wonderful worker—but he doesn't seem happy about being with us. He never smiles or laughs. And he's never said a word to either my husband or myself."

The woman shrugged. "It don't mean anything, Ma'am. Jayse's different. He don't feel things the way most kids do. All he cares about is helping me and the other kids. Don't worry about him. He's doing what he wants to do."

But *is* it what he wants? Irene wondered. She stood at her bedroom window later. She could see the shed where Jayse slept—but he wasn't asleep. He was sitting in the doorway, arms resting slackly on his knees, staring unmovingly into the moonlit night.

"Something's wrong," she said aloud.

"What are you talking about?" her husband asked sleepily.

"Jayse. I've been watching him for half an hour. He's never moved so much as a muscle. With the day he's put in, you'd think he'd have gone to sleep

---

prominent (PROM uh nunt) easy to see; standing out
knobby (NOB ee) lumpy
slackly (SLAK lee) loosely

hours ago. But no—he's just sitting there."

Ernest got up and came to stand at her side. "I could have told you that. He always sits there at night. As far as I know, he never sleeps. I'll admit he's one spooky kid—but he's not really bothering anyone, is he?"

No one but me, Irene thought. As the days wore on, the sight of the boy wrung her heart. His skin, which had been pale, was now yellow and shiny. There were discolored patches on his forehead, cheekbones, and along the ridge of his nose. Even more disquieting, his movements seemed to be slower and more labored.

"Aren't you feeling well, Jayse?" she asked. But the boy only ducked his head and brushed past her. Uneasily, she went to her husband. "Look at Jayse. I think he's sick. He's moving around like an old man."

Ernest peered at Jayse, who was slowly cutting grass. "You're right. What are those dark patches on his skin?"

"I don't know, but I'm sure of one thing. He's going under from malnutrition. I don't care what his mother says— I'm going to get some decent food into him. And tomorrow you can drive him into town to see the doctor."

Protein! Irene thought. Jayse needed some high grade protein, and fast. She went into the kitchen and began to prepare a hearty meal of ham and eggs. That, plus plenty of milk and apple pie, should help.

When it was ready she called Jayse and brought him into the kitchen. "Sit down at the table," she told him. "I've made you a special dinner because you've been here three months today. That's cause for celebration."

Jayse took one bite of the food, then another. He chewed the ham slowly, and swallowed. Then he put down his fork and rose from the table.

"What's the matter?" Irene asked anxiously. "Where are you going?"

But he had already gone. The kitchen door closed behind him. Irene ran to the door and flung it open. The boy had already reached the line of trees that bordered the property. He was moving with long, steady strides. She called his name, but he never looked back.

"Leave him alone," said Ernest, who had just come into the kitchen. "He's going home. His mother was probably right. You shouldn't have given him that food."

Irene slept badly that night. She was up before dawn, walking about the garden. As she feared, Jayse had not come back. But shortly before noon, his mother appeared.

She walked straight up to Irene, her mouth fixed in a hard line. "You did it,

---

disquieting (dis KWY ut ing) disturbing; worrisome
labored (LAY burd) not easy; done with effort
malnutrition (mal noo TRISH un) poor health condition caused by not having enough of the right kinds of food
strides (STRYDZ) long steps

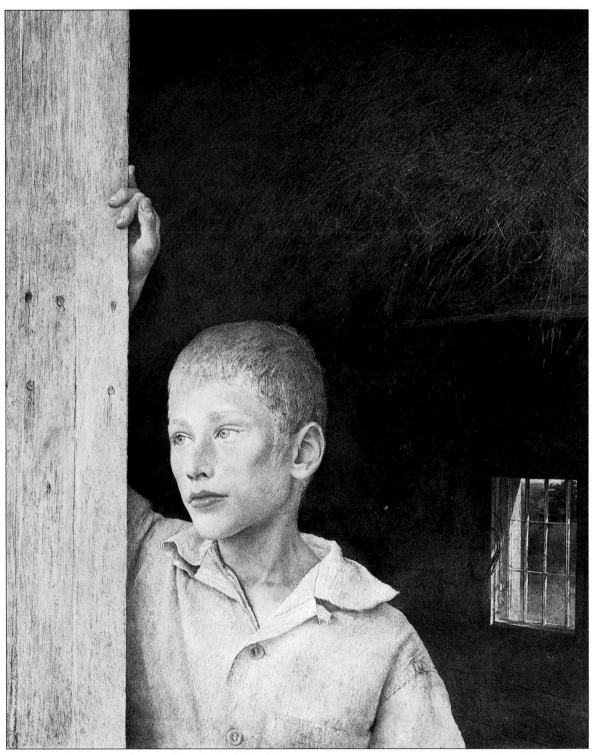

Albert's Son, Andrew Wyeth. Nasjonalgalleriet, Oslo

Journey, Morris Graves. Collection of The Whitney Museum of American Art

didn't you? You fed my boy after I told you not to. What did you give him to eat?"

"Ham and eggs," replied Irene. "Good food, the kind he needed."

"Ham. . ." the woman whispered, "so salty. . . ." Then her voice rose to a shriek. "You're a fool, a meddling fool! Why couldn't you leave well enough alone?"

"I'm sorry if my cooking made Jayse sick," Irene retorted angrily, "but he was starving to death in front of me. I couldn't let it go on. My husband and I will pay any medical bills and see that a doctor takes care of him. Now I want you to take me to him or we will have to notify the authorities."

For a moment the woman was silent, then she began to laugh mirthlessly. "Yes, Ma'am. I'll take you to him. You come with me and see what you've done."

She turned and Irene followed her

---

authorities (uh THAWR uh teez) people with official power
mirthlessly (MURTH lis lee) without humor

through the stretch of woods. For half an hour they climbed through the scraggy foothills. Finally they came to a shabby house where three young children sat listlessly on the stoop. But when Irene stopped, the woman took her arm and pulled her on.

"Isn't that your home?" asked Irene. "Isn't Jayse there?"

The woman shook her head and went on. Presently they came to another stand of trees. Beyond lay an open space with grass-covered mounds. Some of the mounds had wooden markers; others had none.

"What is this place?" Irene cried frantically.

"Old graveyard," replied the woman. "Nobody—hardly nobody uses it anymore. Over here, Ma'am." She pointed to one mound. Irene saw with horror that great tufts of grass had been torn from it, and that someone had tried to scoop a hollow in the dry dirt underneath.

Nothing could have made her go close to the mound. But from where she stood she could see what lay in it—a shriveled, withered something dressed in worn jeans and a stained T-shirt.

"There's Jayse," said the woman. "There's where you sent him. He and his pa died two years ago, that bad winter, of pneumonia. I wished them back, but only Jayse came. He knew I needed him, you see. He wanted to take care of me. He was a good boy, always."

"I don't understand," Irene whispered.

But the woman wasn't listening. She talked on, as if to herself. "I had to take special care of him. You can't feed the dead salt, you know. It makes them forget everything but the last place they rested. That's why Jayse had to come here. Now he won't leave it again, ever."

---

scraggy (SKRAG ee) rough and uneven
tufts (TUFTS) bunches of grass or hair
shriveled (SHRIV uld) dried up
pneumonia (noo MOHN yuh) disease of the lungs

Review the Selection

UNDERSTAND THE SELECTION

Recall

1. Where did the Platts retire?

2. What kind of food did Jayse's mother insist that Jayse eat?

3. What food did Irene Platt prepare for Jayse?

Infer

4. How does the setting contribute to the story?

5. What is the "complication" to the plot that keeps the story going?

6. Why do you think Jayse's mother began to laugh when Irene Platt asked to be taken to see the sick Jayse?

7. Explain the significance of Jayse eating the salty food.

Apply

8. Would you have hired Jayse if you had been Irene Platt? Explain your answer.

9. Would you have liked to have had Jayse for a friend?

10. What is your opinion of the story? Is it believable literally? Symbolically?

Respond to Literature

Does this story have any evil characters or does each character show both good and evil traits? Explain your answer.

WRITE ABOUT THE SELECTION

Years ago, interesting information about a person and his or her life might be inscribed on a headstone marking his or her grave. This was called an epitaph. It could be written in poetry or prose. Suppose Jayse's mother and the Platts have decided to mark Jayse's grave with a headstone and to inscribe something on it. What should they write?

Prewriting Draw a headstone. Next to the headstone, write a list of what you would like to mention about Jayse. Decide if you will write in poetry or prose. Remember that tombstones are not very big, so you cannot write much.

Writing Use your list to write the inscription. Try several versions of your message and decide which you like the best. Write it on the headstone you have drawn. You must keep your epitaph short and to the point.

Revising If you wrote in verse, would rhyming help improve the inscription? Synonyms can be used to make rhymes. If you wrote in prose, would a simile or metaphor help? They were commonly used in inscriptions on old headstones.

Proofreading Reread what you have written and check to make sure all words are spelled correctly. Your inscription will be chiseled into stone, and there must be no mistakes. Use a dictionary to check any words you are not sure of. Because of limited space, delete all unnecessary words.

THINK ABOUT CHARACTER

Margaret Ronan tells us about Jayse directly by describing traits and indirectly by telling how he acted in situations. Each description adds to the mystery surrounding him.

1. In the third paragraph, how is Jayse described? What is your impression of him?

2. In the fourth and fifth paragraphs, what do we learn about Jayse?

3. What do we learn about Jayse from his mother's introduction?

4. When Jayse arrives for work at the Platts, more description is given. Which impression of Jayse seems correct, Mrs. Platt's initial impression or the one given by Jayse's mother?

5. Action tells us more about Jayse after he eats Mrs. Platt's dinner. Explain.

READING FOCUS

Make Predictions As you read, you were able to use clues to make predictions about what would happen next in the story and what the final outcome would be. What prediction did you make about the outcome of the story? What clues helped you make this prediction?

DEVELOP YOUR VOCABULARY

A good way to learn and to remember vocabulary words is to use flashcards. Write the words below on a card. On the back of the card, write the definition and an original sentence.

Use the cards to exercise your vocabulary skills. If you are working alone, shuffle the cards, choose one, and give the definition. Go through all the cards, putting aside those for which you need more practice.

You can also practice your vocabulary skills by first looking at the definitions and then giving the correct words. If working with a partner, you can use the same methods.

1. listless
2. work-scarred
3. hollow-eyed
4. hollow-cheeked
5. haggard-looking
6. disquieting
7. finicky
8. creepy
9. knobby
10. spooky

Learn About

CONFLICT

The plot in literature often focuses on **conflict**, or the meeting of opposing forces. The conflict can be between people, within a single person, between people and things, or between people and nature. A work of literature may contain more than one kind of conflict, but usually only one is the main conflict.

In drama, the conflict can be physical, psychological, or, most often, a combination of the two. Usually, conflict in a play is easier to identify than in fiction because you can see the clash of personalities on stage or infer it from dialogue on the page.

As you read "Sorry, Wrong Number," ask yourself these questions:
1. What conflicts are in the play?
2. What is the main conflict?

WRITING CONNECTION

Think back on the selections you have read in this unit or the previous unit. Describe the main conflict in one of the selections and tell how it is resolved. If there were other lesser conflicts in the same selection, write them down in a sentence or two.

READING FOCUS

Make Inferences From Conversation
Readers can sometimes learn about the characters, plot, and setting of a story through characters' conversations. In a play, almost all of the plot's developments may be revealed through conversation. The play does not give the reader details about the characters or the plot. The reader must make inferences about these elements from the conversation, or dialogue. As you read, pay close attention to the dialogue so that you can see what it reveals about the characters and the plot.

Sorry, Wrong Number

ADAPTED

by Lucille Fletcher

CHARACTERS

MRS. STEVENSON	SERGEANT DUFFY
OPERATOR	THIRD OPERATOR
FIRST MAN	WESTERN UNION
SECOND MAN (GEORGE)	INFORMATION
CHIEF OPERATOR	WOMAN
SECOND OPERATOR	

ACT I

(SOUND: *Number being dialed on phone; busy signal.*)

MRS. STEVENSON (*a complaining, self-centered person*): Oh—dear! (*Slams down receiver. Dials* OPERATOR.)

OPERATOR: Your call, please?

MRS. STEVENSON: Operator? I've been dialing Murray Hill 4-0098 now for the last three quarters of an hour, and the line is always busy. But I don't see how it *could* be busy that long. Will you try it for me, please?

OPERATOR: Murray Hill 4-0098? One moment, please.

MRS. STEVENSON: I don't see how it could be busy all this time. It's my husband's office. He's working late tonight, and I'm all alone here in the house. My health is very poor—and I've been feeling so nervous all day—

OPERATOR: Ringing Murray Hill 4-0098.

---

self-centered (SELF SENT urd) selfish; concerned with oneself

(SOUND: *Phone buzz. It rings three times. Receiver is picked up at other end*)

MAN: Hello.

MRS. STEVENSON: Hello? (*A little puzzled.*) Hello. Is Mr. Stevenson there?

MAN (*into phone, as though he had not heard*): Hello. (*Louder.*) Hello.

SECOND MAN (*slow, heavy voice, faintly foreign accent*): Hello.

FIRST MAN: Hello, George?

GEORGE: Yes, sir.

MRS. STEVENSON (*louder and more commanding, to phone*): Hello. Who's this? What number am I calling, please?

FIRST MAN: We have heard from our client. He says the coast is clear for tonight.

GEORGE: Yes, sir.

FIRST MAN: Where are you now?

GEORGE: In a phone booth.

FIRST MAN: Okay. You know the address. At eleven o'clock the private patrolman goes around to a place on Second Avenue for a break. Be sure that all the lights downstairs are out. There should be only one light visible from the street. At eleven fifteen a subway train crosses the bridge. It makes a noise in case her window is open and she should scream.

MRS. STEVENSON (*shocked*): Oh—*hello!* What number is this, please?

GEORGE: Okay. I understand.

FIRST MAN: Make it quick. As little blood as possible. Our client does not wish to make her suffer long.

GEORGE: A knife okay, sir?

FIRST MAN: Yes. A knife will be okay. And remember—remove the rings and bracelets, and the jewelry in the bureau drawer. Our client wishes it to look like simple robbery.

GEORGE: Okay. I get—

(SOUND: *A soft buzzing signal.*)

MRS. STEVENSON (*clicking phone*): Oh! (*Soft buzzing signal continues. She hangs up.*) How awful! How unspeakably—

(SOUND: *Dialing. Phone buzz.*)

---

client (KLY unt) person who pays for a duty performed
unspeakably (un SPEEK uh blee) horribly; not to be spoken of

OPERATOR: Your call, please?

MRS. STEVENSON (*uptight and breathless, into phone*): Operator, I—I've just been cut off.

OPERATOR: I'm sorry, madam. What number were you calling?

MRS. STEVENSON: Why—it was supposed to be Murray Hill 4-0098, but it wasn't. Some wires must have crossed—I was cut into a wrong number—and—I've just heard the most dreadful thing—a—a murder—and—(*As an order*) Operator, you'll simply have to retrace that call at once.

OPERATOR: I beg your pardon, madam—I don't quite—

MRS. STEVENSON: Oh—I know it was a wrong number, and I had no business listening—but these two men—they were cold-blooded fiends—and they were going to murder somebody—some poor innocent woman—who was all alone—in a house near a bridge. We've got to stop them—we've got to—

OPERATOR (*patiently*): What number were you calling, madam?

MRS. STEVENSON: That doesn't matter. This was a *wrong* number. And *you* dialed it. And we've got to find out what it was—immediately!

OPERATOR: But—madam—

MRS. STEVENSON: Oh, why are you so stupid? Look, it was obviously a case of some little slip of the finger. I told you to try Murray Hill 4-0098 for me—you dialed it—but your finger must have slipped—and I was connected with some other number—and I could hear them, but they couldn't hear me. Now, I simply fail to see why you couldn't make that same mistake again—on purpose—why you couldn't *try* to dial Murray Hill 4-0098 in the same careless sort of way—

OPERATOR (*quickly*): Murray Hill 4-0098? I will try to get it for you, madam.

MRS. STEVENSON: *Thank* you.

(*Sound of ringing; busy signal.*)

OPERATOR: I am sorry. Murray Hill 4-0098 is busy.

MRS. STEVENSON (*madly clicking receiver*): Operator. Operator.

OPERATOR: Yes, madam.

---

cold-blooded fiends (KOHLD blud id FEENDZ) very wicked people
   without mercy

MRS. STEVENSON (*angrily*): You *didn't* try to get that wrong number at all. I asked explicitly. And all you did was dial correctly.

OPERATOR: I am sorry. What number were you calling?

MRS. STEVENSON: Can't you, for once, forget what number I was calling, and do something specific? Now I want to trace that call. It's my civic duty—it's *your* civic duty—to trace that call—and to apprehend those dangerous killers—and if *you* won't—

OPERATOR: I will connect you with the Chief Operator.

MRS. STEVENSON: *Please!*

   (*Sound of ringing.*)

CHIEF OPERATOR (*a cool pro*): This is the Chief Operator.

MRS. STEVENSON: Chief Operator? I want you to trace a call. A telephone call. Immediately. I don't know where it came from, or who was making it, but it's absolutely necessary that it be tracked down. Because it was about a murder. Yes, a terrible, cold-blooded murder of a poor innocent woman—tonight—at eleven fifteen.

CHIEF OPERATOR: I see.

MRS. STEVENSON (*high-strung, demanding*): Can you trace it for me? Can you track down those men?

CHIEF OPERATOR: It depends, madam.

MRS. STEVENSON: Depends on what?

CHIEF OPERATOR: It depends on whether the call is still going on. If it's a live call, we can trace it on the equipment. If it's been disconnected, we can't.

MRS. STEVENSON: Disconnected?

CHIEF OPERATOR: If the parties have stopped talking to each other.

MRS. STEVENSON: Oh—but—but of course they must have stopped talking to each other by *now*. That was at least five minutes ago—and they didn't sound like the type who would make a long call.

CHIEF OPERATOR: Well, I can try tracing it. Now—what is your name, madam?

---

explicitly (ik SPLIS it lee) very clearly
specific (spuh SIF ik) definite; exact
civic (SIV ik) having to do with good citizenship
apprehend (ap rih HEND) seize; arrest

MRS. STEVENSON: Mrs. Stevenson. Mrs. Elbert Stevenson. But—listen—

CHIEF OPERATOR (*writing it down*)**:** And your telephone number?

MRS. STEVENSON (*more bothered*)**:** Plaza 4-2295. But if you go on wasting all this time—

CHIEF OPERATOR: And what is your reason for wanting this call traced?

MRS. STEVENSON: My reason? Well—for heaven's sake—isn't it obvious? I overheard two men—they're killers—they're planning to murder this woman—it's a matter for the police.

CHIEF OPERATOR: Have you told the police?

MRS. STEVENSON: No. How could I?

CHIEF OPERATOR: You're making this check into a private call purely as a private individual?

MRS. STEVENSON: Yes. But meanwhile—

CHIEF OPERATOR: Well, Mrs. Stevenson—I seriously doubt whether we could make this check for you at this time just on your say-so as a private individual. We'd have to have something more official.

MRS. STEVENSON: Oh, for heaven's sake! You mean to tell me I can't report a murder without getting tied up in all this red tape? Why, it's perfectly idiotic. All right, then. I *will* call the police. (*She slams down receiver.*) Ridiculous!

(*Sound of dialing.*)

CHIEF OPERATOR: Your call, please?

MRS. STEVENSON (*very annoyed*): The Police Department—*please.*

SECOND OPERATOR: Ringing the police department.

(*Rings twice. Phone is picked up.*)

SERGEANT DUFFY: Police department. Precinct 43. Duffy speaking.

MRS. STEVENSON: Police department? Oh. This is Mrs. Stevenson— Mrs. Elbert Smythe Stevenson of 53 North Sutton Place. I'm calling to report a murder.

DUFFY: Eh?

MRS. STEVENSON: I mean—the murder hasn't been committed yet. I just overheard plans for it over the telephone . . . over a wrong number that the operator gave me. I've been trying to trace down the call myself, but everybody is so stupid— and I guess in the end you're the only people who could *do* anything.

DUFFY (*not too impressed*): Yes, ma'am.

MRS. STEVENSON (*trying to impress him*): It was a perfectly *definite* murder. I heard their plans distinctly. Two men were talking, and they were going to murder some woman at eleven fifteen tonight—she lived in a house near a bridge.

DUFFY: Yes, ma'am.

MRS. STEVENSON: And there was a private patrolman on the street. He was going to go around for a break on Second Avenue. And there was some third man—a client—who was paying to have this poor woman murdered—They were going to take her rings and bracelets—and use a knife—Well, it's unnerved me dreadfully—and I'm not well—

DUFFY: I see. When was all this, ma'am?

---

red tape (RED TAYP) needless complications of official rules
precinct (PREE singkt) division of a city for police control
unnerved (un NURVD) took away courage; terrified

MRS. STEVENSON: About eight minutes ago. Oh . . . (*relieved*) then you *can* do something? You do understand—

DUFFY: And what is your name, ma'am?

MRS. STEVENSON (*losing patience*): Mrs. Stevenson. Mrs. Elbert Stevenson.

DUFFY: And your address?

MRS. STEVENSON: 53 North Sutton Place. *That's* near a bridge, the Queensborough Bridge, you know—and *we* have a private patrolman on our street—and Second Avenue—

DUFFY: And what was that number you were calling?

MRS. STEVENSON: Murray Hill 4-0098. But—that wasn't the number I overheard. I mean Murray Hill 4-0098 is my husband's office. He's working late tonight, and I was trying to reach him to ask him to come home. I'm an invalid, you know—and it's the maid's night off—and I *hate* to be alone—even though he says I'm perfectly safe as long as I have the telephone beside my bed.

DUFFY (*trying to end it*): Well, we'll look into it, Mrs. Stevenson, and see if we can check it with the telephone company.

MRS. STEVENSON (*using more patience*): But the telephone company said they couldn't check the call if the parties had stopped talking. I've already taken care of *that*.

DUFFY: Oh, yes?

MRS. STEVENSON (*getting bossy*): Personally I feel you ought to do something far more immediate and drastic than just check the call. What good does checking the call do, if they've stopped talking? By the time you track it down, they'll already have committed the murder.

DUFFY: Well, we'll take care of it, lady. Don't worry.

MRS. STEVENSON: The whole thing calls for a search—a complete and thorough search of the whole city. I'm very near a bridge, and I'm not far from Second Avenue. And I know *I'd* feel a whole lot better if you sent around a radio car to *this* neighborhood at once.

DUFFY: And what makes you think the murder's going to be committed in your neighborhood, ma'am?

---

invalid (IN vuh lid) sick person
drastic (DRAS tik) forceful; severe

MRS. STEVENSON: Oh, I don't know. The coincidence is so horrible. Second Avenue—the patrolman—the bridge—

DUFFY: Second Avenue is a very long street, ma'am. And do you happen to know how many bridges there are in the city of New York alone? Not to mention Brooklyn, Staten Island, Queens, and the Bronx? And how do you know there isn't some little house out on Staten Island—on some little Second Avenue you've never heard about? How do you know they were even talking about New York at all?

MRS. STEVENSON: But I heard the call on the New York dialing system.

DUFFY: How do you know it wasn't a long-distance call you overheard? Telephones are funny things. Look, lady, why don't you look at it this way? Supposing you hadn't broken in on that telephone call? Supposing you'd got your husband the way you always do? Would this murder have made any difference to you then?

MRS. STEVENSON: I suppose not. But it's so inhuman—so cold-blooded—

DUFFY: A lot of murders are committed in this city every day, ma'am. If we could do something to stop 'em, we would. But a clue of this kind that's so vague isn't much more use to us than no clue at all.

MRS. STEVENSON: But surely—

DUFFY: Unless, of course, you have some reason for thinking this call is phony—and that someone may be planning to murder *you?*

MRS. STEVENSON: *Me?* Oh, no, I hardly think so. I—I mean—why should anybody? I'm alone all day and night—I see nobody except my maid Eloise—she's a big two-hundred-pounder— she's too lazy to bring up my breakfast tray—and the only other person is my husband Elbert—he's crazy about me— adores me—waits on me hand and foot—he's scarcely left my side since I took sick twelve years ago—

DUFFY: Well, then, there's nothing for you to worry about, is there? And now, if you'll just leave the rest of this to us—

---

coincidence (koh IN suh duns) two or more related events accidentally happening at the same time
vague (VAYG) unclear

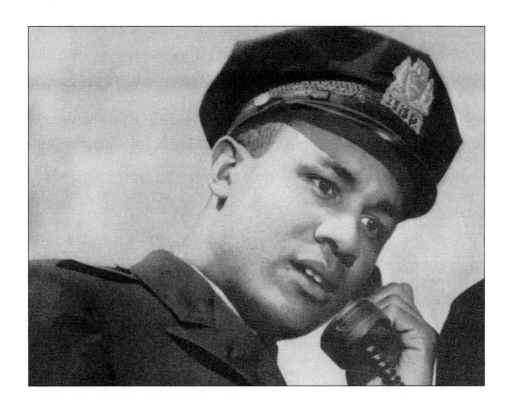

MRS. STEVENSON: But what will you *do?* It's so late—it's nearly eleven o'clock.

DUFFY (*firmly*): We'll take care of it, lady.

MRS. STEVENSON: Will you broadcast it all over the city? And send out squads? And warn your radio cars to watch out—especially in suspicious neighborhoods like mine?

DUFFY (*more firmly*): Lady, I *said* we'd take care of it. Just now I've got a couple of other matters here on my desk that require my immediate—

MRS. STEVENSON: Oh! (*She slams down receiver hard.*) Idiot. (*Looking at phone nervously.*) Now, why did I do that? Now he'll think I am a fool. Oh, why doesn't Elbert come home? *Why* doesn't he?

(*Sound of dialing operator.*)

ACT II

OPERATOR: Your call, please?

MRS. STEVENSON: Operator, for heaven's sake, will you ring that Murray Hill 4-0098 number again? I can't think what's keeping him so long.

OPERATOR: Ringing Murray Hill 4-0098. (*Rings. Busy signal.*) The line is busy. Shall I—

MRS. STEVENSON (*nastily*): I can hear it. You don't have to tell me. I know it's busy. (*Slams down receiver.*) If I could only get out of this bed for a little while. If I could get a breath of fresh air—or just lean out the window—and see the street—(*The phone rings. She answers it instantly.*) Hello. Elbert? Hello. Hello. Hello. Oh, what's the *matter* with this phone? *Hello? Hello?* (*Slams down receiver. The phone rings again, once. She picks it up.*) Hello? Hello— Oh, for heaven's sake, who is this? Hello, Hello, *Hello.* (*Slams down receiver. Dials operator.*)

THIRD OPERATOR: Your call, please?

MRS. STEVENSON (*very annoyed and commanding*): Hello, operator. I don't know what's the matter with this telephone tonight, but it's positively driving me crazy. I've never seen such inefficient, miserable service. Now, look. I'm an invalid, and I'm very nervous, and I'm *not* supposed to be annoyed. But if this keeps on much longer—

THIRD OPERATOR (*a young, sweet type*): What seems to be the trouble, madam?

MRS. STEVENSON: Well, everything's wrong. The whole world could be murdered, for all you people care. And now, my phone keeps ringing—

OPERATOR: Yes, madam?

MRS. STEVENSON: Ringing and ringing and ringing every five seconds or so, and when I pick it up, there's no one there.

OPERATOR: I am sorry, madam. If you will hang up, I will test it for you.

MRS. STEVENSON: I don't want you to test it for me. I want you to put through that call—whatever it is—at once.

OPERATOR (*gently*): I am afraid that is not possible, madam.

---

inefficient (in ih FISH unt) wasteful of time or energy; poorly run

MRS. STEVENSON (*storming*): Not possible? And why may I ask?

OPERATOR: The system is automatic, madam. If someone is trying to dial your number, there is no way to check whether the call is coming through the system or not—unless the person who is trying to reach you complains to the particular operator—

MRS. STEVENSON: Well, of all the stupid, complicated—! And meanwhile *I've* got to sit here in my bed, *suffering* every time that phone rings, imagining everything—

OPERATOR: I will try to check it for you, madam.

MRS. STEVENSON: Check it! Check it! That's all anybody can do. Of all the stupid, idiotic . . . ! (*She hangs up.*) Oh—what's the use . . . (*Instantly* MRS. STEVENSON'S *phone rings again. She picks up the receiver. Wildly.*) Hello. HELLO. Stop ringing, do you hear me? Answer me? What do you want? Do you realize you're driving me crazy? Stark, staring—

MAN (*dull, flat voice*): Hello. Is this Plaza 4-2295?

MRS. STEVENSON (*catching her breath*): Yes. Yes. This is Plaza 4-2295.

MAN: This is Western Union. I have a telegram here for Mrs. Elbert Stevenson. Is there anyone there to receive the message?

MRS. STEVENSON (*trying to calm herself*): I am Mrs. Stevenson.

WESTERN UNION (*reading flatly*): The telegram is as follows: "Mrs. Elbert Stevenson. 53 North Sutton Place, New York, New York. Darling. Terribly sorry. Tried to get you for last hour, but line busy. Leaving for Boston 11 P.M. tonight on urgent business. Back tomorrow afternoon. Keep happy. Love. Signed. Elbert."

MRS. STEVENSON (*shocked, to herself*): Oh—no—

WESTERN UNION: That is all, madam. Do you wish us to deliver a copy of the message?

MRS. STEVENSON: No—no, thank you.

WESTERN UNION: Thank you, madam. Good night. (*He hangs up phone.*)

MRS. STEVENSON (*Softly, to phone*): Good night. (*She hangs up slowly, suddenly bursting into tears.*) No—no—it isn't true! He couldn't do it. Not when he knows I'll be all alone. It's some trick—some fiendish—(*She dials operator.*)

---

stark (STAHRK) absolutely; totally
fiendish (FEEN dish) savagely cruel

OPERATOR (*coolly*): Your call, please?

MRS. STEVENSON: Operator—try that Murray Hill 4-0098 number for me just once more, please.

OPERATOR: Ringing Murray Hill 4-0098. (*Call goes through. We hear ringing at other end. Ring after ring.*)

MRS. STEVENSON: He's gone. Oh, Elbert, how could you? How could you—? (*She hangs up phone, sobbing with pity to herself, turning nervously.*) But I can't be alone tonight. I can't. If I'm alone one more second—I don't care what he says—or what the expense is—I'm a sick woman—I'm entitled—(*She dials Information.*)

INFORMATION: This is Information.

MRS. STEVENSON: I want the telephone number of Henchley Hospital.

INFORMATION: Henchley Hospital? Do you have the address, madam?

MRS. STEVENSON: No. It's somewhere in the seventies, though. It's a very small, private, and exclusive hospital where I had my appendix out two years ago. Henchley. H-E-N-C—

INFORMATION: One moment, please.

MRS. STEVENSON: Please—hurry. And please—what *is* the time?

INFORMATION: I do not know, madam. You may find out the time by dialing Meridian 7-1212.

MRS. STEVENSON (*angered*): Oh, for heaven's sake! Couldn't you—?

INFORMATION: The number of Henchley Hospital is Butterfield 7-0105, madam.

MRS. STEVENSON: Butterfield 7-0105. (*She hangs up before she finishes speaking, and immediately dials number.*)
(*Phone rings.*)

WOMAN (*middle-aged, solid, firm, practical*): Henchley Hospital, good evening.

MRS. STEVENSON: Nurses' Registry.

WOMAN: Who was it you wished to speak to, please?

MRS. STEVENSON (*bossy*): I want the Nurses' Registry at once. I want a trained nurse. I want to hire her immediately. For the night.

---

entitled (en TYT uld) have as a claim or right; empowered
exclusive (ik SKLOO siv) private and expensive
registry (REJ is tree) department where registers, or lists, are kept

WOMAN: I see. And what is the nature of the case, madam?

MRS. STEVENSON: Nerves. I'm very nervous. I need soothing—and companionship. My husband is away—and I'm—

WOMAN: Have you been recommended to us by any doctor in particular, madam?

MRS. STEVENSON: No. But I really don't see why all this catechizing is necessary. I want a trained nurse. I was a patient in your hospital two years ago. And after all, I *do* expect to *pay* this person—

WOMAN: We quite understand that, madam. But registered nurses are very scarce just now—and our superintendent has asked us to send people out only on cases where the physician in charge feels it is absolutely necessary.

MRS. STEVENSON (*growing very upset*): Well, it *is* absolutely necessary. I'm a sick woman. I—I'm very upset. Very. I'm alone in this house—and I'm an invalid—and tonight I overheard a telephone conversation that upset me dreadfully. About a murder— a poor woman who was going to be murdered at eleven fifteen tonight—in fact, if someone doesn't come at once—I'm afraid I'll go out of my mind—(*Almost off handle by now.*)

WOMAN (*calmly*): I see. Well, I'll speak to Miss Phillips as soon as she comes in. And what is your name, madam?

MRS. STEVENSON: Miss Phillips. And when do you expect her in?

WOMAN: I really don't know, madam. She went out to supper at eleven o'clock.

MRS. STEVENSON: Eleven o'clock. But it's not eleven yet. (*She cries out.*) Oh, my clock has stopped. I thought it was running down. What time is it?

WOMAN: Just fourteen minutes past eleven.

(*Sound of phone receiver being lifted on same line as* MRS. STEVENSON'S. *A click.*)

MRS. STEVENSON (*crying out*): What's *that?*

WOMAN: What was what, madam?

MRS. STEVENSON: That—that click just now—in my own telephone? As though someone had lifted the receiver off the hook of the extension phone downstairs—

---

catechizing (KAT uh kyz ing) asking many questions

WOMAN: I didn't hear it, madam. Now—about this—

MRS. STEVENSON (*scared*): But *I* did. There's someone in this house. Someone downstairs in the kitchen. And they're listening to me now. They're—(*Hangs up phone. In a hushed voice.*) I won't pick it up. I won't let them hear me. I'll be quiet—and they'll think—(*with growing terror*) But if I don't call someone now—while they're still down there—there'll be no time. (*She picks up receiver. Soft buzzing signal. She dials operator. Ring twice*)

OPERATOR (*a slow, lazy voice*): Your call, please?

MRS. STEVENSON (*a desperate whisper*): Operator, I—I'm in desperate trouble—I—

OPERATOR: I cannot hear you, madam. Please speak louder.

MRS. STEVENSON (*Still whispering*): I don't dare. I—there's someone listening. Can you hear me now?

OPERATOR: Your call, please? What number are you calling, madam?

MRS. STEVENSON (*desperately*): You've got to hear me. Oh, please. You've got to help me. There's someone in this house. Someone who's going to murder me. And you've got to get in touch with the—(*Click of receiver being put down in* MRS. STEVENSON'S *home. Bursting out wildly.*) Oh, there it is—he's put it down—he's put down the extension—he's coming—(*She screams.*) He's coming up the stairs—(*Wildly.*) Give me the police department—(*Screaming.*) The police!

OPERATOR: Ringing the police department.

(*Phone is rung. We hear sound of a subway train coming nearer. On second ring,* MRS. STEVENSON *screams again, but roaring of train drowns out her voice. For a few seconds we hear nothing but roaring of train, then dying away, phone at police headquarters ringing.*)

DUFFY: Police department. Precinct 43. Duffy speaking. (*Pause.*) Police department. Duffy speaking.

GEORGE: Sorry. Wrong number. (*Hangs up.*)

AUTHOR BIOGRAPHY
Lucille Fletcher (1912–   )

If you look in the mystery section of your local library, you are bound to find at least one book by Lucille Fletcher. Noted as a writer of plays, screenplays, and novels, Fletcher is most famous for her suspense classic, "Sorry, Wrong Number." This work was originally written as a radio play, then later adapted as a novel, TV play, and motion picture.

Born in Brooklyn, New York, Lucille Fletcher attended the public schools there, then later received her bachelor of arts degree from Vassar College in Poughkeepsie. She is married to the novelist Douglass Wallop, who is best known for his book, *The Year the Yankees Lost the Pennant*. Speaking of her life at the time her two daughters were growing up, Ms. Fletcher referred to her writing as a "hobby"—then admitted that "the major part of my life is spent in housekeeping and cooking meals."

Review the Selection

Recall

1. Why is Mrs. Stevenson home alone?

2. How did she get the wrong number?

3. Why is the chief operator unwilling to trace the call?

Infer

4. Why is it the operator's "civic duty" to trace the wrong-number call?

5. Why is Mrs. Stevenson so concerned about the time?

6. How does the policeman try to reassure Mrs. Stevenson?

7. What complications are added to the plot by the telegram?

Apply

8. Do you think Sgt. Duffy handled Mrs. Stevenson's call responsibly?

9. What are the advantages and disadvantages to hearing this on the radio rather than seeing it on stage?

10. Have you ever overheard a private conversation? What was it like to be an eavesdropper?

Respond to Literature

How would you feel if your only way of communicating with the outside world was by telephone?

WRITE ABOUT THE SELECTION

Newspapers almost always report murders. Sometimes the report is long, sometimes short. However, a good reporter will try to learn from everyone who might know something about what happened.

Think of yourself as a reporter. Mrs. Stevenson is murdered, and you must write a story about the murder. You learn that a Sgt. Duffy took a call from Mrs. Stevenson shortly before the killing. You talk with him, and his information forms the basis of your story.

Prewriting   Look at a newspaper story reporting a crime. Notice how it is constructed with the important facts first. Make an informal outline of your story about Mrs. Stevenson's murder.

Writing   Use your informal outline to write the news story. Make sure you include comments from Sgt. Duffy.

Revising   Is your story written in the third person? Is it objective? Make sure that your own opinion is not in the story. Rely instead on the people you interviewed to develop the theme of your story.

Proofreading   Reread what you have written and check for errors. If you have quoted Sgt. Duffy, make sure punctuation and capitalization for the quotations are correct. Also be sure that all your sentences end with periods, quotation marks or exclamation marks. Check interior punctuation as well.

THINK ABOUT CONFLICT

Conflict results from opposing forces—interpersonal, environmental, social, or internal—that drive the plot in many kinds of literature. *Sorry, Wrong Number* contains a number of examples of conflict.

1. What is the main conflict of the story? Who is the conflict between?

2. Conflicts can also be implied, rather than directly stated or described. Do you think there is an implied conflict between Mr. and Mrs. Stevenson?

3. What are some examples of conflict between people in this drama?

4. Is there an example of conflict between people and nature?

5. The final conflict in this story acts as the resolution of the plot. It is the main force behind the story. What is this conflict?

READING FOCUS

Make Inferences From Conversation As you read, you learned a great deal about Mrs. Stevenson from her conversations on the phone. What inference did you make about her relationship with her husband? What things about her conversations led you to make this inference?

DEVELOP YOUR VOCABULARY

Some words are formed by adding prefixes that reverse the meaning. Some common negative prefixes are: *un-*, *in-*, *im-*, *dis-*, *non-*.

Find one word in the sentence that you can make into a negative word. Then use the new negative word in a sentence.

1. Thank you for your efficient service.

2. I appreciate your courteous behavior.

3. "It's possible," she said, "that I made a mistake."

4. The plane became visible as it emerged from the clouds.

5. He was wise to bring an umbrella on such a cloudy day.

6. I'm glad I can count on you to be reliable.

7. I need someone to give me attention.

PLOT

The events in a short story are called the plot. A story's **plot** is its skeleton—the framework that holds it together. It consists of exposition, complication, rising action, climax, and usually resolution. Try to think of a plot as a series of problems that the main character has to overcome. For instance, at the beginning of "The Love Letter" (Unit 1), Jake Belknap has a big decision to make: Should he or should he not try to contact Helen Elizabeth Worley?

Here are two other plot questions Jake confronts in "The Love Letter."

1. How can Jake contact her and how can Helen reply?
2. What are the implications of these letters in the lives of Helen and Jake?

As you read "Thus I Refute Beelzy," think about these questions:

1. What are the plot questions?
2. How do they correspond to the stages of the plot?

WRITING CONNECTION

Review a favorite story you have read in this book. List the plot questions. Which question leads to the climax?

The Sphinx and the Milky Way, Charles Burchfield. Munson-Williams-Proctor Institute Museum of Art

READING FOCUS

Analyze Characters' Responses In order to understand the characters in a story, use the information the author gives you plus your own experience. Avoid making guesses about characters that are not supported by details.

THUS I REFUTE BEELZY

ADAPTED

by John Collier

"There goes the tea bell," said Mrs. Carter. "I hope Simon hears it."

They looked out from the window of the drawing room. The long yard, agreeably neglected, ended in a waste plot. Here a little summer house was passing close by beauty on its way to complete decay. This was Simon's retreat: it was almost completely screened by the tangled branches of the apple tree and the pear tree, planted too close together, as they always are in suburban yards. They caught a glimpse of him now and then, as he strutted up and down, mouthing and gesticulating, performing all the solemn mumbo jumbo of small boys who spend long afternoons at the forgotten ends of long gardens.

"There he is, bless him," said Betty.

"Playing his game," said Mrs. Carter. "He won't play with the other children any more. And if I go down there—the temper! He comes in tired out."

"He doesn't have his sleep in the afternoons?" asked Betty.

"You know what Big Simon's ideas are," said Mrs. Carter. "'Let him choose for himself,' he says. That's what he chooses, and he comes in as white as a sheet."

"Look. He's heard the bell," said Betty. The expression was justified, though the bell had ceased ringing a full minute ago. Small Simon stopped in his parade exactly as if its tinny ring had at that moment reached his ear. They watched him perform certain ritual sweeps and scratchings with his little stick, and come lagging over the hot and flaggy grass toward the house.

Mrs. Carter led the way down to the playroom or garden room, which was

---

gesticulating (jes TIK yoo layt ing) making motions, as in attracting attention or speaking
ritual (RICH oo ul) a set pattern

also the tearoom for hot days. It had been the huge scullery of this tall Georgian house. Now the walls were cream-washed, there was coarse blue net in the windows, canvas-covered armchairs on the stone floor, and a reproduction of Van Gogh's "Sunflowers" over the mantelpiece.

Small Simon came drifting in, and gave Betty a routine greeting. His face was an almost perfect triangle, pointed at the chin, and he was paler than he should have been. "The little elf child!" cried Betty.

Simon looked at her. "No," said he.

At that moment the door opened, and Mr. Carter came in, rubbing his hands. He was a dentist, and washed them before and after everything he did. "You!" said his wife. "Home already!"

"Not unwelcome, I hope," said Mr. Carter, nodding to Betty. "Two people cancelled their appointments: I decided to come home. I said, I hope I am not unwelcome."

"Silly!" said his wife. "Of course not."

"Small Simon seems doubtful," continued Mr. Carter. "Small Simon, are you sorry to see me at tea with you?"

"No, Daddy."

"No what?"

"No, Big Simon."

"That's right. Big Simon and Small Simon. That sounds more like friends, doesn't it? At one time little boys had to call their father 'sir.' If they forgot—a good spanking. On the bottom, Small Simon! On the bottom!" said Mr. Carter, washing his hands once more with his invisible soap and water.

The little boy turned crimson with shame or rage.

"But now, you see," said Betty, to help, "you can call your father whatever you like."

"And what," asked Mr. Carter, "has Small Simon been doing this afternoon, while Big Simon has been at work?"

"Nothing," muttered his son.

"Then you have been bored," said Mr. Carter. "Learn from experience, Small Simon. Tomorrow, do something amusing, and you will not be bored. I want him to learn from experience, Betty. That is my way, the new way."

"I have learned," said the boy, speaking like an old tired man, as little boys so often do.

"It would hardly seem so," said Mr. Carter. "If you sit on your behind all the afternoon, doing nothing. Had *my* father caught me doing nothing, I would not have sat very comfortably."

"He played," said Mrs. Carter.

"A bit," said the boy, shifting on his chair.

"Too much," said Mrs. Carter. "He comes in all nervy and dazed. He ought to have his rest."

"He is six," said her husband. "He is a reasonable being. He must choose for himself. But what game is this, Small Simon, that is worth getting nervy and dazed over? There are very few games as good as all that."

"It's nothing," said the boy.

---

scullery (SKUL er ee) a room for cleaning and storing dishes and pots

Allegory, Ben Shahn. Collection of the Modern Art Museum of Fort Worth. Estate of Ben Shahn/Licensed by VAGA, New York, NY

"Oh, come," said his father. "We are friends, are we not? You can tell me. I was a Small Simon once, just like you, and played the same games you play. Of course there were no airplanes in those days. With whom do you play this fine game? Come on, we must all answer civil questions, or the world would never go round. With whom do you play?"

"Mr. Beelzy," said the boy, unable to resist.

"Mr. Beelzy?" said his father, raising his eyebrows inquiringly at his wife.

"It's a game he makes up," said she.

"Not makes up," cried the boy. "Fool!"

"That is telling stories," said his mother. "And rude as well. We had better talk of something different."

"No wonder he is rude," said Mr. Carter. "If you say he tells lies, and then insist on changing the subject. He tells you his fantasy: you create a guilt feeling. What can you expect? A defense mechanism. Then you get a real lie."

---

civil (SIV ul) here, polite
fantasy (FAN tuh see) something imagined
mechanism (MEK uh niz um) a system whose parts work together like a machine.
    Here, a psychological system of defense

"Like in *These Three*," said Betty. "Only different, of course. *She* was an unblushing little liar."

"I would have made her blush," said Mr. Carter, "in the proper part of her anatomy. But Small Simon is in the fantasy stage. Are you not, Small Simon? You must make things up."

"No I don't," said the boy.

"You do," said his father. "And because you do, it is not too late to reason with you. There is no harm in a fantasy, old chap. There is no harm in a bit of make-believe. Only you have to know the difference between daydreams and real things, or your brain will never grow. It will never be the brain of a Big Simon. So come on. Let us hear about this Mr. Beelzy of yours. Come on. What is he like?"

"He isn't like any thing," said the boy.

"Like nothing on earth," said his father. "That's a terrible fellow."

"I'm not frightened of him," said the child, smiling. "Not a bit."

"I should hope not," said his father. "If you were, you would be frightening yourself. I am always telling people, older people than you are, that they are just frightening themselves. Is he a funny man? Is he a giant?"

"Sometimes he is," said the little boy.

"Sometimes one thing, sometimes another," said his father. "Sounds pretty vague. Why can't you tell us just what he's like?"

"I love him," said the small boy. "He loves me."

"That's a big word," said Mr. Carter. "That might be better kept for real things, like Big Simon and Small Simon."

"He is real," said the boy, passionately. "He's not a fool. He's real."

"Listen," said his father. "When you go down to the yard there's nobody there. Is there?"

"No," said the boy.

"Then you think of him inside your head, and he comes."

"No," said Small Simon. "I have to do something with my stick."

"That doesn't matter."

"Yes, it does."

"Small Simon, you are being obstinate," said Mr. Carter. "I am trying to explain something to you. I have been longer in the world than you have, so naturally I am older and wiser. I am explaining that Mr. Beelzy is a fantasy of yours. Do you hear? Do you understand?"

"Yes, Daddy."

"He is a game. He is a 'let's-pretend.'"

The little boy looked down at his plate, smiling resignedly.

"I hope you are listening to me," said his father. "All you have to do is say, 'I have been playing a game of let's-pretend. With someone I make up, called Mr. Beelzy.' Then no one will say you tell lies, and you will know the difference between dreams and reality. Mr. Beelzy is a daydream."

The little boy still stared at his plate.

"He is sometimes there and sometimes not there," pursued Mr. Carter.

---

anatomy (uh NAT uh mee) here, body

"Sometimes he's like one thing, sometimes another. You can't really see him. Not as you see me. I am real. You can't touch him. You can touch me. I can touch you." Mr. Carter stretched out his big, white, dentist's hand, and took his little son by the shoulder. He stopped speaking for a moment and tightened his hand. The little boy sank his head still lower.

"Now you know the difference," said Mr. Carter, "between a pretend and a real thing. You and I are one thing; he is another. Which is the pretend? Come on. Answer me. Which is the pretend?"

"Big Simon and Small Simon," said the little boy.

"Don't!" cried Betty, and at once put her hand over her mouth, for why should a visitor cry "don't" when a father is explaining things in a scientific and modern way?

"Well, my boy," said Mr. Carter, "I have said you must be allowed to learn from experience. Go upstairs. Right up to your room. You shall learn whether it is better to reason, or to be perverse and obstinate. Go up. I shall follow you."

"You are not going to beat the child?" cried Mrs. Carter.

"No," said the little boy. "Mr. Beelzy won't let him."

"Go on up with you," shouted his father.

Small Simon stopped at the door. "He said he wouldn't let anyone hurt me," he whimpered. "He said he'd come like a lion, with wings on, and eat them up."

"You'll learn how real he is," shouted his father at him. "If you can't learn it at one end, you shall learn it at the other. I'll have your breeches down. I shall finish my cup of tea first, however," said he to the two women.

Neither of them spoke. Mr. Carter finished his tea, and unhurriedly left the room, washing his hands with his invisible soap and water.

Mrs. Carter said nothing. Betty could think of nothing to say. She wanted to be talking: she was afraid of what they might hear.

Suddenly it came. It seemed to tear the air apart. "Good God!" she cried. "What was that? He's hurt him." She sprang out of her chair, her silly eyes flashing behind her glasses. "I'm going up there," she cried, trembling.

"Yes, let us go up," said Mrs. Carter. "Let us go up. That was not Small Simon."

It was on the second-floor landing that they found the shoe, with the man's foot still in it, like that morsel of a mouse which sometimes falls unnoticed from the side of the jaws of the cat.

---

perverse (pur VURS) wrong, improper
obstinate (OB stuh nut) stubborn
morsel (MAWR sul) small piece

Review the Selection

UNDERSTAND THE SELECTION

Recall

1. Where did Simon play?

2. Why is Mr. Carter always washing his hands?

3. What does Mr. Carter hope to accomplish by punishing Simon?

Infer

4. What do you think is the purpose of all the description in the beginning?

5. Do you think Mrs. Carter agrees with her husband's idea of letting Simon "choose for himself"? Explain.

6. What complicates the plot question: What is Simon doing at his retreat?

7. What is the main conflict?

Apply

8. Mrs. Carter seems to allow her husband to determine what Simon can and cannot do. Do you think that is good?

9. Assume that you are Mr. Carter. Would you treat Simon the way he does?

10. Do you like the way the story ends? Would you have ended it differently?

Respond to Literature

Explain why Simon's invention of Mr. Beelzy is unusual.

WRITE ABOUT THE SELECTION

What do you think happened on the second floor when Mr. Carter went to punish Simon? Do you think Mr. Beelzy actually existed and devoured Mr. Carter, or do you think there is a more rational explanation?

Write a postscript to the story, describing what happened. Think of the postscript as continuing the resolution of the story and as being like a short story itself.

Then consider the plot question: What has happened to Mr. Carter? You might want to start with some exposition, perhaps just a sentence or two describing the second floor of the house. Next, begin your answer to the plot question. Present a brief complication that is followed quickly by crisis, climax, and a final resolution.

Prewriting Map your short, short story. Show all the plot development points, and make notes on how you will reach each one.

Writing Use the map to write your postscript. Make sure the plot question is answered.

Revising The author uses vivid language. Can you add a simile or metaphor to add color to your postscript? Check also for redundancy. Your postscript should be tightly written.

Proofreading If you used dialogue in the resolution, be sure each speaker's lines are a separate paragraph. Also check for errors in spelling, usage, and mechanics.

THINK ABOUT PLOT

Rising action builds excitement in a story. The events of a story are called the plot. Plot begins with exposition, then moves to complications where rising action builds excitement. The action reaches a crisis, and then something gives in the climax.

1. What is the first sign of resistance from Simon to his father's questions about the game he plays?

2. Simon gives in by answering his father's question about whom he plays with. What is Simon's answer, and why is it important?

3. How does the crisis build?

4. How do you learn that the climax has been reached?

5. In one short paragraph after the climax, there is the falling action of the resolution. What happens in the resolution?

READING FOCUS

Analyze Characters' Responses As you read, you used the characters' responses to analyze their thoughts and feelings. What responses gave you insight into Small Simon's character?

DEVELOP YOUR VOCABULARY

John Collier sometimes uses different verbs when he tells who says something. Instead of simply saying, "he said," for example, he sometimes says, "he cried." These different verbs give us clues about the state of mind of the person talking. For example:

"I'm going up there," she said.
"I'm going up there," she cried.

The first sentence is neutral. The second sentence tells us the speaker is upset.

Look at the following sentences. Make sure you understand what the italicized verb means, and explain, in a sentence, how it tells us something about the speaker.

1. "Nothing," *muttered* his son.

2. "He is sometimes there and sometimes not there," *pursued* Mr. Carter.

3. "He said he wouldn't let anyone hurt me," he *whimpered*.

4. "Go on up with you," *shouted* his father.

The Three Witches, Henri Fuseli. The Granger Collection

READING FOCUS

Identify Mood Poems often have a certain mood. They may be humorous, scary, or sad, for example. Details in the poem such as sounds, time of day, or weather help create the mood. The poet rarely states directly what the mood of the poem is. It is up to the reader to identify the mood from the details in the poem. As you read, pay attention to details in order to identify the mood.

SOUND SEGMENTS

Poets use segments—vowel sounds and consonant sounds—in patterns to link sounds with meanings or ideas. In descriptive poetry, segments may even combine with rhythm to imitate something being described. The most common ways poets use sound segments are alliteration, onomatopoeia, and assonance.

The repetition of the initial sound of words, for example, *great grow the grizzlies*, is called **alliteration**. A word prounounced out loud that sounds the same as the sound it is describing is called **onomatopoeia**. An example is the *roar* of a lion. When a poet repeats a vowel sound in a line of poetry, he or she is using **assonance**. "Tis hard to say if greater want of skill."

As you read the two poems, ask yourself these questions:

1. Where are alliteration and assonance used?
2. Where is onomatopoeia used?

WRITING CONNECTION

Use alliteration or assonance in a sentence describing something you have done recently. Write a follow-up sentence using onomatopoeia.

Mist Fantasy, J. E. H. MacDonald. Art Gallery of Ontario

hist, whist

by E. E. Cummings

hist   whist
little ghostthings
tip-toe
twinkle-toe

5   little twitchy
witches and tingling
goblins
hob-a-nob   hob-a-nob

little hoppy happy
10 toad in tweeds
tweeds
little itchy mousies

with scuttling
eyes   rustle and run   and
15 hidchidchide
whisk

whisk   look out for the old woman
with the wart on her nose
what she'll do to yer
20 nobody knows

for she knows the devil   ooch
the devil   ouch
the devil
ach   the great

25 green
dancing
devil
devil

devil
30 devil

                              wheeEEE

---

scuttling (SKUT ling) moving quickly

OVERHEARD ON A SALTMARSH

by Harold Monro

Nymph, nymph, what are your beads?
Green glass, goblin. Why do you stare at them?
Give them me.

            No.

5   Give them me. Give them me.

            No.

Then I will howl all night in the reeds,
Lie in the mud and howl for them.

Goblin, why do you love them so?

10   They are better than stars or water,
Better than voices of winds that sing,
Better than any man's fair daughter,
Your green glass beads on a silver ring.

Hush, I stole them out of the moon.

15   Give me your beads, I desire them.

            No.

I will howl in a deep lagoon
For your green glass beads, I love them so.
Give them me. Give them.

20   No.

---

nymph (NIMF) a minor nature goddess in Greek
    and Roman myths
lagoon (luh GOON) a shallow body of water,
    usually connected to a larger one

E. E. Cummings (1894–1962)

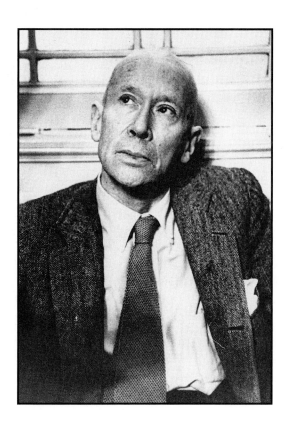

Edward Estlin Cummings was born in Cambridge, Massachusetts, on October 14, 1894. He graduated from Harvard University with a major in English and classics, and spent a part of his life as a volunteer in the army. Cummings' name often appears with lower case spelling— the result of a mistaken belief that the author legally changed his name to lower case letters only.

The unusual punctuation of his name is appropriate, for Cummings is noted for his unique use of punctuation, word forms, and topography.

Words such as "puddle-wonderful" and "mud-luscious" roll from his pen like little jewels. Phrases such as "nonsufficiently inunderstood" seem to sum up feelings more accurately than ordinary language ever could. And his unusual arrangement of words on a page gives Cummings' poetry a visual, as well as a verbal, meaning.

In addition to being a poet, Cummings was a painter, novelist, and playwright. In all of his works, Cummings reveals his disillusionment with most people and celebrates the value of the individual.

Review the Selection

Recall

1. What wears tweeds in "hist, whist"?

2. What distinctive feature does the old woman have in the same poem?

3. Where did the nymph's green glass beads come from in Monro's poem?

Infer

4. Why does Cummings use the word "ghostthings" rather than just "ghosts"?

5. Why does Cummings tell the reader to "look out for the old woman with the wart on her nose"?

6. What do the places where the goblin will howl have in common in Monro's poem?

7. What causes the conflict between the nymph and the goblin?

Apply

8. Explain which character in "hist, whist" is least appealing to you.

9. Do you think the stereotype of the old woman with the wart is fair?

10. What is significant about the fact that the nymph's green glass beads came from the moon?

Respond to Literature

Why do you think poets like to write about mysterious things?

WRITE ABOUT THE SELECTION

You have been asked by poet Harold Monro to provide an introduction to his poem "Overheard on a Saltmarsh." The introduction does not have to be long. You just need to describe the setting of the poem.

Prewriting You first need to make sure you understand what a saltmarsh is. Consult a dictionary if you are not sure. Then visualize standing in a saltmarsh. What would it feel like, smell like, and look like? What sounds would you hear? Write on your paper the five senses "touch," "smell," "sight," "hearing," and "taste." Under each, list several sensations.

Writing Choose from your list of sensations the best ones that provide a vivid description of a saltmarsh. Keep in mind the content and theme of the poem. You may write in poetry or prose. Make sure your thoughts are well-organized.

Revising Can you use alliteration or onomatopoeia anywhere in your description? Remember that these techniques are not limited to poetry. Add more sensory details and vivid words to make your introduction come alive. And eliminate any dead words or phrases that could make your description seem boring.

Proofreading Reread your description to check for errors. Make sure there are no misspellings. Alliteration, onomatopoeia, and other techniques require that you spell correctly. Otherwise the reader is confused and the effect you want to create is lost.

THINK ABOUT SOUND SEGMENTS

Poets use sound segments to link vowel and consonant sounds with ideas. Alliteration repeats consonant sounds while assonance is repetition of vowel sounds. Onomatopoetic words imitate real sounds.

1. Look at the description in "hist, whist" of how "little ghostthings" walk. What technique is this?

2. Identify the onomatopoeia in "Overheard on a Saltmarsh."

3. Cummings likes to play with words. The very first line of the poem is a good example. What is going on here?

4. Find a good example of assonance.

5. How do sound segments help make these poems more interesting?

READING FOCUS

Identify Mood As you read these two poems you were able to identify the different moods in each poem based on details provided. Briefly describe the mood of each poem. Support your response with details from each poem.

DEVELOP YOUR VOCABULARY

Words that mean the same thing are called synonyms. Below are some words from the poems. Consult your dictionary for their precise definitions. Then write a synonym for each. If you can't find a good synonym, make up one, then give a definition for your new word.

1. toad
2. ghostthing
3. wart
4. howl
5. lagoon
6. reeds
7. desire
8. deep

Learn About

READING FOCUS

Use Prior Knowledge When you use prior knowledge to help you understand a story, you use what you know from your own experience and what you know based on what the author has already told you. As you read, use what you already know to help you understand the new events that are occurring and to understand the characters' behaviors.

THEME

Why do we tell stories? Usually it is because we have an important message to relate to our listeners or readers. The central message of a story is called the **theme**.

Sometimes the theme of a story is stated directly. More often, however, the theme is implied, or suggested. The reader must look for clues in the story to discover the theme. Writers often reveal the theme through the words and actions of the characters and through the events in the story. For example, in the selection you are about to read, the main character decides to ignore the warnings of others about the dangers of the judge's house. What theme or message is the writer trying to convey through this character's actions?

As you read "The Judge's House," ask yourself the following questions:

1. What is the theme of this story?
2. What details in the story reveal the theme?

WRITING CONNECTION

At some point in your life, you have probably been asked to tell a story. Think about one such story. What was your purpose in telling it? What was the theme of the story?

The Judge's House

by Bram Stoker

When it was almost time for his exam-
inations, Malcolm Malcolmson went
away to study. He wanted to find a quiet
little town where there would be nothing
to distract him. He bought a ticket for the
first town that he did not know on the
local time table.

At the end of a three-hour trip he was
in Benchurch. He went straight to the one
inn that the sleepy town contained and
got a room for the night. He looked
around the next day to find a place even
quieter and more isolated than "The
Good Traveler." There was only one place
that he liked, and it was certainly quiet. It
was an old rambling house with heavy
gables. Its windows were unusually
small and set higher than was usual in
such houses. It was surrounded with a
high brick wall. It looked more like a
fortress than an ordinary house.

From the post office he got the name of
the agent. He was a friendly old gentleman, delighted that anyone would be
willing to live in the house.

"To tell the truth," said he, "I would be
happy to let anyone have the house rent
free for a term of years. This would get the
people around here used to the idea of
seeing it inhabited. It has been empty for
so long that some kind of absurd prejudice has grown up around it. This can best
be changed if it is occupied, if only by a
scholar like yourself, who wants its quiet
for a time."

Malcolmson did not ask the agent
about the "absurd prejudice." He knew he
would get more information on that subject later. He paid his rent, got the name of
an old woman who would probably keep
house for him, and came away with the
keys in his pocket. He then went to the
landlady of the inn, Mrs. Witham, and
asked her advice about what he might
need at the house. She threw up her hands
in amazement when he told her where he
was going.

"Not the Judge's House!" she said. She
then told him that the house had
belonged to a judge more than a hundred

---

gables (GAY bulz) the triangular top part of an outer wall between the sides of a sloped roof
absurd (ab SURD) unreasonable; ridiculous

years ago. This judge was held in great terror because of his harsh sentences and his hostility to the prisoners. As to what there was against the house itself she could not tell. She had often asked, but no one seemed to know. There was a general feeling that there was something, though. "If you were my boy, you wouldn't sleep there a night!" The good woman was so kind in her intentions that Malcolmson was touched. He told her how much he appreciated her interest.

Then he said, "But, my dear Mrs. Witham, you need not worry about me! A man who is studying for an important test has too much to think of to be disturbed by rumors." Mrs. Witham then kindly offered to see after what he would need, and he went himself to look for the old woman who had been recommended to him as a daytime housekeeper.

He got to the Judge's House with her a few hours later. There, he found Mrs. Witham with several men and boys carrying packages. There was also a man with a bed, for she said, though tables and chairs might be all very well, a bed that hadn't been aired for perhaps fifty years was not proper for young bones to lie on.

After looking through the whole house, Malcolmson decided to settle in the large dining room, which was big enough to serve all his needs. Mrs. Witham, with the aid of the housekeeper, Mrs. Dempster, unpacked. Malcolmson saw that Mrs. Witham had kindly sent from her own kitchen enough food to last for a few days. Before going, she turned at the door and said, "Perhaps, sir, because it is so drafty, you should put one of those big screens around your bed at night. Although I must say I would die myself if

I were to be shut in with all kinds of-of 'things' that put their heads around the sides or over the top to look at me!" The very idea was too much for her nerves, and she fled immediately.

Mrs. Dempster sniffed in a superior manner as the landlady disappeared. She said that for her own part, she wasn't afraid of all the bogies in the kingdom. "There are no 'things' to fear. Rats is bogies, I tell you, and bogies is rats. An old house like this has plenty of them. Don't you get to think anything else!"

"Mrs. Dempster," said Malcolmson, "I'm sure you are right!"

"I know I am, sir. Don't fear anything, and you'll get all the solitude you want here." She got to work with her cleaning. By nightfall, when Malcolmson returned from his walk, he found the room swept and tidied, a fire burning in the old hearth, the lamp lit, and the table spread for supper. "This is comfort, indeed," he said, as he rubbed his hands.

After supper, he got out his books, put fresh wood on the fire, and began studying. He went on without pause until eleven o'clock, when he stopped for a while to fix the fire and to make himself a cup of tea. As he sipped his hot tea, he enjoyed his sense of isolation. It was then that he began to notice for the first time what noise the rats were making.

"Surely," he thought, "they cannot have been at it all the time I was reading. Otherwise, I would have noticed it!" When the noise increased, he was sure that it was really new. It was clear that at first the rats had been frightened at the presence of a stranger and the light of fire and lamp. As the time went on, they had grown bolder and were now acting as they usually did.

How busy they were! Up and down behind the old wainscot, over the ceiling and under the floor they raced and gnawed and scratched! Malcolmson smiled to himself as he remembered Mrs. Dempster's words, "Rats is bogies, and bogies is rats!"

He looked forward to another long spell of work to be done before the night was past. He allowed himself the luxury of a good look around the room. He took his lamp in one hand, and went all around. There were some old pictures on the walls, but they were coated so thick with dust and dirt that he could not see any detail. Here and there he saw some crack or hole blocked for a moment by the face of a rat with its bright eyes glittering in the light. In an instant it was gone, and a squeak and a scamper followed.

The thing that struck him most, however, was the rope of the great alarm bell on the roof. It hung down in a corner of the room to the right of the fireplace. He pulled a carved oak chair up close to the hearth and sat down to his last cup of tea. When this was done he sat back at the table and got to work. He soon got as used to the noise made by the rats as one does to the ticking of a clock. He became so involved with his work that everything else passed away from him.

---

bogies (BOH geez) real or imaginary things that startle or frighten
wainscot (WAYNS koht) a facing for the walls in a room, usually made of wood paneling

Just before dawn, he suddenly looked up. The noise of the rats had stopped. Indeed it seemed to him that the very quiet was what had disturbed him. As he looked around, he was suddenly startled. There on the carved oak chair at the right of the fireplace sat an enormous rat, glaring at him. Malcolmson made a motion to it, but it did not move. He pretended to throw something, and it still did not move. Instead, it showed its great white teeth angrily. Its cruel eyes shone in the lamplight.

Malcolmson felt amazed. He seized the poker from the hearth and ran at it to kill it. Before he could strike it, the rat jumped to the floor and ran up the rope of the alarm bell. It disappeared in the darkness beyond the range of the lamp. Instantly, strange to say, the noisy scampering of the rats in the wainscot began again.

By this time, Malcolmson's mind was quite off the problem. A rooster outside told him of the approach of morning, and he went to bed and to sleep.

By the time he woke up, Mrs. Dempster had already tidied up the room, got his breakfast ready, and tapped on the screen around his bed. He went out for a morning walk, stopping by to see Mrs. Witham and to thank her for her kindness. As they talked, he told her about the rats and about the one who had sat in the oak chair.

"Mercy on us," said Mrs. Witham. "Sitting on a chair by the fireside! Take care, sir! He could be dangerous!" Malcolmson broke into a hearty laugh.

"You needn't laugh, sir. You young folks thinks it easy to laugh at things that makes older ones shudder. Never mind, sir! I hope you'll laugh all the time. It's what I wish you myself!"

"Oh, forgive me!" said Malcolmson. "Don't think me rude, but the idea was too much for me—that a big rat could be dangerous!" At the thought he laughed again.

That evening, the scampering of the rats began earlier. How they squeaked and scratched and gnawed! In spite of the noise, Malcolmson got more and more involved in his work.

All at once everything became silent. The silence was as of the grave. He remembered what happened the night before, and he looked at the chair by the fireside. Then a very odd sensation thrilled through him.

There, on the great old carved oak chair beside the fireplace sat the same enormous rat, steadily glaring at him.

He took a book and flung it at the rat. The book was badly aimed, and the rat did not stir. Again the poker performance of the previous night was repeated. Again, the rat fled up the rope of the alarm bell. Strangely too, this was instantly followed by the renewal of the noise made by the general rat community. As on the previous night, Malcolmson could not see at what part of the room the big rat disappeared, for his lamp left the upper part of the room in darkness.

Looking at his watch he found it was close to midnight. He made up the fire and made himself a pot of tea. He worked for a few hours and then took a break. He sat on the great carved oak chair before the fire. He began to think that he would like to know where the rat had disappeared to, for he thought he might set a rat trap in the morning. He lit another lamp and placed it so that it would shine into the right corner of the wall by the fireplace. He lifted up the rope of the alarm bell and placed the end of it on the table. As he handled it he could not help but notice how flexible it was, especially for such a strong rope, and one not in use. "You could hang a man with it," he thought to himself. When he was ready, he looked around, and thought, "Now, my friend, I think we shall learn something about you next time you come."

He went back to his studies and was soon deep in thought. Again he was distracted suddenly. There was that sudden silence, followed by a slight movement of the rope. As he looked he saw the great rat drop from the rope onto the oak chair and sit there glaring at him. Malcolmson flung a book at it. The rat dodged the book, as he dodged the next three. At last, as Malcolmson stood with another book ready to throw, the rat squeaked and seemed afraid. Malcolmson threw it and struck the rat. It gave a terrified squeak, ran up the back of the chair, and ran up the rope of the alarm bell. Malcolmson kept his eyes on the rat and saw it disappear through a hole in one of the pictures that hung on the wall.

As Malcolmson picked up his books, he noticed that the one that had hit the rat was the Bible his mother had given him. "What an odd coincidence," he murmured to himself. He tried to work some more but was not able to concentrate. At the first streak of dawn, he went to bed.

---

coincidence (koh IN suh duns) two or more related events accidentally happening at the same time

Mrs. Dempster woke him late in the morning. His first request surprised her. "Mrs. Dempster, when I am out today, I'd like you to get the steps and dust or wash those pictures, especially the third one from the fireplace. I want to see what they are."

On his way back from his morning walk, he stopped in to see Mrs. Witham. She introduced him to her visitor, a Dr. Thornhill. They talked about the Judge's House and about what had happened the previous two nights. After listening to Malcolmson's story, Dr. Thornhill asked, "The rat always went up the rope of the alarm bell?"

"Always."

"I suppose you know," said the doctor after a pause, "what the rope is?"

"No!"

"It is the very rope which the hangman used for all the victims of the Judge's anger!"

At this, Mrs. Witham fainted. As the doctor took care of her, Malcolmson looked at his watch and realized that it was close to his dinner hour. He left before she completely recovered.

When Mrs. Witham was herself again, she asked the doctor why he had said that to Malcolmson. "I wanted to draw his attention to the bell rope. He may get in the night some strange fright. If he does, I want him to pull that rope. All alone as he is, it will give us warning. We may reach him in time to help. I shall be sitting up late tonight and shall keep my ears open.

Do not be alarmed if Benchurch gets a surprise before morning."

"Oh, Doctor, what do you mean?"

"I mean this: possibly—even probably—we shall hear the great alarm bell from the Judge's House tonight."

When Malcolmson got home, he found that Mrs. Dempster had already left. He was glad to see that the place was tidy. For a few minutes after his entrance, the noise of the rats ceased. But soon they began again. He was glad to hear them, for he thought of the strange fact that they were quiet only when that big rat came on the scene.

After dinner, Malcolmson sat down to work, determined to make the best use of his time. For an hour or so he worked. Then his thoughts began to wander. The wind outside had turned into a storm. The house, solid though it was, seemed to shake, and the storm roared and raged through its many chimneys and gables, producing strange, unearthly sounds.

As Malcolmson listened to it, he remembered the doctor's words about the rope. He went over to the corner of the fireplace and took it in his hand to look at it. As he stood there, he lost himself in thinking about the victims and about the grim wish of the Judge to have such a ghastly relic in his house. Soon he felt a sort of tremor in the rope, as if something were moving along it.

Looking up, Malcolmson saw the great rat coming slowly down towards him, glaring at him steadily. He dropped the rope, and the rat turned and ran up the rope again and disappeared. It

---

relic (REH lik) something that remains from what has disappeared or been destroyed
tremor (TREH mur) a quick, constant shaking or trembling

occurred to Malcolmson that he had not looked at the pictures, as he had meant to. He held up a lamp and stood opposite the third picture from the fireplace on the right side, where he had seen the rat disappear on the previous night.

The picture had been dusted and washed and now stood out clearly. It was of a Judge dressed in his robes. His face was strong and without mercy. He looked evil, crafty, and cruel. The eyes were quite bright and had an evil expression. They looked exactly like the eyes of the great rat. As he looked at them, Malcolmson realized that the rat was peering out through a hole in the corner of the picture. He also realized that the other rats had stopped making any noise.

In the picture, the Judge was seated in a big carved oak chair on the right side of a great stone fireplace. In the corner a rope hung down from the ceiling, its end lying coiled on the floor. With a feeling of horror, Malcolmson recognized the scene of the very room he was in. Then he looked over to the corner of the fireplace. With a loud cry, he dropped the lamp.

There, in the Judge's chair, with the rope hanging behind, sat the rat with the Judge's eyes. Except for the howling of the storm outside, there was silence.

The fallen lamp brought Malcolmson back to reality. Luckily the lamp was of metal, so the oil was not spilled. He picked it up and got it started again. Then he thought for a moment. "This will not do," he said to himself. "I'm becoming a crazy fool. This must stop! My nerves have been getting into a strange state. I'll be all right now. I shall not be such a fool again."

He sat down to his work. An hour later, he noticed the sudden stillness. The wind was still howling outside, but inside there was no sound. Soon Malcolmson heard a thin, squeaking noise, very faint. It came from the corner of the room where the rope hung down. In the dim light, he saw the great rat clinging to the rope and gnawing it. The rope was nearly gnawed through. He could see the lighter color where the strands were laid bare. As he looked, the job was completed. The cut end of the rope fell clattering to the floor. For an instant the great rat remained like a tassel at the end of the rope, which now began to sway to and fro. Malcolmson felt for a moment a pang of terror as he thought that now the possibility of calling anyone from the town to his assistance was cut off. He threw a book at the rat. Before the book could hit it, the rat dropped off and struck the floor with a soft thud. It darted away and disappeared in the darkness of the shadows of the room.

Malcolmson decided then and there to hunt for the rat. He took off the green shade of the lamp to insure a wider spreading light. As he did so, the gloom of the upper part of the room was lit. In the light, the pictures on the wall stood out boldly. From where he stood, Malcolmson saw right opposite to him the third picture on the wall from the right of the fireplace. He rubbed his eyes in surprise, and then a great fear began to come upon him.

The background was as before, with chair and fireplace and rope. But the figure of the Judge had disappeared.

Malcolmson, almost in a chill of horror, turned slowly around. He began to shake and tremble. His strength seemed to have left him, and he couldn't move. He could only see and hear.

There, on the carved oak chair in the room sat the Judge in his robes, with his eyes glaring, and a smile of triumph on the cruel mouth. He lifted with his hands a black cap. Malcolmson felt as if the blood was running from his heart, as one does in moments of prolonged suspense. There was a singing in his ears. Outside, he could hear the roar and howl of the storm. Then came the striking of midnight by the great chimes in the center of town. As the clock struck, so the look of triumph on the Judge's face intensified. At the last stroke of midnight he placed the black cap on his head.

Slowly and deliberately the Judge rose from his chair and picked up the piece of the rope of the alarm bell that lay on the floor. He drew it through his hands as if he enjoyed its touch. Then deliberately he began to knot one end of it, fashioning it into a noose. Then he began to move along the table on the opposite side to Malcolmson, keeping his eyes on him until he had passed him.

When the Judge stood in front of the door, Malcolmson began to feel that he was trapped and tried to think of what he should do. He saw the Judge approach, still keeping between him and the door. Then the Judge raised the noose and threw it toward him. Malcolmson moved to one side, saw the rope fall beside him, and heard it hit the floor. Again the Judge

---

deliberately (dah LIH bur ayt lee) in an unhurried, slow, and steady manner raised the noose and threw it toward him. This went on many times. Each time the student managed to evade the noose.

The Judge never seemed discouraged, but seemed to be playing as a cat does with a mouse.

At last in despair, Malcolmson looked around him. The lamp seemed to have blazed up. At the many rat-holes and chinks and crannies of the wainscot he saw the rats' eyes. He saw that the rope of the great alarm bell was laden with rats. Every inch of it was covered with them.

More and more were pouring through the small hole in the ceiling, so that with their weight the bell was beginning to sway.

It swayed until the clapper touched the bell. The sound was but a tiny one, but the bell was only beginning to sway, and it would increase.

At the sound the Judge looked up, and a scowl of anger crossed his face. His eyes fairly glowed like hot coals, and he stamped his foot with a sound that seemed to make the house shake. A dreadful peal of thunder broke overhead as he raised the rope again. The rats kept running up and down the rope as though working against time. This time, instead of throwing it, the judge drew close to Mal-

colmson. He held open the noose. As he came closer, there seemed something paralyzing in his very presence. Malcolmson stood rigid as a corpse. He felt the Judge's icy fingers touch his throat as he adjusted the rope. The noose tightened—tightened. Then the Judge, taking the rigid form of the student in his arms, carried him over and placed him standing in the oak chair. Stepping up beside him, he put his hand up and caught the end of the swaying rope of the alarm bell. As he raised his hands, the rats fled squeaking. They disappeared through a hole in the ceiling. Taking the end of the noose which was around Malcolmson's neck, he tied it to the hanging bell rope. Then, descending, he pulled away the chair.

◆ ◆ ◆ ◆ ◆ ◆ ◆

When the alarm bell of the Judge's House began to sound, a crowd soon gathered and hurried to the spot. They knocked loudly at the door, but there was no reply. Then they burst in the door and poured into the great dining room, the doctor at the head.

There at the end of the rope of the great alarm bell hung the body of the student. On the face of the Judge in the picture was a malignant smile.

---

evade (ee VAHD) to keep away from; avoid
rigid (RIH jihd) stiff
malignant (muh LIHG nunt) evil

Review the Selection

UNDERSTAND THE SELECTION

Recall

1. Why did Malcolmson go to Benchurch?

2. Why did the people of Benchurch fear the Judge?

3. Why does Dr. Thornhill tell Malcolmson about the bell rope?

Infer

4. How would you describe Malcolmson's personality?

5. What events did the author use to help the reader predict the ending?

6. In what way is Mrs. Dempster like Malcolmson?

7. What is the theme of this story?

Apply

8. Have you ever, like Malcolmson, ignored the advice of others? What happened as a result?

9. Would you have stayed in the house if you were Malcolmson? What would you have done differently if you had been in Malcolmson's position?

10. Based on this story, how do young people react differently to danger than older people?

Respond to Literature

Why do some people believe in haunted houses? Do you believe in them? Why or why not?

WRITE ABOUT THE SELECTION

Telling a story from a different point of view can drastically change it. Mrs. Dempster, Malcolmson's housekeeper, does not seem to be superstitious or fearful. You are Mrs. Dempster. Explain the events of the story from her point of view.

Prewriting Reread the parts of the story where Mrs. Dempster appears. Make a list of what she does and says. Then think about the end of the story. Assume that she is part of the crowd that finds Malcolmson's body. What do you think she would say and do now?

Writing Begin your story when Mrs. Dempster first meets Malcolmson. Include her observations of Malcolmson and of Mrs. Witham. Use your prewriting list to guide you through the rest of the story, especially the end. Think of how Mrs. Dempster might interpret what the crowd sees when they enter the house. Remember to write in the first person point of view. Use the pronoun *I*.

Revising Reread your story. Keep in mind that Mrs. Dempster is not at all superstitious. Think about how such a person would view the events of the story and describe them. Include some dialogue between Mrs. Dempster and some of the more superstitious characters, like Mrs. Witham and Dr. Thornhill to make your story livelier.

Proofreading Make sure you have used the first person and have spelled the characters' names correctly. Check for correct use of quotation marks in the dialogue.

THINK ABOUT THEME

Theme is the main idea or message in a story or play. One theme of "The Judge's House" is that the evil workings of a person continue long after the person dies. This theme is developed in a number of ways.

1. One way the theme of "The Judge's House" is developed is through the setting. How is the house described when Malcolmson first arrives?

2. Mrs. Witham tells Malcolmson that the Judge, who was greatly feared by the townspeople, lived in the house more than a hundred years ago. How does this fact contribute to the theme?

3. Dialogue is also used to develop theme. Find an example.

4. Plot is also used to develop theme. Explain how.

5. The story ends with this sentence: "On the face of the Judge in the picture was a malignant smile." How does this sentence reinforce the theme?

READING FOCUS

Use Prior Knowledge As you read this story, you were able to draw from your own experiences and from early events in the story to make predictions. How did your prior knowledge help you to anticipate the outcome of the story?

DEVELOP YOUR VOCABULARY

Language changes over time. Many words that we use in everyday speech were unknown a hundred years ago. Likewise, many common words used at the time this story was written are no longer used today.

Below are some sentences from the story. Each contains a word or phrase that is not in common use today. These words are italicized in the sentences. Rewrite the sentences by replacing the italicized words with words we would use today. Use a dictionary as needed.

1. ". . . a bed that hadn't been aired for perhaps fifty years was not proper for *young bones to lie on*."

2. "She said that for her own part, she wasn't afraid of *all the bogies in the kingdom*."

3. "Up and down behind the old *wainscot*, over the ceiling and under the floor they raced and gnawed and scratched!"

4. "Mrs. Dempster, . . . I'd like you to get *the steps* and dust or wash those pictures."

5. "Then deliberately he began to knot one end of it [the rope], *fashioning it* into a noose."

NARRATIVE POETRY

Many poems are written simply to give you an impression or feeling about the subject. They have no real story to tell. Other poems, however, do tell a story. They are like short, short stories written in verse.

Poems that tell a story are called **narrative poems**. They have the elements of a short story—setting, characters, plot, and theme. These elements may not be as well developed as in a short story, however, since a poem is usually shorter.

Why do authors tell stories in poetry rather than prose? That is a question to keep in mind as you read the next two selections. Remember that techniques such as imagery, rhyme, personification, and metaphor can often be used to best advantage in poetry.

As you read "The Listeners" and "Eldorado," ask yourself:

1. What are the poems' elements?
2. What would the story be like if it were in prose rather than poetry?

WRITING CONNECTION

Nursery rhymes, which are poems, are usually a form of narrative poetry. Think of a nursery rhyme. Tell its plot in a paragraph or two.

READING FOCUS

Draw Conclusions When you draw conclusions, you have to decide why certain events take place or why characters do certain things. You can use details in stories and poems and your own experience to draw conclusions about unstated events or actions. Drawing conclusions helps you to understand characters' motivations and why certain events occur. As you read, use what you know and what the author tells you to draw conclusions.

The Listeners

by Walter de la Mare

"Is there anybody there?" said the Traveller,
    Knocking on the moonlit door;
And his horse in the silence champed the grasses
    Of the forest's ferny floor:
5   And a bird flew up out of the turret,
    Above the Traveller's head:
And he smote upon the door again a second time;
    "Is there anybody there?" he said.
But no one descended to the Traveller;
10   No head from the leaf-fringed sill
Leaned over and looked into his grey eyes,
    Where he stood perplexed and still.
But only a host of phantom listeners
    That dwelt in the lone house then
15   Stood listening in the quiet of the moonlight
    To that voice from the world of men:
Stood thronging the faint moonbeams on the dark stair,
    That goes down to the empty hall,
Hearkening in an air stirred and shaken
20   By the lonely Traveller's call.
And he felt in his heart their strangeness,
    Their stillness answering his cry,
While his horse moved, cropping the dark turf,
    'Neath the starred and leafy sky;
25   For he suddenly smote on the door, even
    Louder, and lifted his head:—
"Tell them I came, and no one answered,
    That I kept my word," he said.
Never the least stir made the listeners,

---

champed (CHAMPT) bit or chewed, usually impatiently
turret (TUR it) small tower on top of a building
smote (SMOHT) pounded; struck
perplexed (pur PLEKST) confused; puzzled
host (HOHST) large group
thronging (THRAWNG ing) crowding; jostling
cropping (KROP ing) biting off the tops
turf (TURF) short grass

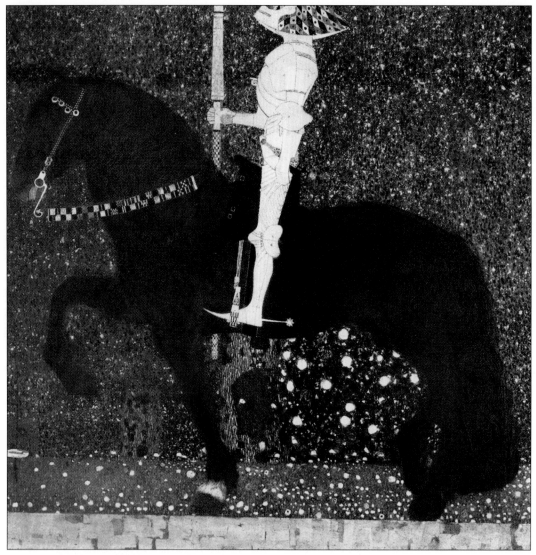

The Battle of Life (*Golden Knight*), Gustave Klimt, Galerie St. Etienne, New York

30   Though every word he spake
        Fell echoing through the shadowiness of the still house
           From the one man left awake:
        Ay, they heard his foot upon the stirrup,
           And the sound of iron on stone,
35   And how the silence surged softly backward,
        When the plunging hoofs were gone.

---

surged (SURJD) rolled; swelled up

182 ▪ Unit 2

ELDORADO

by Edgar Allan Poe

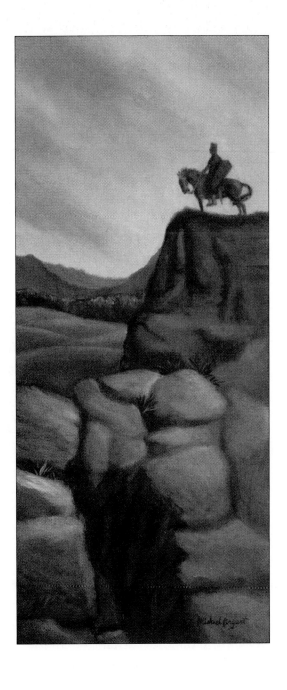

Gaily bedight,
A gallant knight,
In sunshine and in shadow,
Had journeyed long,
5   Singing a song,
In search of Eldorado.

But he grew old—
This knight so bold—
And o'er his heart a shadow
10   Fell, as he found
No spot of ground
That looked like Eldorado.

And, as his strength
Failed him at length
15   He met a pilgrim shadow—
"Shadow," said he,
"Where can it be—
This land of Eldorado?"

"Over the Mountains
20   Of the Moon,
Down the Valley of the Shadow,
Ride, boldly ride,"
The shade replied,
"If you seek for Eldorado!"

---

bedight (bih DYT) adorne
Eldorado (el duh RAH doh) a fabled place full of money-making opportunities

Review the Selection

UNDERSTAND THE SELECTION

Recall

1. Where is the house the traveler stopped at in "The Listeners"?

2. What does the traveler do at the end of the poem?

3. From whom did the knight in "Eldorado" ask directions?

Infer

4. Who do you think the listeners are?

5. Why did the traveler knock on the door a third time?

6. When do you think the knight in "Eldorado" began his search?

7. What does Poe mean by the lines "And o'er his heart a shadow fell"?

Apply

8. Have you ever been in an empty building but felt as if someone else were there? Explain.

9. Why do you think a knight is used as the character in "Eldorado"?

10. Will the knight ever find Eldorado?

Respond to Literature

Can you think of other characters in books you have read who are like the knight in "Eldorado"? What are they looking for?

WRITE ABOUT THE SELECTION

Let us go back to a question asked in the opening discussions of these selections. Why do authors sometimes tell stories in poetry when they could write in prose? Maybe you can find an answer by experimenting with the Edgar Allan Poe poem. Like every narrative poem, it has all the elements of a short story. Rewrite Poe's poem as a short story.

Prewriting Make sure you understand all the words and phrases in the poem. Use a dictionary if you are not sure of any meanings. Then freewrite about the events in the poem to flesh out the narrative with details.

Writing The poem is a natural outline for your story. Use it and your freewriting to write your version, changing the poetry to prose. Do a stanza at a time. Each stanza could be one paragraph. You will probably need to add details and even events to make your tale logical and enjoyable.

Revising Read your story through without stopping to make any changes or corrections. Does it read smoothly? Is the theme as clear as in the original poem? Check the transitions between paragraphs. Then go back and make any changes you think are needed.

Proofreading Reread your story and check for errors. Make sure you use correct punctuation, particularly at the ends of sentences. The poem uses many dashes, which you should not use for end punctuation in your prose story.

THINK ABOUT NARRATIVE POETRY

A narrative poem tells a story. The poem will have elements similar to a short story —plot, setting, characters, and theme. In addition, narrative poems can have other poetic elements. The structures of "Eldorado" and "The Listeners" show one of the strengths of using poetry to tell a story.

1. What is the plot of the two poems?

2. Describe the main characters in "The Listeners" and "Eldorado." How are they similar?

3. What is the setting of "The Listeners"? Of "El Dorado"? What do the settings have in common?

4. Explain the themes of both poems in your own words.

5. Rhythm and rhyme together can give a poem a distinctive feeling. What feeling do they create in these poems?

READING FOCUS

Draw Conclusions For each poem that you read, describe one conclusion that you drew about a character or an event. What clues in the poem helped you come to this conclusion?

DEVELOP YOUR VOCABULARY

You often find odd verbs and verb forms in poems. This might be because the poet is trying to find one word to rhyme with another. Perhaps, as in the case of "The Listeners," it might be because the poem was written about a long time ago when different verbs and verb forms were used commonly.

An example of an old verb is the word *smote*, which appears twice in the poem. A dictionary can help you understand both its meaning and whether it still is used.

Here is the entry:
smote (smōt) v., past tense of *smite*.

If you look up *smite*, you will find all the forms of the verb. You will find also that *smite* as a verb meaning "to hit or strike hard" is "Now Rare."

Choose five old verbs from the poems. Then use them in original sentences. Use a dictionary to find the present/past tenses and definitions of these "old" verbs.

Learn About

Exposition is one of the four types of nonfiction composition. Often when you are asked to write an essay in science or history about types of animals or the causes of World War I, you are writing exposition. The purpose of **exposition** is to explain something to your readers.

While exposition can exist in a form of its own, it is often combined with other types of writing. Exposition can be used to support arguments in persuasive writing, and descriptive writing can blend with exposition to offer examples that explain an important point.

As you read the next selection, ask yourself these questions:

1. What is John McPhee explaining to his readers?
2. What other types of writing does the author use in this essay?

READING FOCUS

Evaluate the Writer's Purpose Every author has a purpose for writing. The purpose may be to inform, to entertain, or to persuade the reader. The way they present information is the way you can determine their purpose. As you read, look for factual, humorous, or persuasive details. This will help you decide the author's purpose. It is up to the reader to decide the writer's purpose.

WRITING CONNECTION

Think about something you really enjoy or something that you are good at doing. Use exposition to explain about your "something" to a reader who knows very little about your subject. What do your readers really need to understand?

THE LOCH NESS MONSTER

ADAPTED

by John McPhee

The road—the A-82—stayed close to the lake, often on ledges that had been blasted into the mountainsides. The steep forests continued, broken now and again, on one shore or the other, by fields of fern, clumps of bright-yellow shrubs and isolated stands of cedar. Along the far shore were widely separated houses and farms, which to the eyes of a traveller appeared almost unbelievably green and fertile after the spare desolation of some of the higher glens. We came to the top of the rise and suddenly saw, on the right-hand side of the road, on the edge of a

glens (GLENZ) narrow, secluded valleys

high meadow that sloped sharply a considerable distance to the lake, a cluster of caravans and other vehicles, arranged in the shape of a C, with an opening toward the road—much like a circle of covered wagons formed for protection against savage attack. All but one or two of the vehicles were painted bright lily-pad green. The compound, in its compact half acre, was surrounded by a fence, to keep out, among other things, sheep, which were grazing all over the slope in deep-green turf among buttercups, daisies, and thistles. Gulls above beat hard into the wind, then turned and planed toward the south. Gulls are inland birds in Scotland, there being so little distance from anywhere to the sea. A big fireplace had been made from rocks of the sort that were scattered all over the meadow. And on the lakeward side a platform had been built, its level high position emphasizing the slope of the hill, which dropped away below it. Mounted on the platform was a thirty-five-millimeter motion-picture camera with an enormous telephoto lens. From its point of view, sticking out at two hundred feet above the lake, the camera could take in a dazzling scene that covered thousands of acres of water.

This was Expedition Headquarters, the principal field station of the Loch Ness Phenomena Investigation Bureau—dues five pounds per annum,[1] life membership one hundred pounds, tax on donations recoverable under covenant.[2] Those who join the bureau receive newsletters and annual reports, and are allowed to participate in the fieldwork if they so desire. I turned into the compound and parked between two bright-green reconditioned old London taxis. The central area had long since been worn grassless and was covered at this moment with fine-grain dust. People were coming and going. The place seemed rather public, as if it were a depot. No one even halfway interested in the natural history of the Great Glen would think of driving up the A-82 without stopping in there. Since the A-82 is the principal route between Glasgow and Inverness,[3] it is not surprising that the apparently amphibious creature as yet unnamed, the so-called Loch Ness Monster, has been seen not only from the highway but on it.

The atmosphere around the headquarters suggested a scientific frontier and also a boom town, much as Cape Canaveral and Cocoa Beach do. There were, as well, hints of show business and fine arts. Probably the one word that might have been applied to everyone present was adventurer. There was, at any

---

caravans (KAR uh vanz) in Great Britain, camping trailers
telephoto (TEL uh foht oh) a camera lens that is able to make faraway things appear large
amphibious (am FIB ee us) able to live on land and in water
[1]**dues five pounds per annum:** amount of British money per year that it costs to belong
[2]**tax on donations recoverable by covenant:** Taxes paid on donations will be refunded
[3]**Glasgow and Inverness:** cities in southern and northern Scotland

rate, nothing really laboratorial about the place, although the prevailing mood seemed to be one not of holiday but of matter-of-fact application and patient dedication. A telephone call came in that day, to the caravan that served as an office, from a woman who owned an inn south of Inverarigaig, on the other side of the lake. She said that she had seen the creature that morning just forty yards offshore—three humps, nothing else to report, and being very busy just now, thank you very much, good day. This was recorded, with no particular display of excitement, by an extremely attractive young woman who appeared to be in her late twenties, an artist from London who had missed but one summer at Loch Ness in seven years. She wore sandals, dungarees, a black pullover, and gold earrings. Her name was Mary Piercy, and her toes were painted pink. The bulletin board where she recorded the sighting resembled the kind used in railway stations for the listing of incoming trains.

The office walls were decorated with photographs of the monster in various postures basking, cruising, diving, splashing, looking up questioningly. A counter was covered with some of the essential publications: the bureau's annual report (twenty-nine sightings the previous year), J. A. Carruth's *Loch Ness and Its Monster* (The Abbey Press, Fort Augustus), Tim Dinsdale's *Loch Ness Monster* (Routledge and Kegan Paul, London), and a report

by the joint Air Reconnaissance Center of the Royal Air Force on a motion picture of the monster swimming about half a mile on the lake's surface. These books and documents could, in turn, lead the interested reader to less available but nonetheless highly important works such as R. T. Gould's *The Loch Ness Monster and Others* and Constance Whyte's *More Than a Legend*.

My children looked over the photographs with absorption but not a great deal of awe, and they bought about a dozen postcards with glossy prints of a picture of the monster—three humps showing, much the same sight that the innkeeper had described—that had been taken by a man named Stuart, directly across the lake from Urquhart Castle. The three younger girls then ran out into the meadow and began to pick daisies and buttercups. Their mother and sister sat down in the sun to read about the creature in the lake, and to write postcards. We were on our way to Inverness, but with no need to hurry. "Dear Grammy, we came to see the monster today."

From the office to the camera-observation platform to the caravan that served as a pocket cafeteria, I wandered around among the crew, was offered and accepted tea, and squinted with imaginary experience up and down the lake, where the water had grown even rougher. Among the crew at the time were two

---

basking (BASK ing) warming oneself pleasantly, as in sunlight
reconnaissance (rih KON uh sens) quick survey of information

Canadians, a Swede, an Australian, three Americans, two Englishmen, a Welshman, and one Scot. Two were women. When I asked one of the crew members if he knew what jobs some of the others had when they were not at Loch Ness, he said, "I'm not sure what they are. We don't go into that." This was obviously a place where now was all that mattered, and in such surroundings it is distinctly pleasant to accept that approach to things. Nonetheless, I found that I couldn't stick completely to this principle, and I did find out that one man was a medical doctor, another a farmer, another a retired naval officer, and that several were students, as might be expected. The daily watch begins at four in the morning and goes on, as one fellow put it, "as long as we can stand up." It has been the pattern among the hundreds of sightings reported that the early-morning hours are the most promising ones. Camera stations are manned until ten at night, dawn and sunset being so close to midnight at that latitude in summer, but the sentries tend to thin out with the lengthening of the day. During the autumn, the size of the crew reduces almost to one.

One man lives at the headquarters all year long. His name is Clem Lister Skelton. "I've been staring at that piece of water since five o'clock," he said, while he drank tea in the mess caravan.

"Is there a technique?" I asked him.

"Just look," he said. "Look. Run your eye over the water in one quick skim. What we're looking for is not hard to see. You just sit and sort of gaze at the loch, that's all. Mutter a few incantations. That's all there is to do. In wintertime, very often, it's just myself. And of course one keeps a very much more perfunctory watch in the winter. I saw it once in a snowstorm, though, and that was the only time I've had a clear view of the head and neck. The neck is obviously very mobile. The creature was quite big, but it wasn't as big as a seventy-foot MFV. Motor fishing vessel. I'd been closer to it, but I hadn't seen as much of it before. I've seen it eight times. The last time was in September. Only the back. Just the sort of upturned boat, which is the classic view of it."

Skelton drank some more tea, and refilled a cup he had given me. "I must know what it is," he went on. "I shall never rest peacefully until I know what it is. Some of the largest creatures in the world are out there, and we can't name them. It may take ten years, but we're going to identify the genus. Most people are not as fanatical as I, but I would like to see this through to the end, if I don't get too broke first."

Skelton is a tall, informed man, English, with reddish hair that is uncombed in long strings from the thinning crown of his head. In outline, Skelton's life

---

technique (tek NEEK) method of doing something
incantations (in kan TAY shunz) magical words used in enchantment
perfunctory (pur FUNK tuh ree) routine; superficial
genus (JEE nus) main subdivision of a family of closely related species
fanatical (fuh NAT ih kul) incredibly devoted, to the point of being unreasonable

there in the caravan on the edge of the high meadow over the lake, in a place that must be uncorrectably gloomy during the wet rains of winter, seemed cagelike and hopeless to me—unacceptably lonely. The impression he gave was of a man who had drawn a circle around himself many hundreds of miles from the rest of his life. But how could I know? He was saying that he had flown Supermarine Spitfires[4] for the R.A.F. during the Second World War. His father had been a soldier, and when Skelton was a boy, he lived, as he put it, "all over the place." As an adult, he became first an actor, later a writer and director of films. He acted in London in plays like *March Hare* and *Saraband for Dead Lovers*. One film he directed was, in his words, "a dreadful thing called *Saul and David*." These appearances on the surface apparently did not occur so frequently that he needed to do nothing else for a livelihood. He also directed, in the course of many years, several hundred educational films. The publisher who distributed some of these films was David James, a friend of Skelton's, and at that time a Member of Parliament.[5] James happened to be, as well, the founder of the Loch Ness Phenomena Investigation Bureau—phenomena, because, for breeding purposes, there would have to be at least two monsters living in the lake at any one time, probably more, and in fact two had on occasion been sighted at the same time. James asked Skelton if he would go up to the lake and give the bureau the benefit of his technical knowledge of movie cameras. "Anything for a laugh," Skelton had said to James. This was in the early nineteen-sixties. "I came for a fortnight," Skelton said now, in the caravan. "And I saw it. I wanted to know what it was, and I've wanted to know what it was ever since. I thought I'd have time to write up here, but I haven't. I don't do anything now except hunt this beast."

Skelton talked on about what the monster might be—a magnified newt, a long-necked variety of giant seal, still existing *Elasmosaurus*. Visitors wandered by in groups outside the caravan, and unexplained strangers kept coming in for tea. In the air was a feeling, utterly hidden by the relative permanence of the place, of a country carnival on a two-night stand. The caravans themselves, in their placement, suggested a section of a carnival. I remembered a woman shouting to attract people to a big caravan on a carnival midway one night in May in New Jersey. That was some time ago. I must have been nineteen. The woman, who was standing on a small platform, was fifty or sixty, and she was trying to get people to go into the caravan to see big jungle cats, I suppose, and brown bears—"Ferocious Beasts," at any rate, according to block lettering on the side of the caravan. A steel cage containing a

---

fortnight (FAWRT nyt) two weeks
newt (NOOT) small salamander found in damp places
[4]**Supermarine Spitfires** for the **R.A.F.:** Fighter planes for the British Royal Air Force
[5]**Parliament:** The national legislative body of Great Britain

small black bear had been set up on two sawhorses outside the caravan—a fragment to suggest what might be found on a large scale inside.

So young that it was no more than two feet from nose to tail, the bear was engaged in desperate motion, racing along one side of the cage from corner to corner, striking the steel bars bluntly with its nose. Whirling then tossing its head over its shoulder like a racing swimmer, it turned and bolted crazily for the opposite end. Its eyes were deep red and shining in a kind of full-sighted blindness. It had gone mad there in the cage and its motion, rhythmic and tortured, never stopped, back and forth, back and forth, the head tossing with each jarring turn. The animal skinned its sides on the steel bars as it ran. Hair and skin had scraped from its sides so that pink flesh showed in the downpour of the carnival arc lights. Blood drained freely through the thinned hair of its belly and dropped onto the floor of the cage. What had a paralyzing effect on me was the animal's almost perfect and now involuntary rhythm—the wild toss of the head after the crash into the corner, the turn, the scraping run, the crash again at the other end, never stopping, regular—the exposed interior of some brutal and living time piece.

Beside the cage, the plump, critical woman, red-faced, red-nosed, kept shouting to the crowds, but she said to me, leaning down with her eyes bloodshot,

"Why don't you move on, sonny, if you ain't going to buy a ticket? Beat it. Come on, now. Move on."

"I argue about what it is," Skelton said. "I'm inclined to think it's a giant slug, but there is an amazingly impressive theory for its being a worm. You can't rule out that it's one of the big dinosaurs, but I think this is more wishful thinking than anything else." In the late nineteen-thirties, a large and strange-looking footprint was found along the shore of Loch Ness. It was carefully studied by various people and was assumed, for a time, to be an impression from a foot or flipper of the monster. Eventually, the print was identified. Someone who owned the preserved foot of a hippopotamus had successfully brought off a trick that put layers of mockery and incredibility over the creature in the lake for many years. The Second World War further turned aside any serious interest that amateurs or naturalists might have taken. Sightings continued, however, in a regular pattern, and finally, in the early nineteen-sixties, the Loch Ness Phenomena Investigation Bureau was established. "I have no plans whatever for leaving," Skelton said. "I am prepared to stay here ad infinitum. All my worldly goods are here."

A dark-haired young woman had stepped into the caravan and poured herself a cup of tea. Skelton, introducing her to me, said, "If the beast has done nothing else, it has brought me a wife.

---

slug (SLUG) a small animal like a snail, but without such a hard, outer shell
ad infinitum (ad in fuh NYT um) Latin phrase meaning forever

She was studying Gaelic and Scottish history at Edinburgh University, and she walked into the glen one day, and I said, 'That is the girl I am going to marry.'" He gestured toward a window of the caravan, which framed a view of the hills and the lake. "The Great Glen is one of the most beautiful places in the world," he continued. "It is peaceful here. I'd be happy here all my life, even if there were nothing in the loch. I've even committed the unforgivable sin of going to sleep in the sun during a flat calm. With enough time, we could shoot the beast with a crossbow, and a line, and get a bit of skin. We could also shoot a small transmitter into its hide and learn more than we know now about its habits and characteristics. "

The creature swims with remarkable speed, as much as 12 to 18 mph when it is really moving. It makes no noise other than sudden splashes, but it is apparently responsive in a highly sensitive way to sound. A shout, an approaching engine, any loud report, will send it into an immediate dive, and this shyness is in large part the cause of why it can't be found, and therefore of its mystery. Curiously, though, the echoing sound was what apparently brought the creature wide attention, for the first series of frequent sightings occurred in 1933, when A-82 was blasted into the cliffsides of the western shore of the lake. Immense boulders kept falling into the depths, and shock waves from dynamite repeatedly ran through the water, causing the creature to lose confidence in its environment and to alter, at least temporarily, its shy and preferred nightlife. In that year it was first observed on land, perhaps attempting to seek a way out forever from the blasts that had alarmed it. A couple named Spicer saw it, near Inverarigiag, and later described its long, serpent-like neck, followed by an awkward hulk of a body, lurching toward the lake and disappearing into high undergrowth as they approached.

With the exception of one report recorded in the sixth century, which said that a monster (fitting the description of the current creatures in the lake) had killed a man with a single bite, there have been no other examples of savagery on its part. To the contrary, its sensitivity to people seems to be sharp, and it keeps a wide margin between itself and mankind. In all likelihood, it feeds on fish and particularly on eels, of which there are millions in the lake. Loch Ness is unparalleled in eel-fishing circles, and has drawn commercial eel fishermen from all over the United Kingdom. The monster has been observed with its neck bent down in the water, like a swan feeding. When the creatures die, they apparently settle into the seven-hundred-foot floor of the lake, where the temperature is always forty-two degrees Fahrenheit—so cold that the lake is known for never

---

Gaelic (GAYL ik) A Celtic language spoken in Scotland and Ireland
crossbow (KRAWS boh) a kind of bow that is set flat for firing
transmitter (trans MIT ur) radio device that sends out signals

giving up its dead. Loch Ness never freezes, despite its high latitude, so if the creature breathes air, as has seemed apparent from the reports of observers who have watched its mouth rhythmically opening and closing, it does not lose access to the surface in winter. It clearly prefers the smooth, sunbaked waters of summer, however, as it seems to love to bask in the sun, like an upturned boat, slowly rolling, plunging, squirming around with what can only be taken as pleasure. By observers' reports, the creature has two pairs of side flippers, and when it swims off, tail thrashing, it leaves behind it a trail of water as impressive as the track of a small warship. When it dives from a still position, it unexplainably goes down without leaving a bubble. When it dives as it swims, it leaves on the surface a churning signature of foam.

Skelton leaned back against the wall of the caravan in a lazy and calm posture. He was wearing a dark blue tie that was monogrammed in small block letters sewn with white thread—L.N.I. (Loch Ness Investigation). Above the monogram and embroidered also in white thread was a small picture of the monster-humps rising regularly, head high, tail extending in back. Skelton gave the tie a tap with one hand. "You get this with a five-pound membership," he said.

The sea-serpent effect given by the white thread on the tie was less a cartoon-like drawing than an attempt toward a naturalistic sketch. As I studied it there, framed on Skelton's chest, the thought occurred to me that there was something inconvenient about the monster's actual appearance. In every sense except possibly the sense that involves cruelty, the creature in Loch Ness is indeed a monster. An average taken from many films and sightings gives its mature length at about forty feet. Its general appearance is very unattractive, in the sense in which reptiles are repulsive to many human beings, and any number of people might find difficulty in accepting a creature that looks like the one that was slain by St. George.[6] Its neck, about six feet long, column-like, powerfully muscled, is the neck of a serpent. Its head, scarcely broader than the neck, is a serpent's head, with uncompromising, lens-shaped eyes. Sometimes as it swims it holds its head and neck erect. The creature's mouth is at least a foot wide. Its body rises and falls with the waves. Its skin glistens when wet and appears coarse, spotted, gray, and elephant-like when exposed to the air long enough to become dry. The tail, long and column-like, stretches back to something of a point. It seemed to me, sitting there at Headquarters, that the classical, mythical, dragon likeness of this living thing—the modified dinosaur, the fantastically exaggerated newt—was an obstacle to the work of the investigation bureau. The bureau has no real interest in what the monster resembles or calls to mind but a great deal in what it actually is. Their goal is a final and positive identification of the genus.

---

[6]**St. George:** Christian saint who supposedly killed a large dragon.

"What we need is a good, lengthy, basking sighting," Skelton said. "We've had one long surfacing—twenty-five minutes. I saw it. Opposite Urquhart Castle. We only had a twelve-inch lens then, at four and a half miles. We have thirty-six-inch lenses now. We need a long, clear, close-up—in color."

My children had watched, some months earlier, the killing of a small snake on a lawn in Maryland. About eighteen inches long, it came out from a basement-window well, through a covering screen of redwood, and was noticed with shouts and shrieks by the children and a young retriever that barked at the snake and leaped about it in a circle. We were the weekend guests of another family, and eight children in all crowded around the snake, which had been gliding slowly across the lawn during the moments after it had been seen, but had now stopped and was turning its head from side to side in apparent indecision. Our host hurried into his garage and came running back to the lawn with a long shovel. Before he killed the snake, his wife urged him not to. She said the snake could not possibly be poisonous. He said, "How do you know?" The children, mine and theirs, looked back and forth from him to her. The dog began to bark more rapidly and at a higher pitch.

"It has none of the markings. There is nothing triangular about its head," she told him.

"That may very well be," he said. "But you can't be sure."

"It is *not* poisonous. Leave it alone. Look at all these children."

"I can't help that."

"It is *not* poisonous."

"How do you know?"

"I know."

He hit the snake with the flat of the shovel, and it twisted. He hit it again. It kept moving. He hit it a third time, and it stopped. Its underside, whitish green, turned up. The children moved in for a closer look.

Review the Selection

UNDERSTAND THE SELECTION

Recall

1. Describe the cluster of trailers.

2. What two places does Expedition Headquarters remind McPhee of?

3. What is the only report of the monster's hurting people?

Infer

4. Why do you think McPhee writes in first-person point of view?

5. Why does McPhee include so many details in his story?

6. Why do you think McPhee describes what his children did when they looked at the Expedition exhibits?

7. Explain the significance of the story about the New Jersey carnival show.

Apply

8. Standing all day next to a camera seems an inefficient way to track the monster. Do you have any better ideas?

9. Do you think John McPhee believes the Loch Ness Monster exists? Explain.

10. Do you believe the Loch Ness Monster exists? Give some reasons.

Respond to Literature

Why do some people believe creatures like Nessie and Bigfoot exist?

WRITE ABOUT THE SELECTION

John McPhee is an expert nonfiction writer. You can learn from the way he writes, particularly his use of exposition.

In the selection opening, you were asked to explain about something you enjoyed or are good at. Look again at what you wrote. Do you have any ideas for improving it?

Prewriting   Think of a reason or purpose for telling about your hobby or talent. McPhee always has a purpose for his writing. What is the purpose of yours? Will you entertain, inform, persuade? Write that purpose at the top of your paper. Then freewrite for five minutes on your topic.

Writing   Keeping the purpose in mind, use any parts of what you have written already to write a new explanation. Add new details, or focus in on one or two important features.

Revising   Look at a single descriptive paragraph in McPhee's story. Then read your paragraph. Can you borrow any of McPhee's techniques to improve your writing? Make sure you vary sentence structures. Too many sentences constructed in the same way can bore readers.

Proofreading   Reread your description and check that you have used initial capital letters for all proper nouns: the name of your school, football team, school newspaper, and so forth. Check the spelling of each proper noun you include.

THINK ABOUT EXPOSITION

This selection uses more description and exposition than any other selection you've read so far. The purpose of exposition is to explain something. While it can be used by itself, it is often combined with other types of composition. McPhee combines exposition and description but other writers blend persuasion or narration with exposition.

1. How does the story begin? What feeling do you have after reading the first paragraph?

2. Look at the third paragraph which talks about the atmosphere of the headquarters. How does McPhee describe it? What does he explain with his description?

3. Why do you think McPhee provides names of books about the monster in the next paragraph?

4. Why is it important for McPhee to try to report about the "adventurers'" jobs?

5. What is John McPhee explaining to his readers?

READING FOCUS

Evaluate the Writer's Purpose As you read, you were able to ask questions about why the author presented certain information and why he used a certain style of writing. What do you think the author's purpose in writing this story was? Did he achieve the results he wanted?

DEVELOP YOUR VOCABULARY

People in Britain sometimes use different words for things than do people in the United States. For example, the *hood* of a car is called a *bonnet* in Britain and what Americans call the *trunk* is the *boot* to the British. Some words commonly used in Britain are not used in the United States. *Fortnight*, for example, means two weeks. People in the United States do not usually use this word.

You can check for alternative or new meanings of words in the dictionary. If a word is used mainly in Britain rather than the U.S., the note [Chiefly Brit.] will come before the definition. Knowing about the background of a new word can help you understand a selection.

Use a dictionary to help you find definitions people in Britain might have for these words. Then use the words in sentences.

1. caravan
2. chips
3. crisp
4. boot
5. nappy
6. hoover
7. goods
8. lorry
9. petrol
10. holiday

READING FOCUS

Make Inferences About Setting Sometimes an author will directly state where a story takes place. At other times, the reader must infer where the story takes place, or other details about the setting, by using clues that the author provides. As you read, look for clues that tell you more about the setting of this story.

PERSUASION

Is it possible that monsters, ghosts, and spirits really exist? In this selection, the author tells us about "poltergeists," or ghosts that create noisy disturbances. He did not believe in ghosts until he did some investigative work of his own. After his investigation, he was persuaded that poltergeists are real. He says he has seen what they can do.

"The Great Amherst Mystery" was written to persuade you, too. **Persuasion** is writing or speech that attempts to convince the reader or listener to adopt an opinion or course of action. The author tries to establish the truth of a proposition by presenting facts, testimony of reliable witnesses, and other evidence. He also uses other types of composition such as exposition, description, and narration. He wants to convince you to believe ghosts might exist.

As you read the next selection, ask yourself these questions:

1. How does the author try to persuade us that poltergeists exist?
2. Are the author's points convincing?

WRITING CONNECTION

Try to persuade a friend to eat a certain kind of food he or she does not like. Write one paragraph arguing your case.

The Great Amherst Mystery

by Walter Hubbell

It's a strange world, this one we live in. I don't believe in ghosts. That is, I didn't believe in ghosts before I investigated the mystery of Esther Cox. Now the only question is what to call them—ghosts, spirits, poltergeists, or what?

My name is Walter Hubbell. By vocation, I'm an actor. By avocation, I'm an investigator of the "supernatural." During the past few years, I've investigated many people who claimed they could talk to the spirits of the dead. They were all fakes, and I exposed them. As an actor, I know all the tricks that we use on the stage. I also know most of the tricks that magicians use to fool the public. I am, beyond doubt, able to judge whether or not deception was used in the case of Esther Cox. And it was not.

Truth is often stranger than fiction. What I have written here is truth—not fiction—and it is *very strange*.

I was acting in Canada when I first heard of Esther Cox. She was 19 years old at the time. She and her sister Jennie, age 22, lived in the home of an older married sister, Olive Teed. Daniel Teed, Olive's husband, was a foreman in a shoe factory. The Teeds had two small boys. Before the trouble started, all lived together in a rented house in the town of Amherst.

Then things started to happen. One night Esther thought she heard a mouse somewhere in her bed. She awakened her sister

---

poltergeist (POHL tur gyst) a noisy ghost
vocation (voh KAY shun) profession; career
avocation (av uh KAY shun) hobby
deception (dih SEP shun) trickery; action intended to fool another person

Jennie, who slept in the same room. They listened in silence, and soon went back to sleep. But the next night, both sisters heard the noise again, louder than ever. "It's in that box, under my bed," declared Esther. Together the two sisters pulled the green cardboard box out from under the bed. It jumped, and both girls screamed. Jennie slowly took hold of the box and placed it in the middle of the room. It jumped again, rising a foot in the air and falling back on its side. The girls' screams brought Daniel Teed hurrying into the room. He listened to their story. "You're both crazy," he announced, shaking his head as he kicked the box back under the bed. "Now go to sleep and don't disturb me again!"

This was just the beginning. A few nights later, another scream echoed through the house. It was Esther: "What's happening to me? I'm swelling up! I'm going to burst!" This time the whole family ran to the bedroom, and there was Esther, confused and worried, her whole body swollen beyond belief. What had happened? What could they do? Daniel Teed was about to call a doctor, when, quite suddenly, came a loud rapping noise, as if someone were pounding with a heavy hammer on the floor under Esther's bed. The swelling started to go down. The rapping continued, and Esther looked more comfortable. Soon she fell into a tired, troubled sleep.

The next morning Daniel Teed hurried to the family doctor. Dr. Thomas W. Carritte listened patiently, but he didn't believe a word. "I'll come this evening, and I'll stay through the night if I have to," he told Daniel. "But I guarantee you, none of this nonsense is going to happen while I'm in the house."

The doctor couldn't have been more wrong. After supper that evening, as he sat in Esther's room, he watched in wonder as an unseen hand seemed to slide the pillow out from under her head. A sheet and a light blanket were pulled from her bed. She began to swell up. Now the doctor had a job to do—but it was not he who cured Esther. It was, again, the loud rapping noises.

Dr. Carritte was as puzzled as everyone else. He knew the family, and he felt sure that no one was trying to fool him. As the rapping went on, he walked outside the house to see if he could discover what caused the noise. From outside the rapping sounded louder, like someone pounding on the roof. But there was no one—on the roof, in the yard, or anywhere.

Not long after, my acting job in Canada having ended, I arrived at the troubled house myself. At the time, I did not believe in ghosts, poltergeists, or spirits of any kind. I did believe that everything that happens has an explanation. From what I'd heard about Esther Cox, it didn't seem likely that she was playing tricks on people. But still, there had to be an explanation. Fortunately, I was able to rent a room from the Teeds, to be nearer the mystery I had come to investigate.

Esther Cox was a short, stout girl who could only be described as plain (her sister Jennie was the pretty one). Though far from dumb, she was not overly intelligent. She certainly didn't understand what was going on. Neither, I was soon persuaded, could she have planned it.

After I'd rented the room, I hadn't been in the house five minutes when my umbrella suddenly seemed to come to life. It flew across the living room. Soon after, Esther appeared in the kitchen doorway, carrying a plate. From behind her, something came flashing through the air—a large knife. It narrowly missed me. I rushed into the kitchen to see who had thrown it. That was my first introduction to ghosts. There was no one there.

"It looks like they don't like you," said Esther.

By "they," it turned out, Esther meant two poltergeists (or *ghosts*, as she called them). One she called "Maggie," the other "Bob." She claimed sometimes that she could see them. Once, as Olive Teed and I looked on in amazement, Esther stared at the thin air in the middle of the living room and told us that Maggie was standing there. Even more strange, the girl swore that Maggie was wearing a pair of black and white socks that belonged to Esther. Feeling a little foolish, I shouted, "Now Maggie, take off Esther's socks—and be quick about it!" A minute later, a pair of black and white socks appeared from out of nowhere. They dropped from the air in front of us to the floor.

After that I stopped looking for explanations. The only explanation was . . . the supernatural.

Whoever—or whatever—"Maggie" and "Bob" were, they seemed to be always in action. With my own eyes, I saw a heavy ash tray leave its place on a table and come whizzing at me, crashing into the wall as I ducked. Furniture constantly slid around the floors. As I entered the dining room one time, every chair fell over with a crash. Another time, needing a light for my pipe,

I remarked, "Bob, give me a few matches, if you please." Immediately, a lighted match fell out of the air.

But the poltergeists were not always so helpful. As the weeks passed, Esther's spells continued, and even grew worse. Sometimes she would lie on her bed as if dead, her body swelling up like a balloon, and then collapsing, over and over. Also, the poltergeists were ruining the furniture and damaging the walls. When they started lighting small fires, the Teeds were asked to move. The owner of the house had risked enough. The Teeds were good people, but they would have to go.

As an experiment, the Teeds decided to see what would happen if only Esther left. She was sent to live with a family named Van Amburgh on a farm in the country. And here the affair came to an end with the biggest mystery of all. With Esther out of the house, everything returned to normal. The rappings, the flying objects, the sliding furniture, the fires—all stopped at once.

And perhaps even more strangely, Esther's life in her new home was completely untroubled. Like all poltergeists, "Maggie" and "Bob" had departed as mysteriously as they had come.

It must be stated that the Teeds made no attempt to keep the strange events secret. Dr. Carritte and others were constantly in and out of the house. I have a statement signed by 16 persons who witnessed at least some of the happenings I've described. I have a letter from Olive Teed declaring that *all* I've written here is true. And Dr. Carritte writes:

"I take pen in hand to say that what Mr. Walter Hubbell has written about the mysterious Esther Cox is entirely correct. The young lady was a patient of mine both previous to and during those wonderful demonstrations. I tried various experiments, but with no satisfactory results. Honestly doubtful persons were on all occasions soon convinced that there was no fraud or deception in the case. Were I to publish the case in medical journals, as you suggest, I doubt it would be believed by doctors generally. I am certain I could not have believed such miracles had I not witnessed them."

---

wonderful (WUN dur ful) curious; strange
demonstration (dem un STRAY shun) any happening that can be observed

Review the Selection

UNDERSTAND THE SELECTION

Recall

1. How did poltergeists first appear?

2. Why is Dr. Carritte called to the house?

3. What incident convinces Hubbell supernatural forces must be at work?

Infer

4. Why is it important that we know Hubbell's profession?

5. What effect does the doctor's presence in the story have?

6. Give an example of the poltergeists' being helpful.

7. Explain the significance of Esther's departure from the house to live in the country.

Apply

8. Would you have conducted the poltergeist investigation any differently?

9. Hubbell gives both opinions and facts. Which are more convincing?

10. Can you think of a rational, natural explanation for one of the incidents involving a poltergeist? Explain your answer.

Respond to Literature

What seemed to be the most believable events in the mysterious happenings that occurred? What seemed least believable?

WRITE ABOUT THE SELECTION

Have you ever tried something you did not want to do at first, and ended up really liking it? Did you then try to convince others they should try it because they, too, might like it?

You were persuaded by that experience to change your mind. You now want to try to persuade others by relating your experience in writing.

Prewriting   You need a topic. Brainstorm for a few minutes to come up with some ideas. You could write about an experience involving food, music, a sport—anything. Once you have chosen a topic, make notes about what happened.

Writing   Refer to your notes when writing your story. Keep in mind your purpose, which is to persuade the reader to try what you are describing or to accept an opinion that you hold. Facts are needed to support your opinion that your experience is worthwhile.

Revising   Use specific language in your description. If a new kind of music sounded nice to you, for example, tell why. Did it have a driving beat? Which instruments were particularly good? Tell your reactions, but try to combine them with facts.

Proofreading   Reread your paper to check for errors in verb forms, particularly irregular verbs. Check also that you use the correct tense throughout the story. Use a dictionary to check any tense forms you are not sure of.

THINK ABOUT PERSUASION

The purpose of Hubbell's story is to persuade us that supernatural forces might exist. The author uses a large amount of exposition and description of events, to provide evidence supporting his view.

In the previous selection, John McPhee was like a detective collecting facts. In this selection, Hubbell is like a detective and lawyer together. He gathers facts and uses them to argue his case.

1. Is the first paragraph of the story fact or opinion?

2. Is the second paragraph fact or opinion?

3. The story shifts gears after the third paragraph. What happens?

4. What is the effect of the doctor's statement?

5. Read the first paragraph of the story again. Do you think a reader is more likely to accept Hubbell's statements after reading the whole story?

READING FOCUS

Make Inferences About Setting As you read, you were able to use clues to infer things about the setting of the story. In the beginning, it seems that the author is describing a typical "haunted house." Does this end up being the case? What can you infer about the house based on the ending of the story?

DEVELOP YOUR VOCABULARY

Many words that we use in English are actually borrowed from foreign languages. *Poltergeist* is a good example. It comes from these German words:

poltern: to make noise, rumble
geist: ghost

You can find information on the foreign roots of words in the dictionary. The information is given in brackets [ ] following the part-of-speech designation.

Find the foreign word in the following sentences. Use a dictionary to explain its roots.

1. The tall buildings shoot into the air like walls of a canyon.

2. My baby brother goes to kindergarten.

3. He likes buffet dinners because he can take exactly what he wants.

4. No anchovies on my pizza, please.

5. Old Faithful is a famous geyser out west.

6. Is her attitude a bit naive for her age?

UNIT 2 Review

Write About Theme

One summer day you are sitting in your backyard, and a strange-looking creature walks up to you.

"Hello," it says.

You realize you are facing an unknown being. You, for some unexplained reason, have been chosen to have the first human contact with this creature.

Write a dialogue of your encounter with this creature. What will you learn about the unknown?

Prewriting Decide first what the creature will be: perhaps an extraterrestrial being. For five minutes freewrite questions you would like to ask the creature. Then take another five minutes to freewrite possible answers.

Writing Put your questions in a logical order, and fill in the answers. Use this form for writing:

Me:
Creature:

Revising The best dialogues are those that flow logically from one question-and-answer to the next. This may be hard when you are talking with a strange being, but consider revising any sections that seem to "jump around" too much. Be sure you have the creature explain elements of the unknown with sharp detail.

Proofreading Although you have written a dialogue, you still need to punctuate correctly. Carefully use special punctuation marks, such as exclamations, for emphasis.

Write About Genre

You have learned in this unit that all short stories have four basic elements: plot, characters, setting, and theme. It helps in analyzing stories if you look very closely at these elements.

Choose one selection you particularly liked. Analyze how plot, characters, setting, and theme add to the story.

Prewriting Review any work you did for the "Think About . . . " sections that discuss the elements. How does the author of the story you have chosen develop a particular element? On the other hand, maybe he or she does not develop another element, and that interests you. Write the elements in the middle of a piece of paper, and make a cluster of your ideas around it.

Writing Use the cluster to write your analysis. Make sure you have a clear thesis statement, such as "Although all elements are present, plot is not important in John McPhee's nonfiction narrative 'The Loch Ness Monster.'" Develop your analysis from there.

Revising An analysis is similar to persuasion. You want to convince the reader that what you say is correct. Readers are more convinced by facts than opinions. Can you add more facts, or evidence, from the story to support your opinions?

Proofreading Reread your analysis carefully. Do you need new paragraphs when you discuss each element?

Vocabulary

Idioms are groups of words that have a special meaning all their own. You cannot add up the meanings of the individual words. You must know the new meaning of the entire group. An example is *over one's head.* The literal meaning is that something is positioned right over your head.

However, look at the phrase's meaning in this sentence: *Trigonometry is simply over my head.* Here, *over my head* means too difficult.

Each sentence below contains an idiom. Find it, and explain its meaning.

1. Please, put your best foot forward this time.

2. The forty-year-old man was getting gray above the ears.

3. The boy lit up when the teacher asked the question about computers.

4. I got a load of their shoulder holsters when they leaned over.

5. We rested on the stoop for awhile, getting our nerves back in shape.

6. "This particular problem," he said, "is only the tip of the iceberg."

7. The red leather basketball shoes in the wind caught Sam's eye.

8. Peggy's new haircut was cuter than a bug's ear.

Grammar, Usage and Mechanics

Three or more words linked in a series by the conjunctions *and* or *or* must be correctly punctuated as follows: I have ordinary abilities, looks, and thoughts. Note that a comma is used after all the words in a series except the last. One easy way to remember how many commas you need is to count the items in a series and then use one less comma. However, if there is a conjunction between every word in the series, you need no commas.

Correct the punctuation errors in the following sentences:

1. They were sitting kneeling or squatting in an easy way.

2. We have electricity washing machines vacuum cleaners modern bathrooms and modern medicine.

3. But there are no radios televisions telephones or cars.

4. They have dances card parties weddings birthdays block parties swimming and sports of all kinds.

5. Verna is a planet of air sun land and sea, like Earth.

6. Now the only question is what to call them—ghosts spirits poltergeists or what?

7. John McPhee used photographs testimony and legends as support for Nessie's existence.

SPEAKING AND LISTENING

It is human nature to want to share experiences with others. If you see a movie, you may want to talk about a scene that you particularly liked. If you hear a new song, you often want to tap the melody out for friends so they can get a feel for it, too. For this activity, you will be telling an incident you remember from a selection in this unit.

Before you share an incident from one of the selections in this unit, read over the following directions. They will help make your assignment clear.

1. You will have about two minutes to share your choice with the class. Remember to focus on one incident. Also, try to get to the point and keep to it.

2. In this assignment, the selection itself is not as important as the incident that you choose. Therefore, instead of thinking about a certain story, think about a single incident. It can be frightening, exciting, suspenseful, or just your favorite.

3. Go back to the selection, skim through it, find the incident, and reread it.

4. Now, paraphrase the incident in your mind. Think about how you would relate this incident to a friend. If necessary, take a few notes to help you focus on what you will say.

5. It is easy to get personally involved when you are talking about an incident that was your favorite. It is also easy to get caught using slang expressions. For this assignment, try to use vocabulary and expressions that are suitable for a literary discussion.

6. Do not be afraid to quote. Perhaps there was a particular way a character said something that added to the sheer excitement of this incident. Let the class in on it by sharing the exact words.

7. Be sure to tell why the incident was memorable to you. Think about the feelings you had after you read it, and express them to your audience.

By following the hints given above, you will find it easy to relate your favorite incident from this unit to your classmates. One last suggestion: Before you begin to talk about the incident, tell the title of the selection it came from; others might be interested in reading the entire story.

CRITICAL THINKING

Fact and Opinion This unit has contained selections about the unknown. It is a tricky subject to write about. The very word *unknown* presents a challenge. How can anyone write something about which he or she does not know much?

The writers of the nonfiction selections in this unit solved the problem through investigation. They went to the places where monsters or ghosts had supposedly been seen or felt, and gathered facts.

In the case of "The Great Amherst Mystery," the writer then used the facts to back up an opinion. Walter Hubbell said he believes that poltergeists and other such supernatural beings really do exist. If there had been no facts to back up his opinion, Hubbell would have looked very funny. However, he had fact after fact, supported by a number of people and their testimonies, to give his opinion credibility. It was far easier to accept his ideas on poltergeists after the facts had been presented.

When you write, support your opinions with facts. They are the things that convince readers. Remember Mr. Gradgrind's comment in Charles Dickens's *Hard Times:* "Now, what I want is, Facts . . . Facts alone are wanted in life."

Choose either "The Great Amherst Mystery" or "The Loch Ness Monster." List ten facts that the author used to tell his story.

EFFECTIVE STUDYING

Developing Study Habits Good study habits can help when you are working in any subject.

It helps to choose a study setting, one place you go regularly. If you associate that place just with studying, it is easier to work there. Ideally, the place would be quiet and away from distractions.

You should develop a study schedule. When will you work? Consider two things here. First, when can you study? If you play sports, obviously you cannot study after school. You need to find another time. Second, what times of day are you at your best? Some people cannot function after 8 P.M. Others are just getting going then. When you have a choice of study times, pick the time you are at peak power.

A third tip is to keep an assignment book. Write all of your assignments and when they are due.

Where and when do you study? Describe your special space and your study schedule.

Test Preparation

Try this memory game the next time you study for a test. Relate the facts you are studying to specific objects in your study area. Associating facts with familiar things may help you recall the facts later.

UNIT 3

Suspense

I tell you a tale to-night
  Which a seaman told to me,
With eyes that gleamed in the lanthorn light
  And a voice as low as the sea.

—Alfred Noyes

The Whale Ship, Joseph Mallord William Turner. The Metropolitan Museum of Art, Wolfe Fund, 1896. Catharine Lorillard Wolfe Collection

Suspense

Everyone loves the excitement of not knowing what is going to happen next. You think, you feel, you imagine a dozen different possibilities.

Suspense means waiting. In literature, a good author knows how to use that waiting period to get you more and more interested in the story. You see the setting and characters in your mind. You feel the plot and theme taking you on a roller coaster ride. A part of you seems to be with the characters as the suspense builds. Explore the world of suspense in this unit.

■ CRIMES

Crimes always make good suspense stories. The perpetrators must be found and their motives explained. Detectives piece together clues. They begin making sense out of what seems nonsense. A theory emerges, and it is proven true. The guilty are revealed!

Within this simple framework of the crime story, a writer can add twists and turns that are guaranteed to keep you guessing or to surprise you.

That is what John Savage does in "The Getaway." The story seems rather simple at first, but look for clues that will prepare you for the ending.

The master crime storyteller of all time is probably Arthur Conan Doyle. He created the greatest detective of all detectives, Sherlock Holmes, and his sidekick, Dr. Watson. Holmes and Watson try to solve a strange murder in a dramatized version of "Sherlock Holmes and the Speckled Band."

Trifles is a crime story that goes beyond the usual "whodunit" tale. It is important to know who killed John Wright, but this time understanding the reasons is essential to feeling the real suspense.

■ HAPPY AND NOT SO HAPPY ENDINGS

Suspense cannot go on forever. It must end sometime. How it ends in a story can make you feel happy or sad.

"The Rattlesnake Hunt" presents a different kind of suspense. Instead of people trying to outwit one another, a herpetologist teaches a writer how to outwit rattlesnakes.

Two poems, both titled "Earth," present not-so-happy endings to human existence on this planet. Even so, suspense is built into each.

■ PUZZLES

"The Lady or the Tiger?" is one of the most interesting suspense stories ever written. It ends in a rather puzzling fashion, and you will have to use all of your abilities to figure out the conclusion.

Think whether you could have named the flying animal described in "Displays of Skill: The Bat" if the poem had a different title. Even though "The Bird of Night" has no such giveaway in its title, you should be able to guess what the poet is describing before you reach the end.

Make doubly sure that you keep the title in mind when you read the last short story in the unit, "A Secret for Two." This story about a Montreal milk wagon driver is innocent enough, but there is real mystery behind it.

Now, explore the world of suspense—and hold your breath as the writers tell their tales!

Learn About

SETTING

Setting is the "where" and "when" of a story. It includes the place and the time the story unfolds. Setting is always important to a story, but sometimes it is so important that you cannot imagine the story happening in any other place at any other time. The story requires that the action happen in this specific setting.

When that is the case, setting plays an important part in the story's plot. Somehow, where or when the story takes place will have a big impact on the action. In suspense stories, the answer to "when?" can keep you on the edge of your seat. The answer to "where?" can spell life or death for the characters.

As you read the next selection, ask yourself these questions:

1. Why is the "where" of the setting so important to this story?
2. Is the "when" of the setting also important to this story?

WRITING CONNECTION

Exotic foreign locales are sometimes the setting for stories or parts of stories. Think of a written story or a film where such a scene is important. In two or three sentences, explain why you think so.

READING FOCUS

Make Predictions Authors do not always directly state what the outcome of a story will be. Instead, they give clues, using characters' actions and dialogue, to help the reader predict what will happen next in the story. As you read, pay attention to what characters say and do, and try to make predictions about what will happen next and how the problems in the story will be resolved.

THE GETAWAY

by John Savage

Whenever I get sleepy at the wheel, I always stop for coffee. This time, I was going along in western Texas and I got sleepy. I saw a sign that said GAS EAT, so I pulled off. It was long after midnight. What I expected was a place like a bunch of others, where the coffee tastes like copper and the flies never sleep.

What I found was something else. The tables were painted wood, and they looked as if nobody ever spilled the ketchup. The counter was spick-and-span. Even the smell was OK, I swear it.

Nobody was there, as far as customers. There was just this one old boy—really only about forty, getting gray above the ears—behind the counter. I sat down at the counter and ordered coffee and apple pie. Right away he got me started feeling sad.

I have a habit: I divide people up. Winners and losers. This old boy behind the counter was the kind that they *mean* well; they can't do enough for you, but their eyes have this gentle, faraway look, and they can't win. You know? With their clean shirt and their little bow tie? It makes you feel sad just to look at them. Only take my tip: Don't feel too sad.

He brought the coffee steaming hot, and it tasted like coffee. "Care for cream and sugar?" he asked. I said, "Please," and the cream was fresh and cold and thick. The pie was good, too.

A car pulled up outside. The old boy glanced out to see if they wanted gas, but they didn't. They came right in. The tall one said, "Two coffees. Do you have a road map we could look at?"

"I think so," the old boy said. He got their coffee first, and then started rooting through a pile of papers by the telephone, looking for a map. It was easy to see he was the type nothing's too much trouble for. Tickled to be of service.

---

root (ROOT) dig or search around

I'm the same type myself, if you want to know. I watched the old boy hunting for his map, and I felt like I was looking in a mirror.

After a minute or two, he came up with the map. "This one's a little out of date, but . . ." He put it on the counter, beside their coffee.

The two men spread out the map and leaned over it. They were well dressed, like a couple of feed merchants. The tall one ran his finger along the Rio Grande and shook his head. "I guess there's no place to get across, this side of El Paso."

He said it to his pal, but the old boy behind the counter heard him and lit up like a light bulb. "You trying to find the best way south? I might be able to help you with that."

"How?"

"Just a minute." He spent a lot of time going through the papers by the telephone again. "Thought I might have a newer map," he said. "Anything recent would show the Hackett Bridge. Anyway, I can tell you how to find it."

"Here's a town called Hackett," the tall one said, still looking at the map. "It's on the river, just at the end of a road. Looks like a pretty small place."

"Not any more. It's just about doubled since they built the bridge."

"What happens on the other side?" The short one asked the question, but both of the feed-merchant types were paying close attention.

"Pretty fair road, clear to Chihuahua. It joins up there with the highway out of El Paso and Juarez."

The tall man finished his coffee, folded the map, put it in his pocket, and stood up. "We'll take your map with us," he said.

The old boy seemed startled, like a new kid at school when somebody pokes him in the nose to show him who's boss. However, he just shrugged and said, "Glad to let you have it."

---

feed merchant (FEED MUR chunt) person who buys and sells food for animals
Rio Grande (ree oh GRAND) river that separates the state of Texas from Mexico
El Paso (el PAS oh) a city in western Texas, near the border of Mexico
Chihuahua (chi WAH wah) city in northern Mexico
Juarez (HWAH res) Mexican city across the Rio Grande from El Paso

Chateau Diner, John Baeder. O.K. Harris Works of Art, New York

The feed merchants had a little conference on the way out, talking in whispers. Then they stopped in the middle of the floor, turned around, reached inside their jackets, and pulled guns on us. Automatic pistols, I think they were. "You sit where you are and don't move," the tall one said to me. "And *you*, get against the wall."

Both of us did exactly what they wanted. I told you we were a lot alike.

The short man walked over and pushed one of the keys of the cash register. "Every little bit helps," he said, and he scooped the money out of the drawer. The tall man set the telephone on the floor, put his foot on it, and jerked the wires out. Then they ran to their car and got in. The short man leaned out the window and shot out one of my tires. Then they took off fast.

I looked at the old boy behind the counter. He seemed a little pale, but he didn't waste any time. He took a screwdriver out of a drawer and squatted down beside the telephone. I said, "It doesn't always pay to be nice to people."

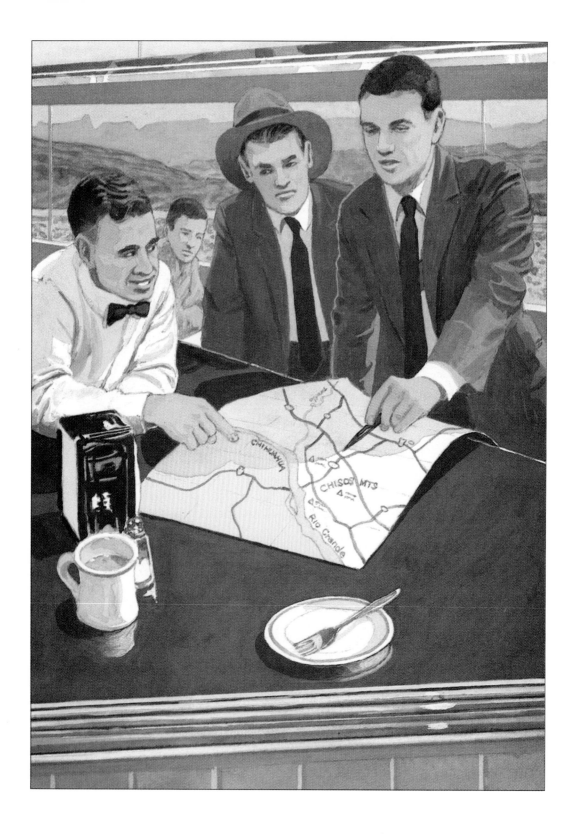

He laughed and said, "Well, it doesn't usually cost anything," and went on taking the base plate off the telephone. He was a fast worker, actually. His tongue was sticking out of the corner of his mouth. In about five minutes he had a dial tone coming out of the receiver. He dialed a number and told the rangers about the men and their car. "They did?" he said. "Well, well, well. . . . No, not El Paso. They took the Hackett turnoff." After he hung up, he said, "It turns out those guys robbed a supermarket in Wichita Falls."

I shook my head. "They sure had me fooled. I thought they looked perfectly all right."

The old boy got me another cup of coffee, and opened himself a bottle of pop. "They fooled me, too, at first." He wiped his mouth. "Then I got a load of their shoulder holsters when they leaned on the counter to look at the map. Anyway, they had mean eyes, I thought. Didn't you?"

"Well, I didn't at the time."

We drank without talking for a while, getting our nerves back in shape. A pair of patrol cars went roaring by outside and squealed their tires around the Hackett turnoff.

I got to thinking, and I thought of the saddest thing yet. "You *knew* there was something wrong with those guys, but you still couldn't keep from helping them on their way."

He laughed. "Well, the world's a tough sort of place at best, is how I look at it."

"I can understand showing them the map," I said, "but I'd never have told about the bridge. Now there's not a chance of catching them. If you'd kept your mouth shut, there'd at least be some hope."

"There isn't any—"

"Not a shred," I went on. "Not with a car as fast as they've got."

The way the old boy smiled made me feel better about him and me. "I don't mean there isn't any hope," he said. "I mean there isn't any bridge."

Review the Selection

UNDERSTAND THE SELECTION

Recall

1. Where does the story take place?

2. At first, who did the narrator think the two men were?

3. When did the counterman say he first thought that the men were criminals?

Infer

4. At the end of the story, is the counterman a "winner" or a "loser"?

5. Do you think the counterman had a newer map than the one he gave the men?

6. Why did the two men cut the telephone line?

7. How does the last sentence help maintain the story's suspense?

Apply

8. Does first-person point of view work well in this story?

9. Are there any hints about the surprise ending earlier in the story?

10. How might you have reacted if you had been the counterman?

Respond to Literature

Do you think that there are any weak points in this story? Is anything not believable? Explain your answer.

WRITE ABOUT THE SELECTION

What did the narrator of the story think when the counterman told him that there was no Hackett Bridge? Imagine that you are the narrator. How would this affect your opinion of the counterman? Imagine that you want to add a postscript describing what you felt and did after you learned that the bridge did not exist.

Prewriting Do a little reviewing before you begin writing. Reread the paragraphs that describe the narrator's feelings about the counterman, especially the third and fourth paragraphs at the beginning and the six paragraphs at the end of the story. How do you feel about those observations now that you know the ending of the story? Make a cluster of your feelings. Then imagine how each of those feelings might make you act. Add a phrase about each of those possible actions to your cluster.

Writing Use your cluster to write your postscript. Try to make a smooth transition from the story's current ending to your addition. Remember that you are telling the story from the narrator's point of view.

Revising Try to imitate the author's writing style. He uses short sentences, informal language, and figures of speech. Add some of these characteristics to your writing.

Proofreading Reread your description to check for errors. Authors often use incomplete sentences. You may, too, but make sure you know how to rewrite them so that they are complete sentences.

THINK ABOUT SETTING

John Savage, the author of "The Getaway," blends the setting so skillfully into the plot of the story that it is easy to overlook the setting's importance. Consider both general and specific time and place when you think about setting.

For example, a story could take place in Los Angeles sometime in the 1980s. That would be the general "where" and "when." The specific setting might be in a house after dinnertime.

1. When do we learn the setting of "The Getaway"?

2. Why is the geographic location of the restaurant important?

3. Why is the restaurant itself important as a setting for the story?

4. Why is setting an important part of the plot of this story?

5. Is the time this story takes place important? Think both about the specific time and the general time.

READING FOCUS

Make Predictions As you read "The Getaway," you were able to use clues from the characters' thoughts, dialogue, and actions to predict what might happen next. What did you predict the ending would be? What clues helped you to make this prediction?

DEVELOP YOUR VOCABULARY

Compound words are made up of two or more root words. Sometimes they are hyphenated.

Often compound words are so common that you do not realize they are made from other words. A good example is the noun in the title of this selection: *getaway* = get + away.

Knowing the root words in a compound word can often help you find its meaning.

There are few strict rules on when a compound word is hyphenated. Check a dictionary if you are unsure which form is correct.

Tell the root words of the following compound words:

1. faraway	4. mother-in-law
2. zigzag	5. turnoff
3. screwdriver	6. newspaper

What compound words are made up of the following root words? Make sure you spell them correctly.

1. law, father, in	3. way, rail
2. noble, man	4. smith, black

Use each compound word from this exercise in an original sentence.

Learn About

CHARACTERS

Stories can have many **characters**. Some of them may not be human.

Usually, however, there is a main character. Likewise, there is usually a character who comes in conflict with the main character. The main character is called the **protagonist**. The character who comes in conflict with him or her is called the **antagonist**.

The conflict between the two characters is very important to the story. Usually, it must be resolved before the story concludes. How it is resolved often determines the ending. A skillful writer can use the conflict between the protagonist and antagonist to develop the story's characters and make them come alive.

As you read the next selection, ask yourself these questions:

1. Who are the protagonist and antagonist?
2. What is the conflict between them?

WRITING CONNECTION

Antagonize is a verb which means "to oppose" or "to provoke to action." A noun with the same root is *antagonist*, one who comes in conflict with or opposes the protagonist. Think of someone or something that antagonizes you. Write a paragraph or two about this.

READING FOCUS

Evaluate the Writer's Craft The purpose of a mystery is to build suspense to keep the reader interested. An author may do this in several ways. One way is to provide some, but not all, details about key events. Instead, the reader has to look for clues and guess what will happen next. As you read this play, see how the author reveals details of plot and setting. Decide how this adds to the suspense and keeps you interested.

SHERLOCK HOLMES AND THE SPECKLED BAND

by Arthur Conan Doyle

DRAMATIZED

CHARACTERS

SHERLOCK HOLMES, *the famous detective*
DR. WATSON, *his friend*
HELEN STONER, *the lady in danger*

JULIA STONER, *her sister*
DR. GRIMESBY ROYLOTT, *her stepfather*

SCENE 1

TIME: About 1900.

SETTING: The parlor in HOLMES'S *apartment on Baker Street, London, England.*

AT RISE[1]: A woman dressed in black and wearing a veil is seated on the window seat in the parlor. The room is comfortably filled with sofas, chairs, old furniture, and the usual belongings of the bachelor detective: books, newspapers, slippers, magnifying glass, pipe rack, various hats, and a violin among them. HOLMES *and* DR. WATSON *enter. The lady rises to greet them.*

HOLMES: Good morning, Madam. I'm Sherlock Holmes. (*Nodding toward* Watson) My close friend, Dr. Watson. You can speak freely in front of him. Please sit down by the fire. I'll order coffee, since I see that you're shivering.

HELEN (*changing her seat*): Not from cold.

HOLMES: What then?

HELEN: Fear, Mr. Holmes. Terror.

(*She raises her veil to reveal a face tired and gray. She looks about 30, but her hair already shows traces of gray. Her eyes are restless and frightened. She looks like a hunted animal.* HOLMES *studies her face.*)

---

[1]**at rise:** at the start of the scene; when the curtain rises

HOLMES: Don't be afraid. Just leave everything to me. Now . . . what sent you all this way by train? And so early in the morning, too.

HELEN: How did you know I . . . ?

HOLMES (*breaking in*): There's the second half of a return ticket in the palm of your left glove. Plain as day. Please relax. That drive in the dogcart must have been difficult.

(HELEN *gives a start of surprise. She stares at* HOLMES.)

HOLMES: It's no mystery, my dear madam. The left arm of your jacket has mud spots in seven places. The marks are fresh. Only a dogcart splashes mud in that way.

HELEN: Well, whatever your reasons, you're right. Mr. Holmes, I can't stand this strain any longer! I'll go mad. I have no one else to turn to, except . . . well, someone who cares for me, but can't help. I've heard of you, Mr. Holmes. Can you help me? I . . . right now, I can't pay you. But in a month or so, I'll be married, and then . . .

HOLMES (*breaking in*): Madam, my work is its own reward. I'll be happy to help you. Now, tell us everything. Everything.

HELEN: I'm afraid that . . . that's the horror of it. It's . . . so vague. My fears—they come from small things that might seem like nothing to you. Even my fiancé thinks it's all just nerves.

HOLMES: He says so?

HELEN: No, but it's in his soothing answers. And the way he turns his eyes from me. But you, Mr. Holmes—I've heard you can see all the evils that lie in the human heart. I'm surrounded by danger. Can you help me?

WATSON: Yes!

HOLMES: Thank you, Watson. Now, Madam—start with your name.

HELEN: It's Helen Stoner.

HOLMES: And you live . . . ?

HELEN: With my stepfather. He's the last member of one of the oldest families in England, the Roylotts of Stoke Moran.

HOLMES: Yes, I've heard the name.

---

vague (VAYG) not clear, hazy
fiancé (fee ahn SAY) husband-to-be
soothing (SOO*TH* ing) calming

HELEN: The family was once very rich. But they were ruined in the last century. Nothing's left but a few acres and the ancient house. And that's crushed under a mortgage. The last Roylott lived out his life there—a horrible life as a penniless nobleman. But his only son—that's my stepfather—he saw that things had to change. He borrowed some money. He got a medical degree and went out to India. He built a large practice there.

HOLMES: But he came back to England? Why?

---

mortgage (MAWR gij) loan given to purchase a house
practice (PRAK tis) the business of a doctor or lawyer

HELEN: A string of robberies in his house in India. He got into a fit of anger about them and beat his native butler to death. They almost hanged him. He spent a long term in prison. Then he came back to England. A sad man. A very disappointed man.

HOLMES: And your mother, his wife?

HELEN: He married my mother in India. She was the widow of a Major-General Stoner. My sister Julia and I were twins. We were only two years old when my mother remarried.

HOLMES: Hm. Was she well-off at the time?

HELEN: Well, yes. She had quite a bit of money—at least £1000 a year. And she gave it all to Dr. Roylott while we lived with him. Julia and I were to each get a certain amount a year when we married.

HOLMES: Is your mother still living?

HELEN: She died soon after we came to England—eight years ago. A railway accident.

HOLMES: And you went on living with your stepfather?

HELEN: Yes, he gave up trying to practice medicine. He took us to live in the family house at Stoke Moran. The money my mother left was more than enough. We had all we needed to be happy.

HOLMES: But?

HELEN: It was my stepfather. A terrible change came over him. At first, the neighbors were so happy to see a Roylott back in the old family home. But instead of making friends, he shut himself up in the house. He hardly ever came out, except to get into fights with anyone who crossed his path. He has a terrible temper. As a matter of fact, some of his ancestors showed traces of . . . well, madness. In his case, it got worse because of those years in India.

HOLMES: What happened?

HELEN: A series of brawls. Two ended in the police court. He became the terror of the village. People would run when they saw him coming.

HOLMES: Is he dangerous?

HELEN: Well, he's a man of huge strength. And when he's angry, he's just out of control. Last week he threw the blacksmith over a bridge into a stream. I had to pay all the money I could get in a hurry to keep it quiet.

---

brawl (BRAWL) noisy fight

HOLMES: He has no friends, then?

HELEN: Only the gypsies. He lets them camp on his land. And they give him the hospitality of their tents. Sometimes for weeks on end. Oh, and he also has animals—Indian animals.

HOLMES: Really?

HELEN: Yes. They're sent over to him by a man in India. He's got a cheetah and a baboon. They just wander loose on the grounds. They scare people almost as much as he does! You can imagine what our life was like, Julia's and mine. No great pleasure. Julia was only 30 when she died, but her hair had already started to turn white. Like mine.

HOLMES: Your sister is dead, then?

HELEN: She died just two years ago. It's her death that I came to see you about.

HOLMES: Go on.

HELEN: Well, living the life we did, Julia and I met very few people our own age. But we had an Aunt Honoria, who lives near Harrow. We went to visit her sometimes. Julia was there at Christmas two years ago, and she met a major of the marines. They got engaged.

HOLMES: What did your stepfather think of that?

HELEN: He didn't object. But within two weeks of the date set for the wedding . . . (*She is very upset.*)

HOLMES: Please go on.

HELEN: The terrible event that . . .

HOLMES (*breaking in*): Please be precise. Details! I must have details.

HELEN: That's easy. It's all burned in my memory.

(*She appears about to cry.*)

HOLMES: Take it easy. Go ahead.

HELEN: The house, as I said, is very old. We use only one wing. The bedrooms are on the ground floor. The first is Dr. Roylott's, the second my sister's, and the third is mine. No connecting doors. But all three rooms open into the same hallway. Is that clear?

HOLMES: Perfectly.

HELEN: The windows of the three rooms open out on the lawn. That night—the night she died—Dr. Roylott had gone to his room early. But we knew he hadn't gone to bed.

---

cheetah (CHEET uh) wild cat with a spotted coat
precise (prih SYS) very exact

HOLMES: How?

HELEN: Because my sister smelled the strong Indian cigars he smokes. So she left her room and came into mine. We sat for a while, talking about the wedding. Then we said goodnight. I remember it all so vividly. She got up to go. . . .

SCENE 2

SETTING: Helen's bedroom in the Roylott mansion.

AT RISE: JULIA *and* HELEN STONER *are seated on the bed. They kiss each other goodnight.* JULIA *walks to the door, then pauses, turning to look back at* HELEN.

JULIA: Helen, have you ever heard anyone whistle in the dead of the night?

HELEN: No! Why?

JULIA: You couldn't be whistling in your sleep, could you?

HELEN: No! What are you talking about?

---

vividly (VIV id lee) very clearly; as if lifelike

JULIA: It's just that the last few nights, I've heard a strange whistling. At about three o'clock in the morning! A low, clear whistle. I'm a light sleeper, and it wakes me up. I can't tell where the sound comes from—the next room, the lawn, I don't know.

HELEN: It must be the gypsies.

JULIA: I guess so. But if it's on the lawn, I wonder why you didn't hear it too.

HELEN: Oh, I sleep like a log.

JULIA: Well, it doesn't matter, anyway. Good night.

SCENE 3

SETTING: The parlor in HOLMES'S *apartment.*

AT RISE: HOLMES, WATSON *and* HELEN STONER *are sitting as before.* HELEN *goes on with her story.*

HELEN: She smiled at me and closed my door. I heard her key turn in the lock.

HOLMES: Her key? Did you usually lock yourselves in at night?

HELEN: Always.

HOLMES: Why?

HELEN: Remember—the cheetah and the baboon! We didn't feel safe unless our doors were locked at night.

HOLMES: Right. Go on.

HELEN: I couldn't sleep that night. It was wild weather, howling wind. The rain beat against the windows. Suddenly I heard a scream—a woman's scream. I knew it was my sister's voice. I rushed into the hall. Then I seemed to hear a low whistle— just as my sister had described it. Then there was a clanging sound, like metal falling. My sister's door was unlocked— and it started to open slowly. I stared at it. I didn't know what would come out! It was Julia. Her face was white with terror. Her hands were groping for help. She swayed as if she was drunk. I ran to her and threw my arms around her, but her knees gave way and she fell to the ground. She was twisting in terrible pain. I bent over her. Then suddenly, she shrieked— I'll never forget her voice! "Oh! Helen! It was the band! The speckled band!"

---

grope (GROHP) feel about blindly

Sherlock Holmes and the Speckled Band ■ 231

HOLMES: That's all? She didn't explain?

HELEN: She tried to say more. She stabbed her finger in the air towards the doctor's room. But then she choked and couldn't get the words out. I called out for my stepfather. But when he got to my sister's side, she was unconscious.

HOLMES: Didn't he do anything to bring her around?

HELEN: He sent for medical help from the village. But it was useless. She died without speaking again.

HOLMES: One moment. Are you sure about this whistle and this metallic sound? Could you swear to it?

HELEN: I don't know. I felt strongly that I heard it. But with the wind crashing, and the creaking of an old house—I don't know.

HOLMES: Was your sister dressed?

HELEN: No, she was in her nightgown. And she had a burnt match in one hand and a matchbox in the other.

HOLMES: So she struck a match and looked about her when it happened. That's important. And what did the coroner find was the cause of death?

HELEN: He was very careful because Dr. Roylott had caused so much trouble in the neighborhood. But he couldn't find the cause of death.

HOLMES: Could anyone have entered her room?

HELEN: The door was locked on the inside. The windows have old-fashioned shutters with broad iron bars, and they were locked every night. The walls are solid all around. So is the floor. The chimney's wide, but it's barred. My sister had to be alone when it happened. Besides, there were no marks of violence on her.

HOLMES: Poison?

HELEN: The doctors examined her for it. There wasn't any.

HOLMES: What do *you* think your sister died of, then?

HELEN: I think she died of pure fear and nervous shock. But what could have frightened her? I can't imagine.

HOLMES: The gypsies—were they on the grounds that night?

HELEN: Yes, there are nearly always some there.

---

coroner (CAWR uh nur) public officer who investigates deaths that may not be due to natural causes

HOLMES: Ah. And what did you think she meant by her last words about a band—a speckled band?

HELEN: I don't know. Sometimes I've thought it was just wild talk—she was dying. Or maybe it meant . . . some band of people. Perhaps the gypsies. Because of the spotted handkerchiefs they wear—she might have called them "the speckled band."

(HOLMES *shakes his head. Clearly, he is far from satisfied.*)

HOLMES: We're in deep waters here. Please tell us the rest.

HELEN: That was two years ago. My life became lonelier than ever—until lately. About a month ago, a friend—a dear friend I've known for years—asked me to marry him. My stepfather hasn't objected. So we're going to be married in the spring.

HOLMES: Then what brings you here?

HELEN: Two days ago, some repairs were started in the west wing of the house. My bedroom wall has been ripped up. So I've had to move into the room where my sister died. And sleep in the bed she slept in. It was terrifying. Last night, I lay awake thinking about her. Her terrible death. I suddenly heard—it was very quiet—I heard the low whistle. Just like the whistle on the night she died. I jumped up and lit the lamp, but there was nothing in the room. I was too shaken to go to bed again. So I got dressed. As soon as it was daylight, I came here.

HOLMES: Very wise. But have you told me everything?

HELEN: Yes. Everything.

HOLMES: You have not, Miss Roylott. You're protecting your stepfather.

HELEN: Why, what do you mean?

(HOLMES *leans toward* HELEN *and pushes back the bit of lace that covers her hand.*)

HOLMES: Ah. Five little black-and-blue spots. Just the sort of spots made by four fingers and a thumb. You've been treated cruelly.

HELEN (*embarrassed*): He's a hard man. Perhaps he doesn't really know his own strength.

(*A silence.* HOLMES *leans his chin on his hands and stares into the fire.*)

---

treat (TREET) deal with

HOLMES: This is a very deep business. I have to know a thousand details before I decide what to do. But we haven't a moment to lose. If we come today to Stoke Moran, will we be able to look over these rooms? Without your stepfather knowing?

HELEN: Well, yes. As a matter of fact, he said he'd be going into town today. He'll probably be away all day.

HOLMES: Good. You wouldn't mind the trip, Watson?

WATSON: I'd love it.

HOLMES: Then we'll both come.

HELEN: Thank you. I feel better already. I'll be waiting for you this afternoon, then.

(HELEN *drops her veil back over her face and exits.*)

HOLMES: Well, what do you think of it all, Watson?

WATSON: Hm. Seems to be a dark, evil business.

HOLMES: Yes, it does.

WATSON: But the floor and the walls were all solid. The door, the windows, and the chimney were all blocked. If she's right about that, then her sister must have been alone when she fell ill.

HOLMES: Then what about those whistles? And what about the "speckled band"?

WATSON: I really couldn't say.

HOLMES: Well, let's put a few things together. First, the whistles at night. Second, the band of gypsies—very friendly with the old doctor. Third, the fact that the doctor has an interest in stopping his stepdaughter's marriage. And finally, the metallic clang. A sound that *might* have been caused by one of the metal bars on the shutters falling into place. I think we can wrap things up along those lines.

WATSON: But how could the gypsies have done it?

HOLMES: I haven't the faintest idea.

WATSON: Holmes, I can think of quite a few objections to this theory.

HOLMES: So can I. That's why we're going to Stoke Moran today. We'll see if the objections make sense. Or if they can be explained away.

---

deep (DEEP) hard to understand
theory (THEE uh ree) guess based on reasoning

(The door has burst open. A huge man stands in the doorway. He wears a black top hat. He has on a long coat and carries a riding whip. He has a wrinkled, sun-burned face, which looks angrily at HOLMES *and* WATSON *in turn.)*

ROYLOTT: Holmes?

HOLMES: Here. And you?

ROYLOTT: Dr. Grimesby Roylott, of Stoke Moran.

HOLMES (*very pleasant*): Have a seat, doctor.

ROYLOTT: I won't. My stepdaughter's been here. I've traced her. What's she been saying to you?

HOLMES: It's a little cold for this time of year, isn't it?

ROYLOTT (*yelling*): What has she been saying to you?

HOLMES (*still pleasant*): But I've heard the crocuses are doing well.

ROYLOTT: Hah! You put me off, do you? (*He takes a step forward and shakes his riding whip at* HOLMES.) I know you, you dog! I've heard of you before. Holmes, the meddler.

(HOLMES *smiles.*)

ROYLOTT: Holmes, the busybody!

(HOLMES *smiles even more broadly.*)

ROYLOTT: Holmes, the Scotland Yard[2] puppet!

HOLMES: Talking with you is very entertaining. When you go out, please close the door. There's a draft.

---

crocus (KROH kus) spring flower
meddler (MED lur) one who butts into other people's business
[2]**Scotland Yard**: detective department of the London police

ROYLOTT: I'll go when I've had my say. Don't you *dare* meddle with my business. I know she's been here. I traced her! I'm a dangerous man to go up against!

(*So saying,* ROYLOTT *picks up an iron poker and bends it over double.*)

ROYLOTT: See that you keep out of my grip.

(ROYLOTT *hurls the poker into the fireplace and stomps out.*)

HOLMES (*laughing*): He seems friendly. Larger than I am, of course. But still, too bad he didn't hang around. We could have matched grips.

(*So saying,* HOLMES *picks up the poker and straightens it out again.*)

HOLMES: He's rude, though. Imagine thinking I'm—I—a puppet of the police! But this little visit makes the job more interesting, though, doesn't it? I only hope Miss Stoner won't be hurt by her carelessness—letting this brute trace her here. Now, Watson, let's have some breakfast. Then I'll do a little detecting.

SCENE 4

SETTING: HOLMES'S *parlor, later that day.*

AT RISE: WATSON *is studying a medical book as* HOLMES *returns.*

HOLMES *holds in his hand a sheet of blue paper. On it are written a bunch of notes and numbers.*

WATSON: Find anything?
HOLMES: I've seen the will of the dead wife, Miss Stoner's mother.
WATSON: And?
HOLMES: Not an easy job! I had to work out the present prices of all these investments. But the result is—at the time she died, the total income was almost £1100 a year. Now, with the fall in farm prices, it's only about £750. Each daughter was to get about £250 if she married.
WATSON: What does that mean for Roylott?
HOLMES: It means that if both girls had married, the old hulk would have had very little for himself. Even one marriage would be a serious blow for him.

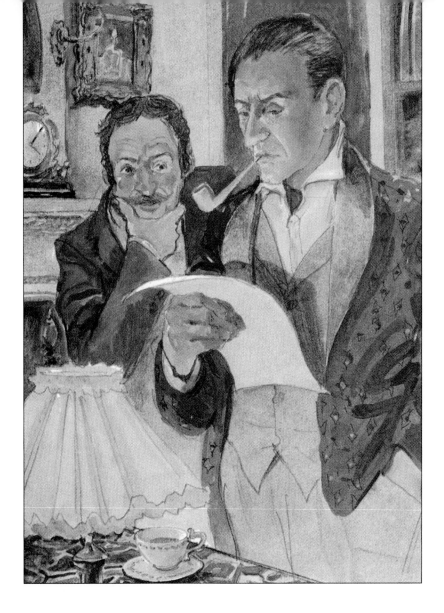

WATSON: So he has a strong motive for standing in the way of their marriages.

HOLMES: Right.

WATSON: What now?

HOLMES: Get your revolver. An Eley's Number 2[3] is an excellent argument with gentlemen who can twist steel pokers into knots. That and a toothbrush should be all you need. Then—let's go!

---

motive (MOHT iv) reason to act
[3]**Eley's Number 2:** old make of pistol

SCENE 5

SETTING: A hallway in the mansion at Stoke Moran.

AT RISE: HOLMES *and* WATSON *are received by* HELEN STONER.

HELEN: I've been waiting. It's turned out very well. He's gone to town. And he's not likely to be back before dark.

HOLMES: Yes, we had the pleasure of meeting the doctor. He followed you to my office. Demanded to know what your business was. Then he threatened us with a poker.

HELEN: Good heavens! You weren't hurt?

HOLMES: Certainly not.

HELEN: He's so tricky. I never know when I'm safe from him. What will we do when he gets back?

HOLMES: Better ask what *he'll* do. He'll have to be on guard. Because now he's got someone more cunning than he is on his track. You must lock yourself in tonight. If he's violent, we'll take you to your aunt's at Harrow. Now, let's examine the outside and then the rooms.

SCENE 6

SETTING: Outside the house.

AT RISE: HOLMES *is walking slowly. He examines the outsides of the windows.*

HOLMES: This window belongs to the room where you used to sleep. The center one is your sister's room, and the one next to the main building is Dr. Roylott's. Correct?

HELEN: Exactly. But now I'm sleeping in the middle room.

HOLMES: Ah, the alterations. I notice there doesn't seem to be any urgent need for repairs there.

HELEN: There isn't. I think it was an excuse to move me from my room.

HOLMES: That's important. Now, on the other side of this narrow wing is the hallway. All three rooms open off it. There are windows in the hallway, of course?

HELEN: Yes, but very small ones. Too narrow for anyone to get through.

---

alteration (awl tuh RAY shun) change made to a building

HOLMES: Anyway, you both locked your doors at night. So your rooms couldn't have been entered from that side. Now, you've bolted these shutters?

HELEN: Yes, they're locked from the inside.

(HOLMES *examines the shutters very closely, trying every way to open them. He tests the hinges with a magnifying glass.*)

HOLMES: No one could pass these shutters—if they were bolted. Hm. This brings up a few problems with my theory.

SCENE 7

SETTING: *A bedroom in the mansion.*

AT RISE: *The bedroom is furnished with fireplace, bed, chest of drawers, dresser, and two chairs.* HOLMES *sits in one of them. He looks over every detail of the room.* HELEN *and* WATSON *stand watching him.*

WATSON: This is the room where your sister died?

HELEN: Yes. And where I'm sleeping now.

(HOLMES *points to a thick bell-rope that hangs down beside the bed. The end of the rope lies on the pillow.*)

HOLMES: This bell-rope[4]—where does the bell ring?

HELEN: In the housekeeper's room.

HOLMES: This rope looks newer than the other things.

HELEN: Yes, it was put there only a couple of years ago.

HOLMES: Your sister asked for it, I suppose.

HELEN: No, I never heard of her using it. We always used to get what we wanted ourselves.

HOLMES: Hm. Then why was such a nice bell-rope put in? Excuse me while I satisfy myself about this floor.

(HOLMES *throws himself face down on the floor. He has his magnifying glass in his hand. He crawls swiftly backward and forward. He examines the cracks between the boards. Then he jumps up and examines the woodwork on the walls. Then he stares at the bed closely. Finally, he takes the bell-rope and yanks it.*)

HOLMES: It's a dummy!

---

[4]**bell-rope:** rope that is attached to a bell that is used to call a servant

WATSON: Won't it ring?

HOLMES: No. It's not even attached to a wire. Interesting. It's tied to a hook just above the little opening for the ventilator.

HELEN: How absurd! I never noticed that before.

HOLMES (*pulling the rope*): Very strange. There are one or two odd points about this room.

WATSON: What are they? I don't see anything odd.

HOLMES: Well, the builder must be a fool to open a vent into another room. With the same trouble, he could have opened it to the outside.

HELEN: The ventilator's quite recent, too.

HOLMES: Done about the same time as the bell-rope?

HELEN: Yes.

HOLMES: *Very* interesting. Dummy bell-ropes. Ventilators that don't ventilate.

WATSON: What does it mean?

HOLMES: Let's carry on in Dr. Roylott's room, please.

SCENE 8

SETTING: A slightly larger bedroom.

AT RISE: The room is plainly furnished. A cot, a shelf of books, an armchair beside the bed, a plain wooden chair, and a round table are the main pieces. There is also a large iron safe. HOLMES *walks slowly around the room. He examines everything,* HELEN *and* WATSON *look on.*

---

ventilator (VEN tuh lay ter) opening to allow fresh air into and stale air out of a room

HOLMES (*tapping the safe*): What's in here?

HELEN: My stepfather's business papers.

HOLMES: Oh. You've seen inside, then?

HELEN: Only once. Years ago. I remember a lot of papers in it.

HOLMES: There isn't a cat inside, for example?

HELEN: No! What a strange idea!

HOLMES: Well, look at this.

(HOLMES *lifts up a saucer of milk that stands on top of the safe.*)

HELEN: We don't keep a cat. But there's the cheetah. And the baboon.

HOLMES: Ah, yes, of course. Well, a cheetah is just a big cat. But a saucer of milk won't do much to satisfy its appetite. There's one thing. . . .

(HOLMES *squats down in front of the wooden chair and examines the seat.*)

HOLMES: Good. That's settled.

WATSON: What's settled? Holmes, what have you . . . ?

HOLMES (*breaking in*): Hello! Here's something interesting.

(HOLMES *picks up a small dog leash hanging on one corner of the bedpost. The leash is curled to make a loop, and tied.*)

HOLMES: What do you make of that, Watson?

WATSON: It's a common enough leash. But I don't know why it's tied that way.

HOLMES: That's not so common, is it? Oh, it's a wicked world. When a clever man turns his brains to crime, it's the worst of all. I think I've seen enough. (HOLMES'S *face is stern.*) Miss Stoner, you *must* follow my advice. In every way.

HELEN: Of course I will.

HOLMES: This is too serious for dilly-dallying. Your life may depend on it.

HELEN: Believe me—I'm in your hands.

HOLMES: Good. In the first place, both my friend and I must spend the night in Julia's room.

(WATSON *and* HELEN *look at* HOLMES *in amazement.*)

HOLMES: I'll explain. (*looking out the window*) Is that the village inn over there?

HELEN: Yes, the Crown.

HOLMES: Good. Your windows could be seen from there?

HELEN: Yes.

HOLMES: All right, here's what you do. Stay in your room. When your stepfather comes back, say you've got a headache. Then when you hear him go to bed, open the shutters of your window. Undo the lock. Put your lamp there as a signal to us. Then take everything you need, and go back to your old room. Even with the repairs, you can manage there for one night, can't you?

HELEN: Oh, yes, easily.

HOLMES: Leave the rest to us.

HELEN: But what will you do?

WATSON: Yes, what *will* we do?

HOLMES: We'll spend the night in that room and find out what caused this whistling noise.

HELEN: I think you already know, Mr. Holmes.

HOLMES: Perhaps.

HELEN: Then please tell me. What caused my sister's death?

HOLMES: I'd rather have proof before I answer that.

HELEN: At least tell me if I'm right—did she die from some sudden shock?

HOLMES: No, I don't think so. I think there was something else. Something more. . . some *thing*. Now, Miss Stoner, we must leave. If Dr. Roylott came back and found us, our trip would have been useless. Be brave. If you do as I've said, we'll soon solve everything.

SCENE 9

SETTING: *A room at the Crown.*

AT RISE: HOLMES *is looking out a dark window.* WATSON *sits nervously.*

HOLMES: Here comes Roylott. Huge monster, isn't he? He's roaring at the poor driver. Look at him shaking his fists! (*turning to* Watson) You know, Watson, I don't know if I ought to take you tonight. It could be dangerous.

WATSON: Will I be any help?

HOLMES: Possibly a great deal.

WATSON: Then I'll come.

HOLMES: Very kind of you.

WATSON: You say danger. You must have seen more in those rooms than I did.

HOLMES: I didn't *see* more. I *deduced* more. I imagine you saw everything I did.

WATSON: I didn't see anything unusual. Except the bell-rope. And what could that be for? I can't imagine.

HOLMES: What about the ventilator?

WATSON: Well, yes, but I don't think that's so unusual—a small opening between two rooms. It was so small, a rat could hardly get through it.

HOLMES: Even before we got here, I knew there'd be a ventilator.

WATSON: What!

HOLMES: Oh, yes. Remember what she told us? Her sister could smell Dr. Roylott's cigar? So there had to be an opening between the two rooms. Nothing was said about it at the coroner's inquest. So it had to be small. Therefore—a ventilator.

WATSON: But what harm could that do?

HOLMES: Well, at the very least, it's an odd coincidence. A ventilator is made. A cord is hung. And a lady who sleeps in the bed dies. Doesn't that strike you?

WATSON: What's the connection? I can't see any.

HOLMES: Notice anything odd about that bed?

WATSON: No.

HOLMES: It was clamped to the floor. Ever see a bed bolted down like that before?

WATSON: Can't say I have.

HOLMES: She couldn't move her bed. It had to stay there right under the ventilator and the rope. We might as well call it a rope, since it was never meant to be used as a bell-rope.

WATSON: Holmes! I'm beginning to guess. If that's it, then . . . Why, we're just in time to prevent a horrible crime. A clever, horrible crime.

HOLMES: Clever enough. And horrible enough. Watson, when a doctor goes wrong, he makes a first-rate criminal. He has nerve, and he has knowledge. Don't *you* ever turn your mind to crime!

---

deduce (dih DOOS) figure out by reasoning
inquest (IN kwest) legal investigation into the cause of death
coincidence (koh IN suh duhns) two related events accidentally happening at the same time

Sherlock Holmes and the Speckled Band ■ 243

WATSON: Never! What a horrible idea!

HOLMES: Believe me, we'll have plenty of horror before the night is over. Would you hand me my pipe, please? Might as well have a few cheerful hours first.

SCENE 10

SETTING: *The same, later.*

AT RISE: HOLMES, *looking out the window, sees a single light appear across the way.*

HOLMES: That's our signal!

(*The two hurry out.*)

SCENE 11

SETTING: JULIA'S *bedroom.*

AT RISE: *The room is dark.* HOLMES *and* WATSON, *their shoes off, enter.* HOLMES *carries a candle and a cane.*

HOLMES (*whispering*): The least sound would be fatal to the plan.

(WATSON *nods.*)

HOLMES (*whispering*): We have to sit without light. He'd see it through the ventilator.

(WATSON *nods again.* HOLMES *blows out the candle. Darkness.*)

HOLMES (*whispering*): Don't go to sleep. Your *life* may depend on it. Have your pistol ready.

(HOLMES *motions to* WATSON *to sit in the chair.* HOLMES *sits on the edge of the bed.* WATSON *takes out his pistol.* HOLMES *places his cane on the side of the bed. They wait. Total silence. Then a bird cries suddenly outside, and the two jump. Then they go back to waiting. A clock strikes twelve.*)

SCENE 12

SETTING: *The same.*

AT RISE: HOLMES *and* WATSON *are sitting in the same places.*

They are slumped over, showing signs of tiredness. WATSON *shakes his head to keep his eyes open. A clock strikes three. Suddenly, there is the sound of something moving. Then comes a gentle, soothing sound—like the sound of steam coming out of a kettle.* HOLMES *strikes a match. He springs from the bed. Then he begins lashing the bell-rope with his cane.*

HOLMES (*yelling*): You see it, Watson? You see it?
WATSON: What? What?

(*There is the sound of a low, clear whistle.* HOLMES *stops striking the bell-rope. He watches it closely. After a moment, a horrible cry is heard off-stage. It becomes louder and louder. It is a hoarse yell of pain and fear and anger.* WATSON *and* HOLMES *look at each other. The scream finally dies away.*)

WATSON: What does it mean?
HOLMES: It means it's all over. Probably for the best, too. Take your pistol, Watson. We'll go into Dr. Roylott's room.

SCENE 13

SETTING: DR. ROYLOTT'S *bedroom.*

AT RISE: HOLMES *and* WATSON, *with his pistol ready, enter the room. They see the iron safe, with its door ajar. Next to it, on a chair, sits* DR. ROYLOTT, *in his bathrobe. The dog leash is across his lap. Rigid, he stares at the ceiling. Around his brow is a yellow band, with brownish speckles. It seems to be bound tightly around his head.*

HOLMES: There's the speckled band!

(WATSON *takes a step forward. The speckled band begins to move! It lifts up a diamond-shaped head. It reveals the puffed neck of a deadly snake.*)

HOLMES: A swamp adder! The deadliest snake in India. Ten seconds after he was bitten—he died! It was obvious. The rope had to be there as a bridge for something passing through the hole and coming to the bed.
WATSON: But who'd think of a snake?
HOLMES: I thought of it right away. Remember, the doctor had pets from India. We knew that. A snake seemed just the sort of

weapon he'd choose. A kind of poison no test could discover. Then, too, it would take effect so quickly. A big advantage from his point of view.

WATSON: A wicked point of view, you mean.

HOLMES: Wickedly clever. Only a sharp-eyed coroner would find the two little punctures left by the fangs. Of course, there was also the whistle. That was a clue.

WATSON: I've been wondering about that. Snakes don't whistle, do they?

HOLMES: Don't be silly, Watson. The *doctor* whistled. The point is, he had to call back the snake before morning. He must have trained it—probably with milk—to return to him when he whistled. He'd put it through the ventilator. He knew it would crawl down the rope and land on the bed.

WATSON: But how could he be sure the snake would bite?

HOLMES: It might or it might not. She might escape every night for a week. But sooner or later . . .

WATSON: Horrible. Yes, I can see now how he must have done it.

HOLMES: Oh, I figured that out before I even went into his room. Then looking at his chair—that settled it.

WATSON: The chair?

HOLMES: Scuff marks. He'd been in the habit of standing on it. He'd have to in order to reach the ventilator. Then there was the speckled band. Let's put this thing back in its den. Then we can get Miss Stoner out of here and get the police in.

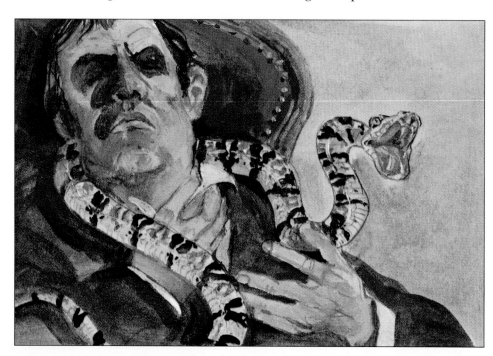

(HOLMES *picks up the dog leash and throws it around the snake's neck. He carries the deadly reptile at arm's length, throws it into the safe, and locks the door.*)

SCENE 14

SETTING: *The parlor in* HOLMES'S *apartment. The next day.*

AT RISE: HOLMES *and* WATSON *sit, having tea.*

HOLMES: I'm afraid I'd had the wrong idea about the case all along, Watson.

WATSON: You too?

HOLMES: That shows you how dangerous it is to reason without having *all* the facts.

WATSON: A natural mistake. After all, the gypsies, the word "band"— it was logical to suspect them.

HOLMES: Not at all. Sloppy thinking. There's only one thing *I* can say in my defense. That is, I instantly changed my mind when I saw the room couldn't be gotten at from outside.

WATSON: You were very clever to notice the ventilator and the bell-rope. I didn't. But even when you pointed them out, I was at sea.

HOLMES: Surely, Watson, after I showed you that the bell-rope was a dummy, you must have guessed . . . safe, the saucer of milk, the loop of cord for a leash. Elementary, my dear Watson.

WATSON: Wait a second. What about that metallic clang heard by Miss Stoner? What was that?

HOLMES: Her stepfather closing the safe, of course. And don't forget the softer noise—that was the snake's hiss. As soon as I heard it, I attacked the thing with my cane.

WATSON: To drive it back through the ventilator.

HOLMES: Exactly. And also, frankly, I had another purpose. My attack roused the snake's temper. Made it fly at the first person it saw.

WATSON: Dr. Grimesby Roylott!

HOLMES: Mmm. You might even say I sort of indirectly caused his death. Can't say it's likely to weigh very heavily on my mind. Will you pass me some toast, please, Watson?

Review the Selection

UNDERSTAND THE SELECTION

Recall

1. How much does Holmes charge Helen Stoner for his work?

2. What is the significance of the whistling that Helen's sister heard?

3. What was odd about Julia's bed?

Infer

4. Describe Helen Stoner's state of mind when she came to see Holmes.

5. The first meeting between Holmes and Dr. Roylott was stormy. How do you know that?

6. What was the real reason for the renovation in Helen's room?

7. Explain the meaning of, "Elementary, my dear Watson."

Apply

8. Why do you think Helen protects Dr. Roylott?

9. Give an example of "deduction," the type of reasoning for which Sherlock Holmes is famous.

10. Did Holmes have the right to cause the death of Dr. Roylott? Explain.

Respond to Literature

Why do you think the Sherlock Holmes mysteries have been popular for a century?

WRITE ABOUT THE SELECTION

Can you write the script for a 60-minute television crime show? Imagine the television producer has agreed to pick the best script submitted and produce it. You must follow the basic rule in crime stories: enough information must be given to allow the viewer to solve the crime. However, you must not make it too easy.

Prewriting First, think of a crime story. You can make up one, or use one you already know. Make a flow chart that shows the action of the story. Next to each box write the dialogue that will be needed for each character.

Writing Use the flow chart to help you write your script. You may use characters and stage directions; you may use a first-person narrator; or you may use third-person point of view. Indicate all stage directions and sound effects.

Revising Can the crime be solved with the information you have given? Check to make sure it can. Can the script be performed in 60 minutes? It will not be accepted for judging unless it can. Finally, make sure transitions between speakers or between thoughts are clear. The script must make sense to the reader.

Proofreading Reread your script and check that the dialogue for each speaker is marked as a new paragraph. Did you use correct punctuation? The script must be tight, with no loose ends.

THINK ABOUT CHARACTERS

Holmes notes at one point in the story, "We're in deep waters here." Indeed, in this episode of Holmes's adventures, he is pitted against an adversary he himself calls "cunning" and "clever." Do you agree? Explain the reasons for your answer.

1. Who is the protagonist and who is the antagonist in the story? Are they equally matched? Explain your answer.

2. Describe the conflict between them. What does each want to accomplish?

3. Do the protagonist and antagonist respect each other? What makes you think so?

4. The one direct confrontation between the protagonist and antagonist ends in a show of physical strength. Who won the confrontation?

5. How does the conflict between the protagonist and antagonist end?

READING FOCUS

Evaluate the Writer's Craft As you read the play, you were able to evaluate the writer's purpose for presenting specific details and information in certain ways. Choose one unusual or unexpected detail. Explain how this added to your enjoyment of the play.

DEVELOP YOUR VOCABULARY

Writing crime stories requires a special vocabulary. You must know terms associated with police work and the legal system.

An example is the word *coroner*. It means a "public officer who investigates deaths that may not be due to natural causes." A coroner can play a very important part in a murder mystery, so you should know the meaning of the word.

Below are some more words associated with crime stories. Make sure that you know how each one is pronounced and what it means. Use a dictionary if you are unsure. Then use each word in a sentence.

1. deduce
2. felony
3. autopsy
4. will
5. inquest
6. plea
7. trial
8. verdict
9. sentence
10. forensic
11. defendant
12. perpetrator

Focus ON DRAMA

A drama is a play that tells a story that revolves around a conflict. Drama is made up of dialogue and action. When you go to the theater to see a play, you are not only hearing what the characters say, you are also seeing what they do.

When you read a drama, you are reading what the characters say, but you obviously do not see what they are doing. You must imagine this. Often notes called **stage directions**, in parentheses or brackets, indicate actions.

Since a drama tells a story, it shares the elements of all stories: plot, characters, setting, and theme. A part of the plot often stressed in drama is conflict. Conflict, usually between human characters, creates the action that keeps the play moving.

Plot Since you have already studied the short story, you know that plot is the series of events, or actions, in a story. The plot of a story often begins with **exposition**, or background information. Then a **complication** develops. The **action rises**, leading to a **climax**. **Resolution** of any unanswered questions comes about after the climax, in **falling action**.

You should pay particular attention to plot clues when reading a drama because the events of the plot are presented differently than in a short story. Plot develops solely through the conversation of the characters. There is often no narrator so you must interpret the information the characters provide and piece it together.

Characters It is the presentation of information through conversation that makes the characters an important element in any drama. You read exactly what the characters say, not what someone else reports them to have said.

The characters in a drama are, of course, the people in the story. You are introduced to them at the very beginning of the play, in the list of characters. This introduction is just that—a list. Unless you are already familiar with the drama, you have no idea which characters are the main ones and how they interact. You learn this through the dialogue.

To help your imagination, stage directions are sometimes given to describe characters' actions. Besides what we learn through these actions, any ideas or descriptions about the characters come indirectly, from what other characters say about them.

Setting   The setting of a drama is stated usually at the beginning of the play. If the setting changes during the play, the new setting is given at the opening of a scene or act.

When you see a drama performed on stage, you learn the "where" of the setting by looking at the stage set. You learn the "when" of the setting also by looking at the stage set and by seeing how the characters are dressed. The objects, or props, used in the setting, as well as the clothes, or costumes, of the characters, provide clues to the time that the drama takes place.

Theme   Theme is the message of the drama. It is the central idea behind the drama. As in short stories, there might be more than one theme in a drama. Sometimes there is no theme of real importance. Usually, however, from studying the conflict, a single, clear theme will emerge.

Conflict   Conflict is what keeps a drama moving. The need to resolve the conflict creates dramatic action that drives the plot to a climax. Conflict usually develops between characters, because characters and their actions are the basis of any play. In "Sherlock Holmes and the Speckled Band," the conflict is between a protagonist and an antagonist.

Conflict can also be within a character. If a character struggles to perform a difficult physical feat, for example, the conflict is between the character and his or her own fear.

As you read the next selection in this unit, look for the elements of drama. Ask yourself these questions:

1. How are the literary elements presented differently in a drama than they are in a short story?
2. What is the conflict in the drama?

TRIFLES

by Susan Glaspell

CHARACTERS

GEORGE HENDERSON, *county attorney*   MRS. PETERS

HENRY PETERS, *sheriff*   MRS. HALE

LEWIS HALE, *a neighboring farmer*

Scene: *The kitchen in the now abandoned farmhouse of* JOHN WRIGHT, *a gloomy kitchen, and left without having been put in order—unwashed pans under the sink, a loaf of bread outside the breadbox, a dish towel on the table—other signs of incompleted work. At the rear the outer door opens and the* SHERIFF *comes in followed by the* COUNTY ATTORNEY *and* HALE. *The* SHERIFF *and* HALE *are men in middle life, the* COUNTY ATTORNEY *is a young man; all are much bundled up and go at once to the stove. They are followed by the two women—the* SHERIFF'S *wife first, she is a slight wiry woman, a thin nervous face.* MRS. HALE *is larger and would ordinarily be called more comfortable looking, but she is disturbed now and looks fearfully about as she enters. The women have come in slowly, and stand close together near the door.*

COUNTY ATTORNEY (*rubbing his hands*): This feels good. Come up to the fire, ladies.

MRS. PETERS (*after taking a step forward*): I'm not—cold.

SHERIFF (*unbuttoning his overcoat and stepping away from the stove as if to mark the beginning of official business*): Now, Mr. Hale, before we move things about, you explain to Mr. Henderson just what you saw when you came here yesterday morning.

COUNTY ATTORNEY: By the way, has anything been moved? Are things just as you left them yesterday?

---

attorney (uh TUR nee) lawyer. A county attorney is a lawyer responsible for bringing criminal charges against someone.
wiry (WYR ee) lean and strong

January, 1940, Grant Wood. Estate of Grant Wood/Licensed by VAGA, New York, NY

SHERIFF (*looking about*): It's just the same. When it dropped below zero last night I thought I'd better send Frank out this morning to make a fire for us—no use getting **pneumonia** with a big case on, but I told him not to touch anything except the stove—and you know Frank.

COUNTY ATTORNEY: Somebody should have been left here yesterday.

SHERIFF: Oh—yesterday. When I had to send Frank to Morris Center for that man who went crazy—I want you to know I had my hands full yesterday. I knew you could get back from Omaha by today and as long as I went over everything here myself—

COUNTY ATTORNEY: Well, Mr. Hale, tell just what happened when you came here yesterday morning.

HALE: Harry and I had started to town with a load of potatoes. We came along the road from my place and as I got here I said, "I'm going to see if I can't get John Wright to go in with me on

Notice how the characters of the sheriff and the county attorney are developed through dialogue. The county attorney seems businesslike and thorough. The sheriff seems to be confronted with a great many problems. Still, he worries about things such as heat in the old farmhouse.

Here is the main question of the plot: What happened at the Wright farmhouse yesterday morning? The plot develops as the characters search for an answer.

pneumonia (noo MOHN yuh) disease of the lungs; caused by an infection a party telephone." I spoke to Wright about it once before and he put me off, saying folks talked too much anyway, and all he asked was peace and quiet—I guess you know about how much he talked himself, but I thought maybe if I went to the house and talked about it before his wife, though I said to Harry that I didn't know as what his wife wanted made much difference to John—

COUNTY ATTORNEY: Let's talk about that later, Mr. Hale. I do want to talk about that, but tell now just what happened when you got to the house.

HALE: I didn't hear or see anything; I knocked at the door, and still it was all quiet inside. I knew they must be up, it was past eight o'clock. So I knocked again, and I thought I heard somebody say "Come in." I wasn't sure, I'm not sure yet, but I opened the door—this door (*indicating the door by which the two men are still standing*) and there in that rocker—(*pointing to it*) sat Mrs. Wright.

(*They all look at the rocker.*)

COUNTY ATTORNEY: What—was she doing?

HALE: She was rockin' back and forth. She had her apron in her hand and was kind of—pleating it.

COUNTY ATTORNEY: And how did she—look?

HALE: Well, she looked queer.

COUNTY ATTORNEY: How do you mean—queer?

HALE: Well, as if she didn't know what she was going to do next. And kind of done up.

COUNTY ATTORNEY: How did she seem to feel about your coming?

HALE: Why, I don't think she minded—one way or other. She didn't pay much attention. I said, "How do, Mrs. Wright, it's cold, ain't it?" And she said, "Is it?"—and went on kind of pleating at her apron. Well, I was surprised; she didn't ask me to come up to the stove, or to set down, but just sat there, not even looking at me, so I said, "I want to see John." And then she—laughed. I guess you would call it a laugh. I thought of Harry and the team outside, so I said a little sharp: "Can't I see John?" "No," she says, kind o' dull like. "Ain't he home?"

These notes in parentheses are stage directions. An actor would use them playing the part of Hale on the stage. However, they also help us to "see" the action and to understand what is happening.

This is a story within a story. It is a way for more background information to be introduced, even though the people mentioned are not characters in the play.

---

pleating (PLEET ing) pressing cloth together

says I. "Yes," says she, "he's home." "Then why can't I see him?" I asked her, out of patience. "'Cause he's dead," says she. *"Dead?"* says I. She just nodded her head, not getting a bit excited, but rockin' back and forth. "Why—where is he?" says I, not knowing what to say. She just pointed upstairs— like that (*himself pointing to the room above*). I got up, with the idea of going up there. I walked from there to here—then I says, "Why, what did he die of?" "He died of a rope round his neck," says she, and just went on pleatin' at her apron. Well, I went out and called Harry. I thought I might—need help. We went upstairs and there he was—lyin'—

COUNTY ATTORNEY: I think I'd rather have you go into that upstairs, where you can point it all out. Just go on now with the rest of the story.

HALE: Well, my first thought was to get that rope off. It looked— (*stops, his face twitches*)—but Harry, he went up to him, and he said, "No, he's dead all right, and we'd better not touch anything." So we went back down stairs. She was still sitting that same way. "Has anybody been notified?" I asked. "No," says she, unconcerned. "Who did this, Mrs. Wright?" said Harry. He said it businesslike—and she stopped pleatin' of her apron. "I don't know," she says. "You don't *know?*" says Harry. "No," says she. "Weren't you sleeping in the bed with him?" says Harry. "Yes," says she, "but I was on the inside." "Somebody slipped a rope round his neck and strangled him and you didn't wake up?" says Harry. "I didn't wake up," she said after him. We may have looked as if we didn't see how that could be, for after a minute she said, "I sleep sound." Harry was going to ask her more questions but I said maybe we ought to let her tell her story first to the coroner, or the sheriff, so Harry went fast as he could to Rivers' place, where there's a telephone.

COUNTY ATTORNEY: And what did Mrs. Wright do when she knew that you had gone for the coroner?

HALE: She moved from that chair to this one over here (*pointing to a small chair in the corner*) and just sat there with her hands held together and looking down. I got a feeling that I ought to

Here is the plot complication: Did Mrs. Wright kill her husband? A few lines further on the county attorney is already trying to determine a motive for the killing.

---

twitches (TWICH iz) pulls with a sudden jerk
notified (NOHT uh fyd) advised; informed
strangled (STRANG guld) choked; killed by squeezing

The Judges c. 1907, Georges Rouault.
The Portland Museum of Art

make some conversation, so I said I had come in to see if John wanted to put in a telephone, and at that she started to laugh, and then she stopped and looked at me—scared. (*The* COUNTY ATTORNEY, *who has had his notebook out, makes a note.*) I dunno, maybe it wasn't scared. I wouldn't like to say it was. Soon Harry got back, and then Dr. Lloyd came, and you, Mr. Peters, and so I guess that's all I know that you don't.

COUNTY ATTORNEY (*looking around*): I guess we'll go upstairs first— and then out to the barn and around there. (*To the* SHERIFF) You're convinced that there was nothing important here— nothing that would point to any motive?

SHERIFF: Nothing here but kitchen things.

(*The* COUNTY ATTORNEY, *after again looking around the kitchen, opens the door of a cupboard closet. He gets up on a chair and looks on a shelf. Pulls his hand away, sticky.*)

---

cupboard (KUB urd) a closet fitted with shelves for holding cups

COUNTY ATTORNEY: Here's a nice mess.

(*The women draw nearer.*)

MRS. PETERS (*to the other woman*): Oh, her fruit; it did freeze. (*To the* COUNTY ATTORNEY.) She worried about that when it turned so cold. She said the fire'd go out and her jars would break.

SHERIFF: Well, can you beat the women! Held for murder and worrying about her preserves.

COUNTY ATTORNEY: I guess before we are through she may have something more serious than preserves to worry about.

HALE: Well, women are used to worrying over trifles.

(*The two women move a little closer together.*)

COUNTY ATTORNEY (*With the gallantry of a young politician*): And yet, for all their worries, what would we do without the ladies? (*The women do not unbend. He goes to the sink, takes a dipperful of water from the pail and pouring it into a basin, washes his hands. Starts to wipe them on the roller towel, turns it for a cleaner place*) Dirty towels! (*Kicks his foot against the pans under the sink*) Not much of a housekeeper, would you say, ladies?

MRS. HALE (*stiffly*): There's a great deal of work to be done on a farm.

COUNTY ATTORNEY: To be sure. And yet (*with a little bow to her*) I know there are some Dickson County farmhouses which do not have such roller towels.

(*He gives it a pull to expose its full length again.*)

MRS. HALE: Those towels get dirty awful quick. Men's hands aren't always as clean as they might be.

COUNTY ATTORNEY: Ah, loyal to your sex, I see. But you and Mrs. Wright were neighbors. I suppose you were friends, too.

MRS. HALE (*shaking her head*): I've not seen much of her of late years. I've not been in this house—it's more than a year.

COUNTY ATTORNEY: And why was that? You didn't like her?

MRS. HALE: I liked her all well enough. Farmers' wives have their hands full, Mr. Henderson. And then—

The word "*trifles*", as used here, is important. "Trifles" is also the title of the play, but here it is a tip-off: Pay attention to small details such as broken jam jars. They might have something to do with the theme of the drama.

Here is an example of where you must piece together information from dialogue and stage directions to understand what is happening. What clues show that the county attorney really does not understand the harsh life of a farmer's wife?

---

preserves (prih ZURVZ) fruit kept from spoiling by special treatment
trifles (TRY fulz) anything of little value or importance
gallantry (GAL un tree) heroic courage; elaborate politeness to women
expose (ik SPOHZ) to lay open; uncover

COUNTY ATTORNEY: Yes—?

MRS. HALE (*looking about*): It never seemed a very cheerful place.

COUNTY ATTORNEY: No—it's not cheerful. I shouldn't say she had the homemaking instinct.

MRS. HALE: Well, I don't know as Wright had, either.

COUNTY ATTORNEY: You mean that they didn't get on very well?

MRS. HALE: No, I don't mean anything. But I don't think a place'd be any cheerfuller for John Wright's being in it.

COUNTY ATTORNEY: I'd like to talk more of that a little later. I want to get the lay of things upstairs now.

(*He goes to the left, where three steps lead to a stair door.*)

SHERIFF: I suppose anything Mrs. Peters does'll be all right. She was to take in some clothes for her, you know, and a few little things. We left in such a hurry yesterday.

COUNTY ATTORNEY: Yes, but I would like to see what you take, Mrs. Peters, and keep an eye out for anything that might be of use to us.

MRS. PETERS: Yes, Mr. Henderson.

The action shifts gears right here. The sheriff and county attorney leave the kitchen and go upstairs to continue their investigation. The women remain downstairs.

(*The women listen to the men's steps on the stairs, then look about the kitchen.*)

This is an important comment, for it indicates a general conflict between men and women.

MRS. HALE: I'd hate to have men coming into my kitchen, snooping round and criticizing.

(*She arranges the pans under the sink which the* LAWYER *had shoved out of place.*)

MRS. PETERS: Of course it's no more than their duty.

MRS. HALE: Duty's all right, but I guess that deputy sheriff that came out to make the fire might have got a little of this on. (*Gives the roller towel a pull*) Wish I'd thought of that sooner. Seems mean to talk about her for not having things slicked up when she had to come away in such a hurry.

MRS. PETERS (*who has gone to a small table in the left rear corner of the room, and lifted one end of a towel that covers a pan*): She had bread set.

---

instinct (IN stingkt) a natural tendency; unconscious skill

snooping (SNOOP ing) searching or looking into other people's property or affairs without permission

(*Stands still*)

MRS. HALE (*Eyes fixed on a loaf of bread beside the breadbox, which is on a low shelf at the other side of the room. Moves slowly toward it.*): She was going to put this in there. (*Picks up loaf, then abruptly drops it, as though returning to familiar things.*) It's a shame about her fruit. I wonder if it's all gone. (*Gets up on the chair and looks*) I think there's some here that's all right, Mrs. Peters. Yes—here; (*holding it toward the window*) this is cherries, too. (*Looking again*) I declare I believe that's the only one. (*Gets down, bottle in her hand. Goes to the sink and wipes it off on the outside.*) She'll feel awful bad after all her hard work in the hot weather. I remember the afternoon I put up my cherries last summer.

> Mrs. Hale is a natural detective just because she understands "women's" work. Do you agree? Her character will now develop more fully, as will Mrs. Peters's. Pay attention to what they say and what they do.

(*She puts the bottle on the big kitchen table, center of the room. With a sigh, is about to sit down in the rocking-chair. Before she is seated realizes what chair it is, with a slow look at it, steps back. The chair which she has touched rocks back and forth.*)

MRS. PETERS: Well, I must get those things from the front room closet. (*She goes to the door at the right, but after looking into the other room, steps back.*) You coming with me, Mrs. Hale? You could help me carry them.

(*They go in the other room; reappear,* MRS. PETERS *carrying a dress and a skirt,* MRS. HALE *following with a pair of shoes.*)

> There is no change in the setting, not even a minor one. The action continues to take place in the farmhouse kitchen.

MRS. PETERS: My, it's cold in there.

(*She puts the clothes on the big table and hurries to the stove.*)

MRS. HALE (*examining the skirt*): Wright was close. I think maybe that's why she kept so much to herself. She didn't even belong to the Ladies' Aid. I suppose she felt she couldn't do her part, and then you don't enjoy things when you feel shabby. She used to wear pretty clothes and be lively, when she was Minnie Foster, one of the town girls singing in the choir. But that was—oh, that was thirty years ago. This all you was to take in?

> Mrs. Hale gives us information that might be important. Minnie Foster seemed a different person from Mrs. John Wright.

MRS. PETERS: She said she wanted an apron. Funny thing to want, for there isn't much to get you dirty in jail, goodness knows.

---

shabby (SHAB ee) seedy; poorly dressed

But I suppose just to make her feel more natural. She said they was in the top drawer in this cupboard. Yes, here. And then her little shawl that always hung behind the door.

(*Opens stair door and looks*) Yes, here it is.

(*Quickly shuts door leading upstairs*)

MRS. HALE (*abruptly moving toward her*): Mrs. Peters?

MRS. PETERS: Yes, Mrs. Hale?

MRS. HALE: Do you think she did it?

MRS. PETERS (*in a frightened voice*): Oh, I don't know.

MRS. HALE: Well, I don't think she did. Asking for an apron and her little shawl. Worrying about her fruit.

MRS. PETERS (*Starts to speak, glances up, where footsteps are heard in the room above. In a low voice*): Mr. Peters says it looks bad for her. Mr. Henderson is awful sarcastic in a speech and he'll make fun of her sayin' she didn't wake up.

MRS. HALE: Well, I guess John Wright didn't wake when they was slipping that rope under his neck.

MRS. PETERS: No, it's strange. It must have been done awful crafty and still. They say it was such a—funny way to kill a man, rigging it all up like that.

MRS. HALE: That's just what Mr. Hale said. There was a gun in the house. He says that's what he can't understand.

MRS. PETERS: Mr. Henderson said coming out that what was needed for the case was a motive; something to show anger, or—sudden feeling.

MRS. HALE (*who is standing by the table*): Well, I don't see any signs of anger around here, but (*She puts her hand on the dish towel which lies on the table, stands looking down at the table, one half of which is clean, the other half messy.*) It's wiped to here. (*Makes a move as if to finish the work, then turns and looks at loaf of bread outside the breadbox. Drops towel. Speaks in that voice of coming back to familiar things.*) Wonder how they are finding things upstairs. I hope she had it a little more red-up there.

---

shawl (SHAWL) a loose scarf used by women to cover the shoulders
abruptly (uh BRUPT lee) suddenly
sarcastic (sahr KAS tik) sneering or ironic, and meant to hurt feelings
crafty (KRAFT ee) shrewd; tricky
rigging (RIG ing) any gear or tackle

Ground Hog Day, Andrew Wyeth. Philadelphia Museum of Art

You know, it seems kind of *sneaking*. Locking her up in town and then coming out here and trying to get her own house to turn against her!

MRS. PETERS: But Mrs. Hale, the law is the law.

MRS. HALE: I s'pose 'tis. (*unbuttoning her coat*) Better loosen up your things, Mrs. Peters. You won't feel them when you go out.

(MRS. PETERS *takes off her fur tippet, goes to hang it on hook at back of room, stands looking at the under part of the small corner table.*)

MRS. PETERS: She was piecing a quilt.

Here sympathy is created for Mrs. Wright and the situation she is in. Mrs. Hale feels a kind of common bond with Mrs. Wright. Do you think so?

---

tippet (TIP it) garment like a scarf that covers the neck and shoulders
quilt (KWILT) a bed cover made by stitching a layer of cotton between
    two layers of fabric

Again, the women show an understanding that the men lack of Mrs. Wright's work and life. Yet the men are the ones who are officially gathering the evidence.

(*She brings the large sewing basket and they look at the bright pieces.*)

MRS. HALE: It's log cabin pattern. Pretty, isn't it? I wonder if she was goin' to quilt it or just knot it?

(*Footsteps have been heard coming down the stairs. The* SHERIFF *enters followed by* HALE *and the* COUNTY ATTORNEY.)

SHERIFF: They wonder if she was going to quilt it or just knot it?

(*The men laugh, the women look abashed.*)

COUNTY ATTORNEY (*rubbing his hands over the stove*): Frank's fire didn't do much up there, did it? Well, let's go out to the barn and get that cleared up.

(*The men go outside.*)

MRS. HALE (*resentfully*): I don't know as there's anything so strange, our takin' up our time with little things while we're waiting for them to get the evidence. (*She sits down at the big table smoothing out a block with decision.*) I don't see as it's anything to laugh about.

MRS. PETERS (*apologetically*): Of course they've got awful important things on their minds.

(*Pulls up a chair and joins* MRS. HALE *at the table.*)

What is Mrs. Hale doing here? What do you think she is thinking?

MRS. HALE (*examining another block*): Mrs. Peters, look at this one. Here, this is the one she was working on, and look at the sewing! All the rest of it has been so nice and even. And look at this! It's all over the place! Why, it looks as if she didn't know what she was about!

(*After she has said this they look at each other, then start to glance back at the door. After an instant* MRS. HALE *has pulled at a knot and ripped the sewing.*)

MRS. PETERS: Oh, what are you doing, Mrs. Hale?

MRS. HALE (*mildly*): Just pulling out a stitch or two that's not sewed very good. (*Threading a needle*) Bad sewing always made me fidgety.

---

knot (NOT) tie a knoblike lacing
abashed (uh BASHT) embarrassed
resentfully (rih ZENT ful ee) angrily
apologetically (uh pol uh JET ik lee) defensively; spoken with excuses

MRS. PETERS (*nervously*): I don't think we ought to touch things.

MRS. HALE: I'll just finish up this end. (*Suddenly stopping and leaning forward*) Mrs. Peters?

MRS. PETERS: Yes, Mrs. Hale?

MRS. HALE: What do you suppose she was so nervous about?

MRS. PETERS: Oh—I don't know. I don't know as she was nervous. I sometimes sew awful queer when I'm just tired. (MRS. HALE *starts to say something, looks at* MRS. PETERS, *then goes on sewing.*) Well I must get these things wrapped up. They may be through sooner than we think. (*Putting apron and other things together.*) I wonder where I can find a piece of paper, and string.

MRS. HALE: In that cupboard, maybe.

MRS. PETERS (*looking in cupboard*): Why, here's a bird cage. (*Holds it up.*) Did she have a bird, Mrs. Hale?

It is Mrs. Peters's turn to play detective, although she might not be doing it consciously.

MRS. HALE: Why, I don't know whether she did or not—I've not been here for so long. There was a man around last year selling canaries cheap, but I don't know as she took one; maybe she did. She used to sing real pretty herself.

MRS. PETERS (*glancing around*): Seems funny to think of a bird here. But she must have had one, or why would she have had a cage? I wonder what happened to it.

MRS. HALE: I s'pose maybe the cat got it.

MRS. PETERS: No, she didn't have a cat. She's got that feeling some people have about cats—being afraid of them. My cat got in her room and she was real upset and asked me to take it out.

MRS. HALE: My sister Bessie was like that. Queer, ain't it?

MRS. PETERS (*examining the cage*): Why, look at this door. It's broke. One hinge is pulled apart.

MRS. HALE (*looking, too*): Looks as if someone must have been rough with it.

MRS. PETERS: Why, yes.

(*She brings the cage forward and puts it on the table.*)

MRS. HALE: I wish if they're going to find any evidence they'd be about it. I don't like this place.

---

fidgety (FIJ it ee) nervous or uneasy

MRS. PETERS: But I'm awful glad you came with me, Mrs. Hale. It would be lonesome for me sitting here alone.

MRS. HALE: It would, wouldn't it? (*Dropping her sewing*) But I tell you what I do wish, Mrs. Peters. I wish I had come over sometimes when *she* was here. I—(*looking around the room*)—wish I had.

MRS. PETERS: But of course you were awful busy, Mrs. Hale—your house and your children.

MRS. HALE: I could've come. I stayed away because it weren't cheerful—and that's why I ought to have come. I—I've never liked this place. Maybe because it's down in a hollow and you don't see the road. I dunno what it is, but it's a lonesome place and always was. I wish I had come over to see Minnie Foster sometimes. I can see now—

(*Shakes her head.*)

MRS. PETERS: Well, you mustn't reproach yourself, Mrs. Hale. Somehow we just don't see how it is with other folks until—something comes up.

MRS. HALE: Not having children makes less work—but it makes a quiet house, and Wright out to work all day, and no company when he did come in. Did you know John Wright, Mrs. Peters?

MRS. PETERS: Not to know him; I've seen him in town. They say he was a good man.

MRS. HALE: Yes—good; he didn't drink, and kept his word as well as most, I guess, and paid his debts. But he was a hard man, Mrs. Peters. Just to pass the time of day with him—(*shivers*) Like a raw wind that gets to the bone. (*Pauses, her eye falling on the cage*) I should think she would'a wanted a bird. But what do you suppose went with it?

MRS. PETERS: I don't know, unless it got sick and died.

(*She reaches over and swings the broken door, swings it again, both women watch it.*)

MRS. HALE: You weren't raised round here, were you? (MRS. PETERS *shakes her head.*) You didn't know—her?

MRS. PETERS: Not till they brought her yesterday.

Here is some information about the setting tucked into the dialogue.

---

reproach (rih PROHCH) accuse and blame for a fault

Christina's World, Andrew Wyeth, 1948. Tempera on gessoed panel 32¼" × 47¾" (81.9 × 121.3 cm). The Museum of Modern Art, New York. Purchase. Photograph ©2000 The Museum of Modern Art, New York

MRS. HALE: She—come to think of it, she was kind of like a bird herself—real sweet and pretty, but kind of timid and—fluttery. How—she—did—change. (*Silence; then as if struck by a happy thought and relieved to get back to everyday things.*) Tell you what, Mrs. Peters, why don't you take the quilt in with you? It might take up her mind.

MRS. PETERS: Why, I think that's a real nice idea, Mrs. Hale. There couldn't possibly be any objection to it, could there? Now, just what would I take? I wonder if her patches are in here—and her things.

(*They look in the sewing basket.*)

MRS. HALE: Here's some red. I expect this has got sewing things in it. (*Brings out a fancy box*) What a pretty box. Looks like

---

timid (TIM id) shy
fluttery (FLUT ur ee) moving rapidly and with uncertainty

something somebody would give you. Maybe her scissors are in here. (*Opens box. Suddenly puts her hand to her nose.*) Why—(MRS. PETERS *bends nearer, then turns her face away*) There's something wrapped up in this piece of silk.

MRS. PETERS: Why, this isn't her scissors,

MRS. HALE (*lifting the silk*): Oh, Mrs. Peters—it's

(MRS. PETERS *bends closer.*)

MRS. PETERS: It's the bird.

MRS. HALE (*jumping up*): But, Mrs. Peters—look at it! Its neck! Look at its neck! It's all—other side *to*.

MRS. PETERS: Somebody—wrung—its—neck.

(*Their eyes meet. A look of growing comprehension, of horror. Steps are heard outside.* MRS. HALE *slips box under quilt pieces, and sinks into her chair. Enter* SHERIFF *and* COUNTY ATTORNEY. MRS. PETERS *rises.*)

COUNTY ATTORNEY (*as one turning from serious things to little pleasantries*): Well, ladies, have you decided whether she was going to quilt it or knot it?

MRS. PETERS: We think she was going to—knot it.

COUNTY ATTORNEY: Well, that's interesting, I am sure. (*Seeing the bird cage*) Has the bird flown?

MRS. HALE (*putting more quilt pieces over the box*): We think the—cat got it.

COUNTY ATTORNEY (*preoccupied*): Is there a cat?

(MRS. HALE *glances in a quick, covert way at* MRS. PETERS.)

MRS. PETERS: Well, not *now*. They're superstitious, you know. They leave.

COUNTY ATTORNEY (*to* SHERIFF PETERS, *continuing an interrupted conversation*): No sign at all of anyone having come from the outside. Their own rope. Now let's go up again and go over it piece by piece. (*They start upstairs.*) It would have been some-one who knew just the—

---

comprehension (kom prih HEN shun) understanding or knowledge of something
pleasantries (PLEZ un treez) lively, agreeable talks
preoccupied (pree OK yuh pyd) thinking of something else
covert (KOH vurt) hidden or disguised
superstitious (soo pur STISH us) too much fear of the unknown

(MRS. PETERS *sits down. The two women sit there not looking at one another, but as if peering into something and at the same time holding back. When they talk now it is in the manner of feeling their way over strange ground, as if afraid of what they are saying, but as if they cannot help saying it.*)

MRS. HALE: She liked the bird. She was going to bury it in that pretty box.

MRS. PETERS (*in a whisper*): When I was a girl—my kitten—there was a boy took a hatchet, and before my eyes—and before I could get there—(*covers her face an instant*) If they hadn't held me back I would have—(*catches herself, looks upstairs where steps are heard, falters weakly*)—hurt him.

MRS. HALE (*with a slow look around her*): I wonder how it would seem never to have had any children around. (*Pause*) No, Wright wouldn't like the bird—a thing that sang. She used to sing. He killed that, too.

MRS. PETERS (*moving uneasily*): We don't know who killed the bird.

MRS. HALE: I knew John Wright.

MRS. PETERS: It was an awful thing was done in this house that night, Mrs. Hale. Killing a man while he slept, slipping a rope around his neck that choked the life out of him.

MRS. HALE: His neck. Choked the life out of him.

(*Her hand goes out and rests on the bird cage.*)

MRS. PETERS (*with rising voice*): We don't know who killed him. We don't *know.*

MRS. HALE (*her own feeling not interrupted*): If there'd been years and years of nothing, then a bird to sing to you, it would be awful—still, after the bird was still.

MRS. PETERS (*something within her speaking*): I know what stillness is. When we homesteaded in Dakota, and my first baby died—after he was two years old, and me with no other then—

The note, "with rising voice," suggests the action is rising faster and we are heading for the climax. The women seem to have a theory about what happened. What is their theory?

---

peering (PIR ing) looking closely
hatchet (HACH it) a tool for chopping; like an ax
falters (FAWL turz) walks unsteadily; stumbles
homesteaded (HOHM sted id) occupied land as a home

Mrs. Peters, the wife of the sheriff, sees the conflict clearly—crimes must be punished, but what if the crime is justifiable?

MRS. HALE (*moving*): How soon do you suppose they'll be through, looking for the evidence?

MRS. PETERS: I know what stillness is. (*Pulling herself back*) The law has got to punish crime, Mrs. Hale.

MRS. HALE (*not as if answering that*): I wish you'd seen Minnie Foster when she wore a white dress with blue ribbons and stood up there in the choir and sang. (*A look around the room*) Oh, I wish I'd come over here once in a while! That was a crime! That was a crime! Who's going to punish that?

MRS. PETERS (*looking upstairs*): We mustn't—take on.

Here is the theme that has been hinted at before—life for farmers' wives is hard, and the suffering created a common bond among women.

MRS. HALE: I might have known she needed help! I know how things can be—for women. I tell you, it's queer, Mrs. Peters. We live close together and we live far apart. We all go through the same things—it's all just a different kind of the same thing. (*Brushes her eyes, noticing the bottle of fruit, reaches out for it*) If I was you I wouldn't tell her her fruit was gone. Tell her it *ain't*, Tell her it's all right. Take this in to prove it to her. She—she may never know whether it was broke or not.

MRS. PETERS (*Takes the bottle, looks about for something to wrap it in; takes petticoat from the clothes brought from the other room, very nervously begins winding this around the bottle. In a false voice.*): My, it's a good thing the men couldn't hear us. Wouldn't they just laugh! Getting all stirred up over a little thing like a—dead canary. As if that could have anything to do with—with— wouldn't they *laugh*!

(*The men are heard coming down stairs.*)

MRS. HALE (*under her breath*): Maybe they would—maybe they wouldn't.

COUNTY ATTORNEY: No, Peters, it's all perfectly clear except a reason for doing it. But you know juries when it comes to women. If there was some definite thing. Something to show—something to make a story about—a thing that would connect up with this strange way of doing it—

(*The women's eyes meet for an instant. Enter* HALE *from outer door.*)

HALE: Well, I've got the team around. Pretty cold out there.

---

petticoat (PET ee koht) a loose underskirt

COUNTY ATTORNEY: I'm going to stay here a while by myself. (*To the* SHERIFF.) You can send Frank out for me, can't you? I want to go over everything. I'm not satisfied that we can't do better.

SHERIFF: Do you want to see what Mrs. Peters is going to take in?

(*The* LAWYER *goes to the table, picks up the apron, laughs.*)

COUNTY ATTORNEY: Oh, I guess they're not very dangerous things the ladies have picked out. (*Moves a few things about, disturbing the quilt pieces which cover the box. Steps back.*) No, Mrs. Peters doesn't need supervising. For that matter, a sheriff's wife is married to the law. Ever think of it that way, Mrs. Peters?

MRS. PETERS: Not—just that way.

SHERIFF (*chuckling*): Married to the law. (*Moves toward the other room.*) I just want you to come in here a minute, George. We ought to take a look at these windows.

COUNTY ATTORNEY (*scoffingly*): Oh, windows!

SHERIFF: We'll be right out, Mr. Hale.

(HALE *goes outside. The* SHERIFF *follows the* COUNTY ATTORNEY *into the other room. Then* MRS. HALE *rises, hands tight together, looking intensely at* MRS. PETERS, *whose eyes make a slow turn, finally meeting* MRS. HALE'S. *For a moment* MRS. HALE *holds her, then her own eyes point the way to where the box is concealed. Suddenly* MRS. PETERS *throws back quilt pieces and tries to put the box in the bag she is wearing. It is too big. She opens box, starts to take bird out, cannot touch it, goes to pieces, stands there helpless. Sound of a knob turning in the other room.* MRS. HALE *snatches the box and puts it in the pocket of her big coat. Enter* COUNTY ATTORNEY *and* SHERIFF.)

> The bond among women will prevent Mrs. Peters and Mrs. Hale from telling the men what they know about John Wright's death.

COUNTY ATTORNEY (*facetiously*): Well, Henry, at least we found out that she was not going to quilt it. She was going to—what is it you call it, ladies?

MRS. HALE (*her hand against her pocket*): We call it—knot it, Mr. Henderson.

---

supervising (SOO pur vyz ing) inspecting with authority
scoffingly (SKOF ing lee) spoken with scorn or contempt
snatches (SNACH iz) grabs suddenly, rudely, or eagerly
facetiously (fuh SEE shus lee) jokingly, especially at an inappropriate time

Review the Selection

UNDERSTAND THE SELECTION

Recall

1. Why had Lewis Hale stopped at the Wright farmhouse?

2. Why did the sheriff and county attorney go upstairs in the farmhouse?

3. What was Mrs. Wright sewing at the time of John Wright's death?

Infer

4. Mrs. Wright is an absent character we learn much about. Describe her.

5. What does John Wright's not wanting a telephone tell you about him?

6. Why does Mrs. Peters tell about the kitten she had as a little girl?

7. Why does Mrs. Hale consider it a crime not to have visited at the Wrights?

Apply

8. How would you investigate John Wright's death differently?

9. Do you think Mrs. Wright will be found guilty of murder?

10. What keeps the story moving?

Respond to Literature

Investigating a crime is a difficult and challenging job. If you were in charge of investigating this crime, what facts would you consider important? Do you think the suspect's emotional state should be considered?

WRITE ABOUT THE SELECTION

Suppose that Mrs. Hale made a neighborly visit to the Wright Farm. Write a conversation that happens between Mrs. Hale and Mrs. Wright before the murder takes place. Include dialogue about how Mrs. Wright feels about her husband.

Prewriting Make a list of topics Mrs. Hale might talk about. Next to each topic on the list, jot down Mrs. Wright's response. Then make another list of things Mrs. Wright might want to discuss. Next to each item, jot down Mrs. Hale's response.

Writing Use your list of topics and responses to create an imaginary two-character scene for the play "Trifles." Your scene should take place before the murder actually happens. Use the play as a model to write the dialogue between Mrs. Hale and Mrs. Wright. Then add whatever stage directions you think are necessary.

Revising Read your scene aloud. Does your dialogue sound as if two women who are neighbors are actually talking to one another? Change any lines that do not sound real.

Proofreading Do not use quotation marks for dialogue in a play; instead, make sure each speech is preceded by the correct character's name followed by a colon. Also, check to see that you have inserted a parenthesis at the beginning and ending of all stage directions.

THINK ABOUT DRAMA

Trifles is much more than a simple "whodunit." In it, the elements of drama—plot, characters, setting, and theme—combine to make a suspenseful and meaningful play. The author has something important to tell us. She delivers her message through the play's conflicts. Who murdered John Wright quickly becomes secondary to why he was murdered.

1. The theme is closely related to the conflict presented in the play. What conflict exists between the five characters who actually appear in this play?

2. A second important conflict involves the play's absent characters. Explain this conflict.

3. Both of the conflicts involve a lack of understanding. Explain who is involved and what he or she did not understand.

4. Do the characters resolve the conflicts by the end of the play?

5. What do you think the author's message is?

DEVELOP YOUR VOCABULARY

Using specific words or phrases appropriate to a certain lifestyle makes a story seem more real. You must know exactly what the words mean, however, to understand fully what the author is talking about.

In *Trifles* many words associated with country or farm life are used. For example, at one point Hale mentions "Harry and the team outside." Harry is his companion outside, and the team is the horses they are using to haul potatoes to town. The dictionary gives this as a second definition for team: "Two or more horses or oxen harnessed to the same vehicle."

Make sure you know the precise definitions of the following words as they are used in *Trifles*. Consult a dictionary if you need help.

1. party telephone
2. stove
3. pleating
4. load of potatoes
5. put up food
6. dipperful
7. roller towel
8. quilt
9. preserves
10. a hollow

Choose five of the above words and use them in an original paragraph.

Learn About

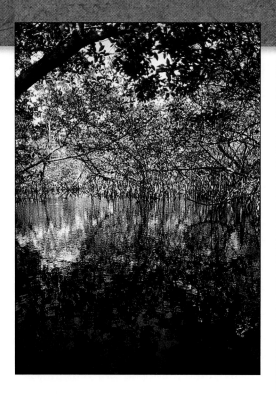

NARRATION

The ability to tell a story has played an important part in human life as long as man has been able to communicate.

At first, stories were told orally. Then with the development of alphabets, stories began to be written down. Even today, however, the oral tradition remains strong in some cultures.

Whether stories are told orally or in writing, narration is the most common form of presenting them. **Narration** is simply the orderly telling of events.

The person doing the telling is the **narrator**. The narrator may be a character within the story. Sometimes the narrator does not take part in the events of the story but reports them from outside. Whether the narrator is inside or outside the action determines the point of view of the story.

As you read the next selection, ask yourself these questions:

1. Who is the narrator?
2. How does narration help organize the telling of the story?

WRITING CONNECTION

Did your parents tell stories to you when you were younger? Do you tell stories to a brother or sister? What is hard about telling a story? Write down three or four ideas.

READING FOCUS

Identify Problems and Solutions Often, a story revolves around one main conflict or problem. In order to solve this problem, characters may need to find solutions to a number of other, smaller problems that help them to overcome the main problem. These problems and solutions in a story are not always clearly defined. Use characters' words and actions to help you identify them.

The Rattlesnake Hunt
from Cross Creek

by Margorie Kinnan Rawlings

I discovered that for me rattlesnakes represented the last outpost of physical fear.

I discovered this when Ross Allen, a young Florida herpetologist, invited me to join him on a hunt in the upper Everglades—for rattlesnakes. . . . Ross and I drove to Arcadia in his coupe on a warm January day.

I said, "How will you bring back the rattlesnakes?"

"In the back of my car."

My courage was not adequate to inquire whether they were thrown in loose and might be expected to appear between our feet. Actually, a large portable box of heavy-meshed wire made a safe cage. Ross wanted me to write an article about his work and on our way to the unhappy hunting grounds I took notes on the mass of data that he had accumulated in his years of herpetological research. . . . As I had discovered with insects and varmints, it is difficult to be afraid of anything about which enough is known, and Ross' facts were fresh from the laboratory.

The hunting ground was Big Prairie, south of Arcadia and west of the northern tip of Lake Okeechobee. Big Prairie is a desolate cattle country, half marsh, half pasture, with islands of palm trees and cypress and oaks. At that time of year the cattlemen and Indians were burning the country, on the theory that the young fresh wire grass that springs up from the roots after a fire is the best cattle forage.

---

herpetologist (hur puh TOL uh jist) someone who studies reptiles and amphibians
everglade (EV ur glayd) a large region of swampland; the Everglades is a region of such land in southern Florida, about 100 miles long and 50 to 75 miles wide
coupe (KOOP) a small, two-door automobile
portable (PAWRT uh bul) capable of being easily carried
meshed (MESHT) made into a net
data (DAYT uh) collected facts
varmints (VAHR munts) animals regarded as troublesome
desolate (DES uh lit) having no people; in a state of ruin
cypress (SY prus) a cone-bearing tree of the pine family
forage (FOR ihj) food eaten by animals

Ross planned to hunt his rattlers in the forefront of the fires. They lived in winter, he said, in gopher holes, coming out in the midday warmth to forage, and would move ahead of the flames and be easily taken. We joined forces with . . . Will, his snake-hunting companion of the territory, and set out in early morning, after a long rough drive over deep-rutted roads into the open wilds.

I hope never in my life to be so frightened as I was in those first few hours. I kept on Ross' footsteps, I moved when he moved, sometimes jolting into him when I thought he might leave me behind. He does not use the forked stick of conventional snake hunting but a steel prong, shaped like an L, at the end of a long stout stick. He hunted casually, calling my attention to the varying vegetation, to hawks overhead, to a pair of the rare whooping cranes that flapped over us. In mid-morning he stopped short, dropped his stick, and brought up a five-foot rattlesnake draped limply over the steel L. It seemed to me that I should drop in my tracks.

"They're not active at this season," he said quietly. "A snake takes on the temperature of its surroundings. They can't stand too much heat for that reason, and when the weather is cool, as now, they're sluggish."

The sun was bright overhead, the sky a translucent blue, and it seemed to me that it was warm enough for any snake to do as it willed. The sweat poured down my back. Ross dropped the rattler in a crocus sack and Will carried it. By noon, he had caught four. I felt faint and ill. We stopped by a pond and went swimming. The region was flat, the horizon limitless, and as I came out of the cool blue water, I expected to find myself surrounded by a ring of rattlers. There were only Ross and Will, opening the lunch basket. I could not eat. . . . Will went back and drove his truck closer, for Ross expected the hunting to be better in the afternoon. The hunting was much better. When we went back to the truck to deposit two more rattlers in the wire cage, there was a rattlesnake lying under the truck.

Ross said, "Whenever I leave my car or truck with snakes already in it, other rattlers always appear. I don't know whether this is because they scent or sense the presence of other snakes, or whether in this arid area they come to the car for shade in the heat of the day."

The problem was scientific, but I had no interest.

---

gopher (GOH fur) a rodent that digs into the ground
companion (kum PAN yun) a friend
jolting (JOHL ting) shaking from sudden jerks
prong (PRAWNG) a sharp-pointed instrument
vegetation (vej uh TAY shun) plant life
sluggish (SLUG ish) lacking energy; slow, inactive
translucent (tranz LOO suhnt) hazy or blurred
crocus sack (KROH kus SAK) a term used in the southern United States for a burlap bag

That night Ross and Will and I camped out in the vast spaces of the Everglades prairies. We got water from an abandoned well and cooked supper under buttonwood bushes by a flowing stream. The camp fire blazed cheerfully under the stars and a new moon lifted in the sky. Will told tall tales of the cattlemen and the Indians, and we were at peace.

Ross said, "We couldn't have a better night for catching water snakes."

After the rattlers, water snakes seemed innocuous enough. We worked along the edge of the stream and here Ross did not use his L-shaped steel. He reached under rocks and along the edge of the water and brought out harmless reptiles with his hands. I had said nothing to him of my fears, but he understood them. He brought a small dark snake from under a willow root.

"Wouldn't you like to hold it?" he asked. "People think snakes are cold and clammy, but they aren't. Take it in your hands. You'll see that it is warm."

Again, because I was ashamed, I took the snake in my hands. It was not cold, it was not clammy, and it lay trustingly in my hands, a thing that lived and breathed like the rest of us. I felt an upsurgence of spirit.

The next day was magnificent. The air was crystal, the sky was aquamarine, and the far horizon of palms and oaks lay against the sky. I felt a new boldness and followed Ross bravely. He was making the rounds of the gopher holes. The rattlers came out in the mid-morning warmth and were never far away. He could tell by their trails whether one had come out or was still in the hole. Sometimes the two men dug the snake out. At times it was down so long and winding a tunnel that the digging was hopeless. Then they blocked the entrance and went on to other holes. In an hour or so they made the original rounds, unblocking the holes. The rattler in every case came out hurriedly, as though anything were preferable to being shut in. All the time Ross talked to me, telling me the scientific facts he had discovered about the habits of the rattlers.

"They pay no attention to a man standing perfectly still," he said, and proved it by letting Will unblock a hole while he stood at the entrance as the snake came out. It was exciting to watch the snake crawl slowly beside and past the man's legs. When it was at a safe distance he walked within its range of vision, which he had proved to be no higher than a man's knee, and the snake whirled and drew back in an attitude of fighting defense. The rattler strikes only for paralyzing and killing its food, and for defense.

"It is a slow and heavy snake," Ross said. "It lies in wait on a small game trail and strikes the rat or rabbit passing by.

---

buttonwood (BUT un wuud) a small sycamore tree
innocuous (ih NAHK yoo uhs) harmless
upsurgence (uhp SER juhns) lifting
aquamarine (AH kwuh muh REEN) blue green
attitude (AT uh tood) in this case, a position or posture of the body
paralyzing (PAR uh lyz ing) losing of power or movement

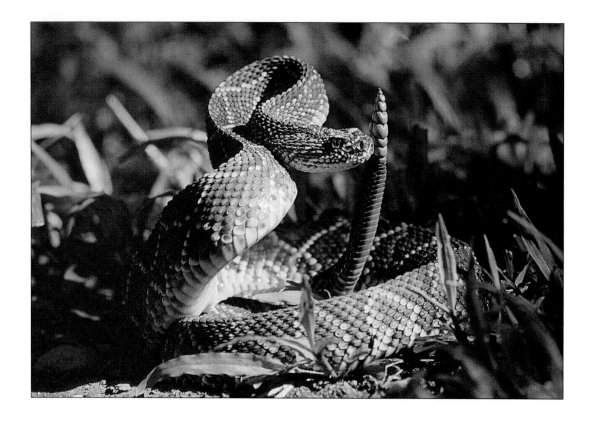

It waits a few minutes, then follows along the trail, coming to the small animal, now dead or dying. It noses it from all sides, making sure that it is dead and ready for swallowing."

A rattler will lie quietly without revealing himself if a man passes by and it thinks it is not seen. It slips away without fighting if given the chance. Only Ross' sharp eyes sometimes picked out the gray and yellow diamond pattern, camouflaged among the grasses. In the cool of the morning, chilled by the January air, the snakes showed no fight. They could be looped up limply over the L and dropped in a sack or up into the wire cage on the back of Will's truck. . . . I went off hunting by myself, and though I found no snakes, I should have known what to do.

The sun was dropping low in the west. Masses of white cloud hung above the flat marshy plain and seemed to be tangled in the tops of distant palms and cypresses. The sky turned orange, then saffron. I walked leisurely back toward the truck. In the distance I could see Ross and Will making their way in too. The season was more advanced than at the Creek, two hundred miles to the north, and I noticed that spring flowers were blooming

---

saffron (SAF run) orange-yellow in color

among the lumpy hummocks. I leaned over to pick a white violet. There was a rattlesnake under the violet.

If this had happened the week before, if it had happened the *day* before, I think I should have lain down and died on top of the rattlesnake, with no need of being struck and poisoned. The snake did not coil, but lifted its head and whirred its rattles lightly. I stepped back slowly and put the violet in a buttonhole. I reached forward and laid the steel L across the snake's neck, just back of the blunt head. I called to Ross:

"I've got one."

He walked toward me.

"Well, pick it up," he said.

I released it and slipped the L under the middle of the thick body.

"Go put it in the box."

He went ahead of me and lifted the top of the wire cage. I made the truck with the rattler, but when I reached up the six feet to drop it in the cage, it slipped off the stick and dropped on Ross' feet. It made no effort to strike.

"Pick it up again," he said. "If you'll pin it down lightly and reach just back of its head with your hand, as you've seen me do, you can drop it in more easily."

I pinned it and leaned over.

"I'm awfully sorry," I said, "but you're pushing me a little too fast."

He grinned. I lifted the snake on the stick and again as I had it at head height, it slipped off, down Ross' boots and on top of his feet. He stood as still as a stump. I dropped the snake on his feet for the third time. It seemed to me that the most patient of rattlers might in time resent being hauled up and down, and for all man's quiet certainty that in standing motionless there was no danger, it would strike at whatever was nearest, and that would be Ross.

I said, "I'm just not man enough to keep this up any longer," and he laughed and reached down with his smooth quickness and lifted the snake back of the head and dropped it in the cage. It slid in among its mates and settled in a corner. The hunt was over and we drove back over the uneven trail to Will's village and left him and went on to Arcadia and home. Our catch for the two days was thirty-two rattlers.

I said to Ross, "I believe that tomorrow I could have picked up that snake."

Back at the Creek, I felt a new lightness. I had done battle with a great fear, and the victory was mine.

---

hummocks (HUM uks) areas of fertile, wooded land, higher than the surrounding swamp
whirred (WHERD) shook, making a buzzing sound
blunt (BLUNT) having a rounded point
resent (rih ZENT) to consider as an insult

Review the Selection

UNDERSTAND THE SELECTION

Recall

1. In what general area of Florida did the rattlesnake hunt take place?

2. What sort of tool does Ross use?

3. Why does a rattler strike?

Infer

4. Why does Ross hunt in January?

5. Describe the narrator's feelings the first few hours of the hunt.

6. What motive does Ross have for hunting water snakes the first night?

7. Why does Ross laugh when, the narrator says, "I'm just not man enough to keep this up any longer"?

Apply

8. How might you react to seeing a snake?

9. The narrator was planning to write an article about Ross Allen's work. Do you think she succeeded in writing an interesting article? Why or why not?

10. The narrator says "it is difficult to be afraid of anything about which enough is known." Do you agree?

Respond to Literature

The narrator overcame her fear of snakes during the snake hunt. How did she do this? Give some examples of fears you have overcome.

WRITE ABOUT THE SELECTION

One of the best ways to practice clear, precise writing is to explain a process to someone. When the process is how to catch a snake, the danger of not explaining things well is real!

Since you are now an authority on rattlesnakes, you have been asked to explain to a scout troop how to catch a rattlesnake.

Prewriting   Identify each step for catching a rattlesnake by scanning "Rattlesnake Hunt" for information. Note the steps explained in the story. As an example, you might write: Step 1, gather equipment and supplies, including a strong cage. Include all steps necessary for success and safety.

Writing   Begin by making a general statement about the process you will describe. Then use your list of steps to write a detailed description of each step in the process.

Revising   Review the information the author gives for hunting snakes, and check to be sure you have not omitted any of her steps. Read your description to someone else. Ask that person to comment about parts that seem unclear. Then revise those parts.

Proofreading   Reread your description to check for errors. Make sure that you have used words correctly and precisely. Change any words that might confuse a reader who is unfamiliar with snake hunting.

THINK ABOUT NARRATION

You have been reading mostly mysteries and detective stories in this unit. "The Rattlesnake Hunt" is a little different. It is a nonfiction narration—reporting true events in their natural order.

1. Who is the narrator? For what purpose did he or she go on the rattlesnake hunt?

2. In what ways does the narrator help to organize the events of the story?

3. Since Ross Allen and his partner are old hands at catching rattlesnakes, the only suspense is created by the narrator's experiences. Which of her experiences provide suspense?

4. Does the narrator take part in the events of the story or report them from outside the action of the story?

5. How might the story have changed if another character had been the narrator?

READING FOCUS

Identify Problems and Solutions What was the main problem the narrator faced? Give two examples of smaller problems she described and the solutions she found.

DEVELOP YOUR VOCABULARY

Ross Allen, the snake hunter in the story, is a herpetologist, a person who studies reptiles and amphibians. The word *herpetologist* includes the suffix *-ist*. A suffix is an addition to the end of a word that forms another related word. The suffix *-ist* means "a person who studies, seeks, makes, or does." For example, an adventurist is a person who seeks adventure. Each word below includes the suffix *-ist*. Tell what each word means. Use a dictionary as needed.

1. scientist
2. geologist
3. phrenologist
4. botanist
5. chemist
6. alchemist
7. journalist
8. physicist
9. philatelist
10. numismatist
11. artist
12. ophthalmologist
13. dentist

Now, use the words in original sentences.

TONE

When people talk, you often can determine how they really feel by listening to their tones. How a person's voice sounds—angry, excited, bored, tired—is sometimes as important as what the person says. What happens when you cannot listen to the person, but instead must read what he or she writes? Does tone still exist? It certainly does. However, you must pay closer attention to discover the tone.

Tone is the writer's attitude toward his or her subject as well as toward the reader. It is expressed indirectly, through the choice of words or the combining of words. Even the construction of a sentence, or punctuation, might hint at how the writer feels.

Look for answers to the following questions as you read the poems:

1. How is tone created?
2. What is the relationship between tone and the theme of the poem?

WRITING CONNECTION

Look in a newspaper or magazine for an advertisement with a catchy slogan. What is the tone of the slogan? How does it fit with the visual message? Report your findings in a paragraph.

READING FOCUS

Evaluate the Author's Style An author's writing style is the manner in which the author makes a point or delivers a message in a story. Often this style is as important as the point being made because it may make an impression on the reader. The style of a story or poem can add to its impact. As you read, pay close attention to the styles of both poems and determine how they add to the poems' message.

EARTH *by John Hall Wheelock*

"A planet doesn't explode of itself," said drily
The Martian astronomer, gazing off into the air—
"That they were able to do it is proof that highly
Intelligent beings must have been living there."

EARTH *by Oliver Herford*

If this little world to-night
    Suddenly should fall through space
In a hissing, headlong flight,
    Shrivelling from off its face,
5 As it falls into the sun,
    In an instant every trace
Of the little crawling things—
    Ants, philosophers, and lice,
Cattle, cockroaches, and kings,
10   Beggars, millionaires, and mice,
Men and maggots all as one
As it falls into the sun—
Who can say but at the same
    Instant from some planet far
15 A child may watch us and exclaim:
    "See the pretty shooting star!"

Martian (MAHR shun) inhabitant of the planet Mars
shrivelling (SHRIV ul ing) shrinking; drying up
lice (LYS) plural of louse, a small insect that lives in the skin and hair of people
cockroaches (KOK rohch is) large black or brown insects that live everywhere
maggots (MAG uts) small wormlike animals that are the young form of flies or other insects

Review the Selection

UNDERSTAND THE SELECTION

Recall

1. Who observes the explosion of Earth in John Hall Wheelock's poem?

2. How is Earth destroyed in Oliver Herford's poem?

3. What does a child on a distant planet think as Earth is being destroyed?

Infer

4. How is Earth destroyed in John Hall Wheelock's poem?

5. Explain the astronomer's attitude as he watches Earth explode.

6. Explain "Men and maggots all as one."

7. What is the theme of the Herford poem?

Apply

8. How is suspense achieved in each poem?

9. What do you think about when you see a shooting star?

10. Have you ever imagined how life on Earth could end? What do you think could be the most likely cause?

Respond to Literature

Both poems suggest that there is intelligent life on other planets. Do you think there is? Why do you think as you do?

WRITE ABOUT THE SELECTION

You are a television news reporter on a distant planet working the night news desk. Suddenly, there is a big explosion in the sky. How would you describe the explosion to your audience? How would you explain what caused it?

Prewriting   You have no film footage, so you must do some quick interviews for your story. Make a list of people you might call for information, such as an astronomer, a military official or an astronaut. Also, you want to locate some eyewitnesses. Imagine what each of these people might tell you. List the information, keeping what each person says separate so you know what information came from what source.

Writing   Organize your information into a news story. Remember, the most important information comes first in a news story, and you should answer the questions: who, what, where, when, and how. You may quote the people you interviewed.

Revising   Since this is a broadcast news story, read your story aloud. Make sure all your information is stated clearly. Ask yourself which parts of your story will create pictures in the listeners' minds. Revise those parts that do not create word pictures. Think of a snappy way to end your story.

Proofreading   Make sure that you correctly pronounce the names and titles of the people you interviewed.

THINK ABOUT TONE

Tone is the way a poet reveals attitudes and feelings. Everything in a poem helps to create tone. You must be a detective in order to discover clues to the way tone is created in a written work.

1. In the first line of Herford's poem, how does the poet indicate his attitude about the importance of the world?

2. How does Herford show his attitude toward living things, including people?

3. Alliteration is often a key to tone. It can be used to show humor, anger, or other feelings. Find an example of alliteration. Identify a feeling the poet is communicating.

4. The attitude of the Martian astronomer in Wheelock's poem could be the poet's attitude, too. What is the attitude about life on the planet in the poem?

5. What is the theme of Wheelock's poem? Does the tone reflect this?

READING FOCUS

Evaluate the Author's Style As you read each poem, you evaluated the style in which the authors delivered their messages. Which poem has a more effective style? How did the style help reveal the poem's message? Why?

DEVELOP YOUR VOCABULARY

A thesaurus can be a useful reference book. If you want to use alliteration, you will find many words with similar initial sounds. You will also find synonyms: words that have the same or similar meanings.

In some thesauruses, you look up the word for which you want a synonym, and the synonyms are listed. In other thesauruses, you look for the word in the index. Following the word is a page number. You then turn to that page to find the word and list of synonyms.

Now that you know how to use a thesaurus, find some synonyms for the word *beggar*. Choose the synonym beginning with *m*. Then find synonyms for the other words listed below. For each numbered word, choose a synonym that starts with the letter indicated.

1. beggar (**m**)
2. philosopher (**i**)
3. proof (**v**)
4. millionaire (**p**)
5. crawling (**c**)
6. exclaim (**s**)

Use each synonym in an original sentence.

King Melchisedech in ceremonial robes,
Flemish tapestry, late 15th century.
Photograph Erich Lessing/Art Resource

READING FOCUS

Make Judgments You can make judgments about a story based on your opinion of the setting, plot, characters, style, or theme of the story. As you read, use the information you gather to make judgments and express opinions about the story. Always support your judgments with details from the story.

IRONY

In Wheelock's poem about Earth exploding, he says, "Intelligent beings must have been living there." It seems like he is complimenting humans, but this is not so. He is really questioning how intelligent a species could be if it blows itself up.

When a writer means the opposite of what he or she actually says, the writer is using irony. **Irony** is a way to call attention to an idea by deliberately saying the opposite.

In literature, characters, settings, and plots can all have ironic features. The farmhouse setting in *Trifles* is in some ways ironic. Rural settings are usually considered peaceful. Farms are places for nurturing plant and animal life. The farmhouse setting in *Trifles* is instead a place of death.

As you read further ask yourself:
1. What is ironic about the king?
2. What is ironic about his justice?

WRITING CONNECTION

Irony is often used in jokes. What we expect to happen does not. Think of examples. Write them down. Then you and a partner create a short routine of ironic comedy to present to the class.

THE LADY OR THE TIGER?

ADAPTED

by Frank R. Stockton

In the very olden time, there once lived a semi-barbaric king. His ideas, though somewhat polished and sharpened by the more civilized ways of distant neighbors, were still raw, savage and reckless, as became the half of him that was still barbaric. He was a man of wild imagination, and his word was law. Whenever he wished, his varied fancies became facts. He was greatly given to self-questioning, and when he and himself agreed upon anything, that thing was done. When everything in his kingdom moved smoothly, his manner was happy and genial; but whenever there was a little trouble, he was happier and more genial still. For nothing pleased him so much as to make the crooked straight, and crush down uneven places.

Among the borrowed ideas by which his barbarism had become softened was that of the public arena. In his arena, both men and beasts displayed their courage.

These displays, the king thought, uplifted the minds of his people.

But even here the wild imagination expressed itself. The arena of the king was not built to let his people watch men fight each other with sword and shield. It was not built to settle arguments between religious opinions and hungry jaws. No, its purpose was far better filled to uplifting the minds of the people. The huge arena, with its many rows of seats, its unseen passages, was a hall of justice. There crime was punished. There goodness was rewarded. There justice was decided by the completely fair and unprejudiced Law of Chance.

The system was simple. First a person had to be accused of a crime of enough importance to interest the king. Then public notice was given that on a certain day the accused man would appear in the king's arena. When the people of the city had gathered, the king entered.

semi- (SEM ih *or* SEM ee) prefix meaning half
barbaric (bahr BAR ik) wild and cruel; not yet civilized
fancies (FAN seez) notions or ideas, usually pleasant
genial (JEEN yul) pleasant; good-natured

Surrounded by his family and servants, he sat on a throne high up on one side of the arena. Suddenly he gave a signal. A door far beneath him opened, and the accused person stepped out.

Right across from the man on trial were two doors, exactly alike and side by side. It was the duty and the privilege of the person on trial to walk straight to the doors and open one of them. He could open either door he pleased. He was given no help but that of the Law of Chance. If he opened the one, there came out of it a hungry tiger, the wildest and most cruel that could be found. The tiger immediately sprang upon him and tore him to pieces, as punishment for his guilt. The moment that the case of the criminal was so decided, doleful iron bells were rung. Great sighs went up, and the people left the arena with bowed heads and broken hearts. Why did one so young and handsome, or so old and well known, deserve so horrible an end?

But if the accused person opened the other door, there came out of it a lady, always well fitted to the man's age and place in life. In fact, she was always the most perfect wife that his majesty's servants could find among his fair subjects. And to this lady the man was immediately married, as a reward for his innocence. It mattered not that he might already have a wife and family, nor that he might be engaged to a woman of his own choice. The king allowed no such details to interfere with his grand ideas about punishment and reward. The wedding took place right away, and in the arena. Another door opened beneath the king, and a priest followed by dancing maidens and a group of singers, advanced to where the pair stood side by side. The wedding was short and joyful. Then the happy brass bells rang out, the people cheered and cheered, and the innocent man, following children throwing flowers in his path, led his bride to his home.

This was the king's semi-barbaric method of handing out justice. Its perfect fairness is clear. The criminal could not know out of which doorway would come the lady. He opened either door he pleased. He had not the slightest idea whether, in the next instant, he was to be devoured or married. Sometimes the tiger came out of one door, sometimes out of the other. The king's justice was not only fair, but also fast. The accused person was instantly punished if he found himself guilty. And if innocent, he was rewarded on the spot, whether he liked it or not. There was no escape from the judgments of the king's arena.

The system was a very popular one. The people never knew whether they were to witness a bloody slaughter or a joyous wedding. There was just no way they could know. This gave an interest to the event which it could not otherwise have had. Thus the masses were entertained and pleased. And even the thinking persons in the community could find no reason to say that the plan was unfair.

---

doleful (DOHL ful) sorrowful
fair (FAIR) nice looking
subject (SUB jehkt) person under authority of a king or government

Tiger, Edward J. Detmold. The Metropolitan Museum of Art, The Elisha Whittelsey Collection

For did not the accused person have the whole matter in his own hands?

This semi-barbaric king had a daughter as blooming as his own lively imagination and with a soul as fiery and as proud as his own. As is usual in such cases, she was the apple of his eye, and was loved by him above all others. And her love? Well . . . among the king's servants was a handsome young man of that fineness of blood and lowness of station common to story-book heroes who love royal maidens.

This royal maiden was well satisfied with her lover. He was better looking and braver than anyone else in all the kingdom, and her love for him had enough of barbarism in it to make it very warm, and very, very strong. The love affair moved on happily for many months, until, one day, the king happened to learn of it. He did not waste an instant! He knew his duty in the matter at once. The youth was immediately put into prison, and a day was set for his trial in the king's arena.

This, of course, was an especially important happening in the kingdom. His majesty, as well as all the people, was greatly interested in the preparation for the trial. Never before had such a case occurred—never before had a subject dared to love the daughter of the king!

The tiger cages of the kingdom were searched for the most savage and relentless of beasts, from which the fiercest monster was to be chosen for the arena. And a search was also made among the ranks of maiden youth and beauty throughout the land. The young man was to have a fitting bride, if bride it was to be. Of course, everyone knew that the act of the accused man had, in fact, been done. He had loved the princess, and neither he, she, nor anyone in the kingdom thought of saying anything else. But the king would not think of letting any fact of this kind interfere with the tribunal, in which he took such great delight and satisfaction. No matter how it turned out, the youth's future would be decided. The king was especially interested in finding out whether the young man had done wrong in allowing himself to love the princess.

The day arrived. From far and near the people gathered, and they soon filled the great arena. Outside, more huge crowds, unable to get in, stood against the walls. The king was in his place, opposite the twin portals—so horrible in their likeness to each other!

All was ready. The signal was given. A door beneath the king opened, and the lover of the princess walked into the arena. Tall and handsome, he was greeted with a low hum of wonder and worry. Half the people had not known that such a youth had lived among them. No wonder the princess loved him! What a terrible thing for him to be there!

---

station (STAY shun) place in life
relentless (rih LENT lis) without pity; harsh and cruel
tribunal (try BYOO nul) court of justice
portals (PAWRT ulz) doors; entrances

As the youth advanced into the arena, he stopped to turn, as the custom was, and bow to the king. But he did not think at all of that royal person. His eyes were fixed on the princess, who sat to the right of her father. Had it not been for the barbaric half of her soul, the lady probably would not have been there. But her strong spirit would not allow her to be absent from an event in which she was terribly interested. From the very moment of the king's order, she had thought of nothing else, night or day. She knew only that her lover's future was to be decided in the king's arena. Having more power and determination than anyone who had ever before been interested in such a case, she had done what no other person had done. She had learned the secret of the doors. She knew about the two little rooms across the arena from them. She knew in which stood the tiger, and in which waited the lady. Gold and power had brought that secret to the princess.

Not only did she know in which room stood the lady, ready to come out, all blushing and radiant, should her door be opened, but she also knew who the lady was. It was one of the most beautiful and lively maidens of the palace—and the princess hated her. Often she had seen, or imagined she had seen, things she didn't like. The lovely girl would throw glances of delight upon her lover, and sometimes, she thought, they had even been returned. Now and then she had seen them talking together. It was only for a moment or two,

but much can be said in a brief time. And what had they talked about? Something unimportant, probably. But how could she know that? The girl was lovely, but she had dared to raise her eyes to the loved one of the princess. With all the strength of the savage blood of her barbaric ancestors, the princess hated the woman who blushed and trembled behind that silent door.

And now, the man in the arena had turned to took at her. She sat there paler and whiter than anyone else in the sea of worried faces around her. His eye met hers. At once he saw, by that power of quick perception given only to those whose souls are one, that she knew! She knew behind which door waited the tiger, and behind which stood the lady. He had expected her to know it. He understood her perfectly. He knew that she would never rest until she had discovered this secret, hidden to all others, even to the king. The only sure hope for the youth was the success the princess had in solving this mystery, and the moment he looked upon her, he knew she had succeeded.

Then it was that his quick and anxious glance asked the question, "Which?" It was as plain to her as if he shouted it from where he stood. There was not an instant to be lost. The question was asked in a flash; it must be answered in another.

Her right arm lay on the cushioned wall before her. She raised her hand, and made a slight, quick movement to the right. No one but her lover saw it. Every eye but his was fixed on the man in the arena.

---

perception (pur SEP shun) awareness; understanding

He turned, and with a rapid step he walked across the empty space. Every heart stopped beating. Every breath was held. Every eye was fixed as if frozen upon that man. Without the slightest pause, he went to the door on the right, and opened it.

Now, the point of the story is this: Did the tiger come out of that door, or did the lady?

The more we reflect upon that question, the harder it is to answer. It involves a study of the human heart. It leads us into a wild jungle of love and hate, out of which it is difficult to find our way. Think of it, fair reader, not as a question that you yourself had to answer. No, the answer involves that hot-blooded, semi-barbaric princess. Think of her soul, at white heat in the combined fires of despair and jealousy. She had lost him, but who should have him?

How often, in her daylight hours and in her dreams, had she thought of her lover opening the door to find the cruel teeth of the tiger? How often had that thought made her tremble in horror and cover her face with her hands?

But how much oftener had she seen him at the other door! To think of his surprised delight as he opened the door of the lady! How her soul had burned! How she had torn her hair when she had seen him rush to meet that woman, with her flashing cheek and sparkling eye! When she had seen him lead her from the door! When she had heard the glad shouts from the crowd! When she had

seen the priest, with his happy followers, advance to make them husband and wife! When she had seen them walk away upon their path of flowers, followed by the tremendous cheers of the people, in which her own shriek of despair was lost and drowned!

---

reflect (rih FLEKT) think

Would it not be better for him to die at once? Would it not be better to think of him waiting for her in some semi-barbaric heaven?

And yet, that awful tiger! Those shrieks! That blood!

The slight wave of her right hand had taken just an instant. But the motion had been made after days and nights of agonizing thought. She had known she would be asked, she had decided what she would answer, and without the slightest pause, she had moved her hand to the right.

The question of her decision is not one to be taken lightly, and it is not for me to set myself up as the one person who can answer it. So I leave it with all of you: Which came out of the opened door—the lady, or the tiger?

Review the Selection

UNDERSTAND THE SELECTION

Recall

1. What law governed the proceedings in the arena?

2. What happened to a person who chose the door that revealed a lady?

3. Which door did the daughter's lover choose?

Infer

4. Explain how the king achieved justice.

5. Why did the king disapprove of the young man chosen by his daughter?

6. Is the Law of Chance being observed in the case of the daughter's lover?

7. Explain the significance of the title.

Apply

8. Is justice really being done in the king's "hall of justice"? Explain your answer.

9. Was the lady or the tiger behind the right door? Why do you think so?

10. What is a basic flaw with the king's system of justice?

Respond to Literature

Think about whether the king will achieve his goal in this story. What will happen if the open door reveals the tiger? What will happen if the open door reveals the lady?

WRITE ABOUT THE SELECTION

Which will it be: the lady or the tiger? Frank Stockton has given you a rather unusual opportunity. He has provided the setting, theme, and characters of a story, and most of the plot. He has left you hanging right before the climax. Now it is up to you to provide an ending.

Prewriting The last section of "The Lady or the Tiger?" has questions to help you decide what will be revealed behind the right door. Reread it. Then choose the lady or the tiger as the basis for an ending. Make an informal plot outline including what happens, as well as the reactions of the princess, the lover, the king, and the crowd.

Writing Use your informal outline to write a conclusion for the story. The length is up to you, but there must be resolution of the questions raised by the story. Imitate Frank Stockton's style as you write your narration.

Revising Reread parts of the story, and analyze what makes Frank Stockton's style distinctive. Revise or make additions to your conclusion to make your writing sound as though Stockton himself has written it. Use questions, as he does, for suspense.

Proofreading Reread your conclusion to check for errors. Pay close attention to end punctuation. Stockton uses many question marks and exclamation points, as well as periods. Make sure you know when to use each.

THINK ABOUT IRONY

Answer the questions below about irony in "The Lady or the Tiger?".

1. What is ironic about this description of the king: ". . . his manner was happy and genial; but whenever there was a little trouble, he was happier and more genial still"?

2. Stockton says about the king's system of justice, "Its perfect fairness is clear." What is ironic about this?

3. "The king was especially interested in finding out whether the young man had done wrong in allowing himself to love the princess." Explain the irony in this statement.

4. "The king's justice was not only fair, but also fast." Given the way the story ends, what is ironic about this?

5. In some stories the reader knows something the characters do not. Is this true for "The Lady or the Tiger?"? Explain how this feature of the story is an example of irony.

READING FOCUS

Make Judgments As you read, you were able to make judgments about the characters, plot, setting, and theme of the story. Choose one of these story elements, and tell why you think it was especially interesting.

DEVELOP YOUR VOCABULARY

Prefixes and suffixes allow you to make additions to a root word to create new words with related meanings. Frank Stockton uses three related words from one base:

semi-barbaric   barbaric   barbarism

If you are familiar with the meaning of the base word and can identify and define the prefixes and suffixes, you can figure out the meaning of each of the following words.

Identify the bases and suffixes or prefixes of the following italicized words. Explain the meaning of the bases and the suffixes or prefixes. Use a dictionary as needed.

1. *Doleful* iron bells were rung.

2. The king was in his place, opposite the twin *portals*.

3. Gold and power had brought that secret to the *princess*.

4. The power of quick *perception* is only given to those whose souls are one.

5. Without the *slightest* pause, she moved her hand to the right.

Learn About

WORD MEANING

When you look for a word in a dictionary you find a specific meaning. Words communicate feelings and attitudes as well as specific meanings. For example, you might describe something as *cheap*, meaning that it is low in price. However, some people have an attitude of contempt about things that are cheap. They look down upon them. Therefore, the word *cheap* also carries a feeling of being of lesser value.

The actual meaning of a word is called **denotation**. The feeling or attitude associated with a word is **connotation**.

Poets choose their words carefully. They use connotation as well as denotation to create tone and emotional impact.

Look for answers to the following questions as you read the poems:
1. What words suggest other meanings in addition to their literal definitions?
2. What feelings do you associate with each word you identified?

WRITING CONNECTION

Think of a word that provokes a strong feeling or attitude. Use a dictionary to find its specific meaning. Then write two sentences showing the denotation and connotation of the same word.

READING FOCUS

Evaluate Facts Stories and poetry often contain factual information about their subjects. An author may use different sources to gather facts, depending upon the subject and purpose of the writing. As you read the two poems in this selection, look for facts. Think about how these facts enhance the poems.

Displays of Skill:
The Bat

by Ruth Herschberger

Being a mammal, I have less care than birds,
Being a flight-borne creature, need no home,
So while the beaver builds its dam, robin its nest,
I hook my hind feet into a wall or ceiling
5   And hang there looking at the world made silly
By being turned around and upside-down.
Sleep, sleep is my nourishment, I sleep
All day, all winter, and my young's but one.
At first I fly with it at my breast, even hunting,
10   But if it bores me I hang it on a wall
And go alone, enjoying insects frankly.
Tons, tons, I devour tons of insects, half
Of my weight is insects eaten within one night,
Yet cleverer than the swift or swallow, I deploy
15   Twist, turn, dodge, catch mosquitoes one by one.
And if the human family finds me odd,
No odder they, locked in their crazy yards.

---

mammal (MAM ul) a member of the highest class of vertebrate animals, including man
flight-borne (FLYT bawrn) able to fly
nourishment (NUR ish munt) food
swift (SWIFT) in this case, a bird of extreme speed in flight
deploy (dih PLOI) spread out systematically over an area

Los Caprichos: El suena de la razon produce monstruos (The Sleep of Reason Produces Monsters), Francisco de Goya. National Gallery of Art, Washington, DC, Rosenwald Collection

The Bird of Night

by Randall Jarrell

A shadow is floating through the moonlight.
Its wings don't make a sound.
Its claws are long, its beak is bright.
Its eyes try all the corners of the night.

5   It calls and calls: all the air swells and heaves
And washes up and down like water.
The ear that listens to the owl believes
In death. The bat beneath the eaves,

The mouse beside the stone are still as death—
10   The owl's air washes them like water.
The owl goes back and forth inside the night,
And the night holds its breath.

---

swells (SWELZ) increases in size, volume, or force
heaves (HEEVZ) lifts up with effort
eaves (EEVZ) lower edges of a roof, especially that part sticking out over the walls of the building

Review the Selection

UNDERSTAND THE SELECTION

Recall

1. What kind of an animal is a bat?

2. Where does a mother bat put her baby if she wants to go hunting alone?

3. What do animals listening to the owl believe or fear?

Infer

4. Why does the bat say it needs no home?

5. Describe what a bat hunting mosquitoes looks like.

6. Describe an owl flying.

7. What are some of the animals an owl preys upon?

Apply

8. "Displays of Skill: The Bat" contains a lot of information about this much-despised animal. What new things did you learn about bats?

9. If a bat weighs about 4 ounces, how many ounces of insects would it eat in one night?

10. Why do you think owls are thought to be wise?

Respond to Literature

In what ways do bats and owls help create suspense? Give examples.

WRITE ABOUT THE SELECTION

"Displays of Skill: The Bat" is written in a first-person point of view, but "The Bird of Night" is written in a third-person point of view.

The tone of each poem is very different. Could that be because of the different point of view in which each is written?

See if you can find out by writing in the first person about owls. Plan to write poetry. You may either adapt "The Bird of Night" to a poem written in the first person, or you may write a new poem.

Prewriting Decide if you will adapt Jarrell's poem or write your own. If you are adapting, circle all the words in Jarrell's poem you will have to change. If you are writing your own poem, make a cluster of words about the owl that you may want to use.

Writing Use either the circled poem or your cluster to write a first-person poem on owls. Remember that information must be presented from the owl's point of view. You may want to consult a reference book to learn more about the owl's habitat.

Revising When you revise your poem, think about adding words with connotations that fit the meaning and feeling you want. Use a thesaurus as needed.

Proofreading Reread your poem to check for errors. Decide where to break lines, where to indent, and whether you want to use end-of-line punctuation. Mark your copy accordingly.

THINK ABOUT WORD MEANING

Poets rely on connotations of words when they use figurative language in their poems. Below are examples from the previous poems.

1. In "The Bird of Night," a simile is used in the second stanza. What is being compared to water? How is the word *swells* connected to water? What feeling or image does the word *swells* connote?

2. What other words in the poem also have a connection to or a connotation involving water?

3. Another simile is used to describe the bat and mouse as the owl floats through the night. What is it?

4. Hyperbole is used in "Displays of Skill: The Bat." Where? What feelings or connotations are associated with this exaggeration?

5. What word fits particularly well with the hyperbole?

6. List five other words with connotations that add to both poems' effectiveness.

READING FOCUS

Evaluate Facts What facts did the author of "Displays of Skill: The Bat" include in her poem? What facts did the author of "The Bird of Night" use? How do these facts enhance the poems?

DEVELOP YOUR VOCABULARY

Knowing the connotation of a certain word requires that you know the denotations of the word as well.

Examine the word *swells*, for example, from "The Bird of Night." Why did the poet use *swells* instead of *expands*? They both mean "to increase in size."

Swell is often used to describe waves at sea. The connotation of *swell* is appropriate for comparing air to water.

Below are other words used in the two poems. Each is paired with a synonym the way *swells* was paired with *expands*. Decide why the poet chose to use the word he did. Write the denotation for each. Then identify the connotation of each word. Be ready to explain why the connotation is appropriate for the poem in which the word is used.

1. floating/flying
2. bright/colorful
3. heaves/moves
4. hook/attach
5. devour/eat
6. deploy/move

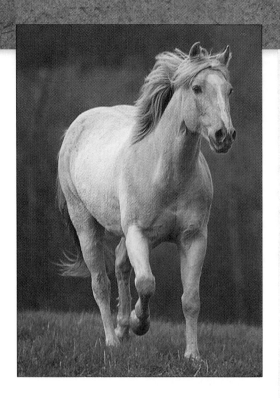

PLOT

The most important element of many stories, dramas included, is **plot**. Such stories depend upon action for their developments. Characters and settings are important, and so are the themes, but the energy of the plot moves the story forward.

You should be familiar with the basic pattern of plots. First, there is **exposition**, or background information. Then a **complication** develops, raising a question or several questions that must be answered during the remainder of the story. The **action rises**, and the **climax** is reached. The **action falls**, and any questions not answered in the climax are answered in the **resolution**.

As you read the selection, ask yourself these questions:

1. What are the main complications or questions in the plot?
2. How is each complication resolved or question answered?

READING FOCUS

Make Inferences An author does not always directly state information about characters, setting, or plot. Usually, the author is more indirect, using dialogue and descriptive detail to give information. It is up to the reader to infer or guess about characters and events in the story. As you read, try to make inferences about the plot and characters using clues from the story.

WRITING CONNECTION

In a few sentences explain the plot of any story you have read in this unit. Describe the major points of the plot, identifying necessary background information, all important complications, the climax, and the resolution.

A SECRET FOR TWO

ADAPTED   *by Quentin Reynolds*

Montreal is a very large city. But, like all large cities, it has some very small streets. Streets, for instance, like Prince Edward Street, which is only four blocks long. No one knew Prince Edward Street as well as did Pierre Dupin. For Pierre had delivered milk to the families on the street for thirty years now.

During the past fifteen years, the horse that drew the milk wagon used by Pierre was a large white horse named Joseph. In Montreal, especially in that part of Montreal that is very French, the animals, like children, are often given the names of saints. When the big white horse first came to the Provincale Milk Company, he didn't have a name. They told Pierre that he could use the white horse. Pierre stroked the softness of the horse's neck. He stroked the sheen of its splendid belly, and he looked into the eyes of the horse.

"This is a kind horse, a gentle and faithful horse," Pierre said. "I can see a beautiful spirit shining out of the eyes of the horse. I will name him after good St. Joseph, who was also kind and gentle and faithful and a beautiful spirit."

Within a year, Joseph knew the milk route as well as Pierre. Pierre used to boast that he didn't need reins—he never touched them. Each morning Pierre arrived at the stables of the Provincale Milk Company at five o'clock. The wagon would be loaded and Joseph hitched to it. Pierre would call, *"Bonjour, vieil ami,"* as he climbed into his seat. Joseph would turn his head, and the other drivers would smile and say that the horse would smile at Pierre. Then Jacques, the foreman, would say, "All right, Pierre, go on."

Montreal (mon tree AWL) city in eastern Canada that has French as its official language
sheen (SHEEN) brightness; shininess

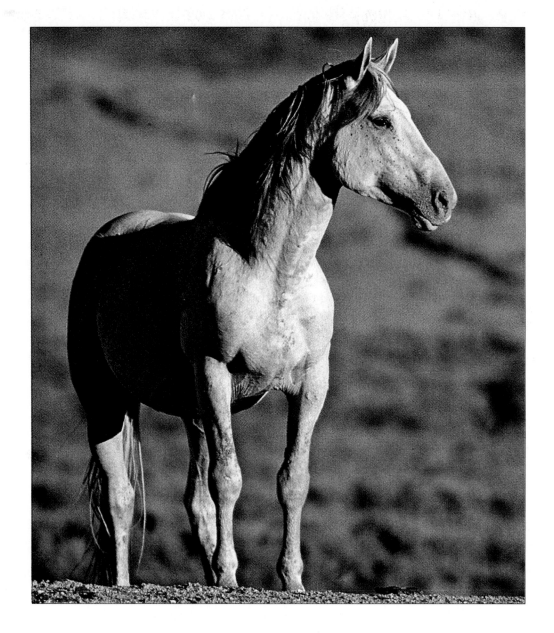

Pierre would call softly to Joseph, "*Avance, mon ami.*" And this splendid combination would stalk proudly down the street.

The wagon, without any direction from Pierre, would roll three blocks down St. Catherine Street, then turn right two blocks along Roslyn Avenue; then left, for that was Prince Edward Street. The horse would stop at the first house, allow Pierre perhaps

---

stalk (STAWK) walk in a stiff, proud way

thirty seconds to get down from his seat and put a bottle of milk at the front door, and would then go on, skipping two houses and stopping at the third. So down the length of the street. Then Joseph, still without any direction from Pierre, would turn around and come back along the other side. Yes, Joseph was a smart horse.

Pierre would boast, at the stable, of Joseph's skill. "I never touch the reins. He knows just where to stop. Why, a blind man could handle my route with Joseph pulling the wagon."

So it went on for years—always the same. Pierre and Joseph both grew old together, but gradually, not suddenly. Pierre's huge walrus mustache was pure white now. Joseph didn't lift his knees so high, or raise his head quite as much. Jacques, the foreman of the stables, never noticed that they were both getting old until Pierre appeared one morning carrying a heavy walking stick.

"Hey, Pierre," Jacques laughed. "Maybe you got the gout, hey?"

"*Mais oui, Jacques,*" Pierre said a bit uncertainly. "One grows old. One's legs get tired."

"You should teach that horse to carry the milk to the front door for you," Jacques told him. "He does everything else."

He knew every one of the forty families he served on Prince Edward Street. The cooks knew that Pierre could neither read nor write. So instead of following the usual custom of leaving a note in an empty bottle if an additional quart of milk was needed, they would sing out when they heard the rumble of his wagon wheels over the cobbled street, "Bring an extra quart this morning, Pierre."

"So you have company for dinner tonight," he would call back gaily.

Pierre had a remarkable memory. When he arrived at the stable, he'd always remember to tell Jacques, "The Paquins took an extra quart this morning. The Lemoines bought a pint of cream."

Jacques would note these things in a little book he always carried. Most of the drivers had to make out the weekly bills and

---

gout (GOUT) painful disease of the joints, usually of the feet and the hands

cobbled (KOB uld) paved with stones, usually referring to a street (when used as an adjective) collect the money. But Jacques, liking Pierre, had always excused him from this task. All Pierre had to do was to arrive at five in the morning, walk to his wagon, which was always in the same spot at the curb, and deliver his milk. He returned some two hours later, got down stiffly from his seat, called a cheery *"Au'voir"* to Jacques, and then limped slowly down the street.

One morning the president of the Provincale Milk Company came to inspect the early morning deliveries. Jacques pointed Pierre out to him and said, "Watch how he talks to that horse. See how the horse listens and how he turns his head toward Pierre? See the look in that horse's eyes? You know, I think those two share a secret. I have often noticed it. It is as though they both sometimes chuckle at us as they go off on their route. Pierre is a good man, Monsieur Président, but he gets old. Would it be too bold of me to suggest that he be retired and be given perhaps a small pension?" he added anxiously.

"But of course," the president laughed. "I know his record. He has been on this route now for thirty years and never once has there been a complaint. Tell him it is time he rested. His salary will go on just the same."

But Pierre refused to retire. He was panic-stricken at the thought of not driving Joseph every day. "We are two old men," he said to Jacques. "Let us wear out together. When Joseph is ready to retire—then I, too, will quit."

Jacques, who was a kind man, understood. There was something about Pierre and Joseph that made a man smile tenderly. It was as though each drew some hidden strength from the other. When Pierre was sitting in his seat, and when Joseph was hitched to the wagon, neither seemed old. But when they finished their work, then Pierre would limp down the street slowly, seeming very old indeed. The horse's head would drop, and he would walk very wearily to his stall.

Then one morning Jacques had dreadful news for Pierre when he arrived. It was a cold morning and still pitch-dark. The air was iced that morning. And the snow that had fallen during the night glistened like a million diamonds piled together.

Monsieur (muh SYUR) French for Mister
pension (PEN shun) retirement pay

Jacques said, "Pierre, your horse, Joseph, did not wake up this morning. He was very old, Pierre. He was twenty-five, and that is like being seventy-five for a man."

"Yes," Pierre said, slowly. "Yes. I am seventy-five. And I cannot see Joseph again."

"Of course you can," Jacques soothed. "He is over in his stall, looking very peaceful. Go over and see him."

Pierre took one step forward, then turned. "No . . . no . . . you don't understand, Jacques."

Jacques clapped him on the shoulder. "We'll find another horse just as good as Joseph. Why, in a month you'll teach him to know your route as well as Joseph did. We'll . . ."

The look in Pierre's eyes stopped him. For years Pierre had worn a heavy cap. The peak came low over his eyes, keeping the bitter morning wind out of them. Now Jacques looked into Pierre's eyes, and saw something that startled him. He saw a dead, lifeless look in them. The eyes were mirroring the grief that was in Pierre's heart and his soul. It was as though his heart and soul had died.

"Take today off, Pierre," Jacques said. But already Pierre was hobbling off down the street; and had one been near, one would have seen tears streaming down his cheeks and have heard half-smothered sobs. There was a warning yell from the driver of a huge truck that was coming fast. There was the scream of brakes. But Pierre apparently heard neither.

Five minutes later an ambulance driver said, "He's dead. Was killed instantly."

"I couldn't help it," the driver of the truck protested. "He walked right into my truck. He never saw it, I guess. Why, he walked into it as though he were blind."

The ambulance doctor bent down. "Blind? Of course the man was blind. See those cataracts? This man has been blind for five years." He turned to Jacques. "You say he worked for you? Didn't you know he was blind?"

"No . . . no . . . " Jacques said softly. "None of us knew. Only one knew—a friend of his named Joseph. . . . It was a secret, I think, just between those two."

---

peak (PEEK) front part of a cap
cataract (KAT uh rakt) clouding of the eye's lens that can cause blindness

Review the Selection

UNDERSTAND THE SELECTION

Recall

1. In what city is "A Secret for Two" set?

2. How do Pierre's customers order extra milk?

3. How long had Pierre worked for the Provincale Milk Company?

Infer

4. How do you know that Pierre is not blind at the beginning of the story?

5. Give an example showing that Pierre has a good relationship with his boss.

6. Find an example of foreshadowing.

7. What was Jacques's reaction when he learned that Pierre had been blind for five years?

Apply

8. Do you think Pierre was happy with his life? Why or why not?

9. Do you think it is possible for someone to be blind without others knowing about it?

10. This unit has as its theme "suspense." Is "A Secret for Two" a suspense story? Explain your answer.

Respond to Literature

Why do foreign cities make especially good settings for stories?

WRITE ABOUT THE SELECTION

A **eulogy** is a speech or piece of writing praising someone who has died. What might be said to eulogize Pierre Dupin? On the surface, he was a simple man. He could not read or write. However, inside, he must have been patient, strong, and trusting, as well as dedicated.

Imagine you are speaking at Pierre Dupin's funeral delivering the eulogy.

Prewriting   Start by thinking of an epitaph you could write for Pierre's tombstone. (An epitaph is an inscription on a headstone in memory of the person buried there.) The epitaph will serve as an outline for writing a longer, more complete eulogy. List qualities that you admire which were exhibited by Pierre Dupin in the story.

Writing   Write the eulogy based on the epitaph you wrote and the list of qualities you compiled. Expand on any ideas you have mentioned, and add new ones.

Revising   As you revise the eulogy, think back on the information about Pierre given in the story. Are there any traits or characteristics you have neglected to mention? Add them. Make sure you have provided examples from the story for each of the traits mentioned.

Proofreading   Reread your eulogy and check for errors. Make sure that all verbs agree with their subjects. Check to see that verb tenses are consistent. If you begin speaking of Pierre in past tense, make sure all verbs are past tense.

THINK ABOUT PLOT

The **plot**, or the action of a story, is based on conflicting human motivations and responses. To develop a plot successfully, the sequence of events must include human motivations. For instance, some motivations in "The Lady or the Tiger?" are jealousy, protectiveness, and love. In the story "A Secret for Two," human motivations are a major element of the plot. However, other literary elements also affect the plot.

1. The plot of this story requires a certain kind of character. What kind of person is Pierre? What does he value? What motivates his behavior?

2. The plot also requires a certain kind of setting. What characteristics of the neighborhood in Montreal where Pierre works are important to the plot?

3. What complications develop in the story?

4. What is the climax of the story?

5. How does Pierre's boss, Jacques, affect the plot of "A Secret for Two"?

6. What is the conflict in the story? How does this conflict affect the plot?

READING FOCUS

Make Inferences As you read, you were able to make inferences about the characters and plot in the story. What clues allowed you to infer that Pierre was losing his sight?

DEVELOP YOUR VOCABULARY

Using context clues can sometimes help in understanding the meaning of foreign words and expressions. Follow these steps to use context clues:

a. Reread the sentence in which the foreign word or phrase appears; also reread the sentences before and after.

b. Substitute words that you think are similar to the English words.

c. If the English words make sense, your choice of meaning is probably accurate.

Use context clues to discover the meaning of the French phrases from "A Secret for Two." Copy the sentences substituting an English meaning for each French phrase.

1. Pierre would call, "*Bonjour, vieil ami,*" as he climbed into his seat.

2. Pierre would call softly to Joseph, "*Avance, mon ami.*"

3. "*Mais oui, Jacques,*" Pierre said a bit uncertainly.

4. He returned some two hours later, got down stiffly from his seat, and called a cheery "*Au'voir*" to Jacques.

5. Pierre is a good man, *Monsieur* President, but he gets old.

WRITING APPLICATIONS

Write About Theme

In this unit, you have been introduced to some interesting characters who have been involved in some exciting situations. Two stories were dramas, so you have studied the elements of drama. Why not put your knowledge of drama to work?

Write an original play, using any of the characters from any of the selections in this unit. Make the play suspenseful. After all, suspense is what these characters are accustomed to!

Prewriting   Choose the characters you would like to use in your play. List them. Then think of a plot. Map the plot, with each major development in a box. Write some ideas on the map about how the dialogue or the stage directions will advance the plot.

Writing   Use the plot map, your list of characters, and your notes about the dialogue and stage directions to write the play.

Revising   Make sure you have paced the action of the play. Review the steps in plot development, and check to see that you have followed them.

Proofreading   Reread your play to check for errors. Make any changes you feel are necessary.

Write About Genre

The elements of drama are the same as those for all stories, with added emphasis on the conflict. Conflicts in dramas are usually between human characters. The conflict is caused by a clash between their personalities, traits, or beliefs. How the characters struggle with one another is a very important part of the drama.

Take a closer look at the conflict in one of the dramas you have read.

Prewriting   Review the work you did for the "Thinking About" sections. Then choose the drama that most interests you. Make a chart, listing the conflict and the characters involved. Under each character's name, write all of the traits important to the conflict.

Writing   Use the chart to write a description of the conflict. Then analyze the role of the conflict in the drama. How does it relate to other elements, particularly theme?

Revising   When you are revising, think of ways to use material from the drama itself to illustrate what you are saying. For example, can you quote something a character says to illustrate a point?

Proofreading   Reread what you have written as a check for errors. Try to vary the structure of sentences. If too many sentences are constructed in the same way, the reader could become bored.

Vocabulary

Characters are developed through description. The words the author chooses for the description are important. Pay attention not only to the **denotations**, or "dictionary definitions," of the words, but also to their **connotations**, or "emotional meanings."

Many words used to describe people have negative or positive connotations. These connotations help the reader form an impression of the character.

Below are some words used in the selections in this unit to describe characters. Make a "+" after positive words, and a "−" after negative words. Then use each in a sentence.

1. kind
2. gentle
3. faithful
4. smart
5. reckless
6. raw
7. wildly imaginative
8. genial
9. fiery
10. proud
11. brave
12. cunning
13. clever
14. rude

Grammar, Usage, and Mechanics

Verbs must agree with their subjects. If the subject is singular, the verb must be singular. If the subject is plural, the verb must be plural. Make sure you match the verb correctly with the subject.

In the sentences below, what is the correct form of the verbs in parentheses? Write the verb, and tell whether it is singular or plural.

1. This old boy behind the counter was the kind that (mean) well.

2. Both of the feed-merchant types (were) paying close attention.

3. It (lead) us into a wild jungle of love and hate.

4. (Do) the tiger come out of the door, or (do) the lady?

5. There (was) only Ross and Will opening the lunch basket.

SPEAKING AND LISTENING

A theme is the meaning or message of a piece of literature. Some stories and poems have more than one theme, and others have a theme of only minor importance.

Sometimes plot and theme are confused. A plot is the "what happens" in a poem or story. For example, the plot of a story might concern a young soldier during his first battle. The events of the plot might include the man's thoughts, the battle itself, and the outcome of the battle. However, the theme of the story might be the idea that fighting solves nothing.

Understanding the plot and theme of a story is sometimes easier if you share your ideas with classmates and talk about how the events of a story help illustrate the theme.

Before you begin a discussion of the plot and theme of a selection in this unit, consider the following:

1. Read the selection carefully. Try to identify the author's message. Since a story or play can contain more than one idea, it is possible to have several themes. Be aware that although there may be several, only one is the main theme.

2. Think about the events in the story. As you become familiar with what happens, you will be able to see how these events point toward a theme.

3. Study the characters until you know them well. Notice how personality traits or important characteristics they have make a statement about their outlooks on life.

4. Consider the different points of view of the characters. Decide whether others share their outlooks. Think about general ideas the different characters might represent.

5. Remember that an author may or may not state his theme somewhere in the story. He or she may merely suggest a theme through the events of the plot and the attitudes of the characters. If this is the case in the selection you choose to discuss, be sure to examine the events in the plot, the dialogue of the characters, and the setting for clues to the theme of the story.

Now, as a class or in small groups, choose a poem, play, or story from this unit that you believe has a strong theme: one that seems to be written to get a certain idea across to the reader. First, discuss what you believe the main theme to be. Then talk about how the events and characters in the selection illustrate the theme. Discuss elements of the setting that contribute to the theme. Keep the steps and suggestions above in mind as you and your classmates discuss the selection.

CRITICAL THINKING

Deductions   Sherlock Holmes's detecting skills are based on deduction. "You must have seen more in those rooms than I did," states Watson in "Sherlock Holmes and the Speckled Band." The master detective replies, "I didn't see more. I *deduced* more. I imagine you saw everything I did."

Actually, Holmes's first deductions about who killed Julia Stoner were wrong. He had reached an unsound conclusion. Why? Holmes himself explains: It is dangerous "to reason without having *all* the facts."

There are three parts to deductive reasoning. They are called a **syllogism**: a major premise, a minor premise, and a conclusion. You must be sure the two premises are correct before making a deduction. If any facts are missing or incorrect, your conclusion will be wrong, or unsound.

Example:
Policemen wear blue uniforms.
Mr. Kahil wears a blue uniform.
Mr. Kahil is, therefore, a policeman.

Sound logical? Well, maybe. However, what if you find out that Mr. Kahil is a bus driver? The deduction does not seem very sound, does it? The problem with this syllogism is that the premises may be true, but other important facts are ignored. Many people besides policemen wear blue uniforms.

Rewrite the examples. Make a correct deduction.

EFFECTIVE STUDYING

Using Dictionaries   Reading and writing are not always easy. You might not know the definition of a word. You might want to use a certain synonym that you are sure exists, but that you cannot think of. What if you encounter a foreign word or phrase?

A **dictionary** lists words alphabetically. It also provides information about definitions of words, pronunciations of words, origins of words, and different forms of words, such as noun, verb, adjective and adverb forms.

Two-language dictionaries translate foreign words into English. They are useful if you read stories with foreign phrases.

A **thesaurus** lists synonyms for words, and sometimes antonyms as well. Some thesauruses list words alphabetically, as in a dictionary. Others have indexes that refer you to numbered sections.

Many word-processing programs include **spell-checkers** and thesauruses. These features can be a great help, although a spell-checker is certainly no substitute for a dictionary.

What reference books would you use to find the meaning of *adios*, find a substitute for the word *afraid*, and check the spelling of a difficult word?

Test Preparation

Although you might not have a dictionary with you when you take a test, you should always reread your work to check for spelling. Also check that you have used every word the way you meant to use it.

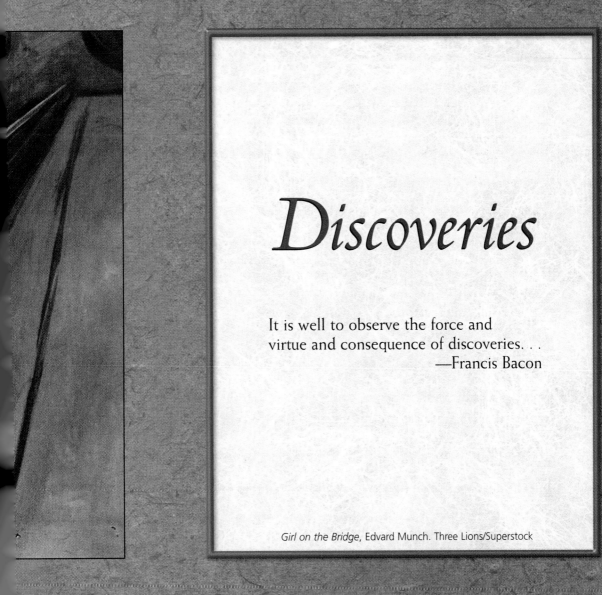

Discoveries

It is well to observe the force and
virtue and consequence of discoveries. . .
—Francis Bacon

Girl on the Bridge, Edvard Munch. Three Lions/Superstock

313

Discoveries

What do you think of when you hear the word *discovery*? Perhaps you think of a great scientific discovery, like the automobile engine. Perhaps you think of discovering something valuable, such as diamonds or gold. You may even think of discovering something new, like a cheap source of energy.

Francis Bacon, the English essayist, wrote about the importance of looking at the effects of discoveries. Think of the changes television, frozen food, and computers have made in the 20th century. Discoveries have the power to change the world, either for better or for worse. Do you see the discovery of nuclear energy as beneficial or destructive? This idea of change also applies to your own discoveries. Once you make a discovery, your world—and your own inner reality—are forever changed. Life is never quite the same again.

The selections in this unit will focus on discoveries that people make about themselves, others, the world around them, and life. The selections will help you think about the discoveries that you have made.

■ DISCOVERIES ABOUT YOURSELF

In the short story "Chee's Daughter," a Navaho man doubts the wisdom of his values when his wife dies and he loses his daughter. A bold plan to win back his daughter succeeds, and Chee discovers that his values were right for him after all. Have you ever experienced self-doubt when faced with difficult circumstances? What did you discover about yourself? The speaker of "Four Skinny Trees" discovers reasons for encouragement and inspiration.

Sometimes a person needs the help of another to find out who he or she really is. In the short story "The Gold Medal," a young African American girl discovers an aspect of her true self through a chance encounter with a wise and kindly old man.

Have you ever taken part in a ritual that is part of your religion or community, such as a bar mitzvah, baptism, or initiation? What did you discover about yourself as a result of this experience?

In the true story "Ta-Na-E-Ka," a young Native American girl describes her participation in the coming-of-age ritual that is part of the tradition of the Kaw Indians. Sent out to spend five days and nights alone in the wilderness, the girl comes up with a clever plan. She discovers that she can survive in the most unusual circumstances.

■ ABOUT OTHERS

People discover things about themselves and one another in relationships. What things have you discovered recently about the people in your life? Did some of these things surprise you? In the short story "Thank You, M'am," a boy is *very* surprised by some things he discovers about a woman whom he meets in an unusual way. "Navaho Chant" helps you recognize how some Native Americans view nature. Nature is beautiful and the crops think like human beings. Why do you think the Navahos see nature in such a positive way?

■ ABOUT THE WORLD

City streets can be very dangerous, but you can make discoveries—good and bad—there. Is nature dangerous, too? Sometimes, nature can be a harsh teacher. In the true story "Starvation Wilderness," a young couple learns that the far north country is no place for two people and a small baby in winter. Yet the story has a positive side, too, as characters discover their own courage and endurance. Poems can also help you make discoveries about the world. The haiku offers insights into nature and human nature. Discover what "Sympathy," "Dreams," and an untitled poem have to say about self-awareness, freedom, and dreams. These poems offer discoveries about a world inside everyone.

Discoveries are a part of everyday living. Most discoveries come about as a result of analysis, disclosure, and exploration. Sometimes, however, discoveries are made purely by accident. What important discoveries have you made? What changes have these discoveries made in your life?

Learn About

SYMBOLISM IN FICTION

A **symbol** is something that stands for something else. For example, a heart is often used as a symbol of love.

Literature is full of symbolism, or the use of symbols. Often in a story, a symbol stands for an idea, a feeling, or a quality. Sometimes a certain symbol is used several times throughout a story. When a symbol is used in this way, you know that it emphasizes an important idea. This type of symbol may appear at the beginning or end of a story, as well as at critical points in the plot.

In the story "Chee's Daughter," symbols convey important ideas about Chee and his values. As you read "Chee's Daughter," ask yourself:

1. What symbol in the story represents Chee's faith in the land?
2. At what points in the story is this symbol used?

WRITING CONNECTION

Writers use symbols to convey important ideas about characters. Think of something you own that is especially important to you. Then write a paragraph explaining how this object could be used as a symbol to describe the kind of person you are.

READING FOCUS

Make Inferences Sometimes a writer tells you directly what is happening. In other cases, the writer gives certain details, and you infer, or draw a conclusion, by putting together the pieces of information that are given.

Consider this description: "No one spoke to me at the party. No one smiled. When I tried to chat with several people, they all turned away." From these details, you can infer that the guest was not welcome at the party. Look for details that can help you make inferences about both the action and characters in "Chee's Daughter."

Chee's Daughter

by Juanita Platero and Siyowin Miller

The hat told the story, the big, black, drooping Stetson. It was not at the proper angle, the proper rakish angle for so young a Navaho. There was no song, and that was not in keeping either. There should have been at least a humming, a faint, all-to-himself "he he he heya," for it was a good horse he was riding, a slender-legged, high-stepping buckskin that would race the wind with light knee-urging. This was a day for singing, a warm winter day, when the touch of the sun upon the back belied the snow high on distant mountains.

Wind warmed by the sun touched his high-boned cheeks like flicker feathers, and still he rode on silently, deeper into Little Canyon, until the red rock walls rose straight upward from the streambed and only a narrow piece of blue sky hung above. Abruptly the sky widened where the canyon walls were pushed back to make a wide place, as though in ancient times an angry stream had tried to go all ways at once.

This was home—this wide place in the canyon—levels of jagged rock and levels of rich red earth. This was home to Chee, the rider of the buckskin, as it had been to many generations before him.

He stopped his horse at the stream and sat looking across the narrow ribbon of water to the bare-branched peach trees. He was seeing them each springtime with their age-gnarled limbs transfigured beneath veils of blossom pink; he was seeing them in autumn laden with their yellow fruit, small and sweet. Then his eyes searched out the indistinct furrows of the fields beside the stream, where each year the corn and beans and squash drank thirstily of the overflow from summer rains. Chee was trying to outweigh today's bitter betrayal of hope by gathering to himself these reminders of the integrity of the land. Land did not cheat! His mind lingered deliberately on all the days spent here in the sun caring for the young plants, his songs to the earth and to the life springing from it: ". . . In the middle of the wide field . . . Yellow Corn Boy . . . He has started both ways . . .," then the harvest and repayment in full measure. Here was the old

rakish (RAYK ish) stylish
transfigured (trans FIG yurd) changed in form or appearance

feeling of wholeness and of oneness with the sun and earth and growing things.

Chee urged the buckskin toward the family compound where, secure in a recess of overhanging rock, was his mother's dome-shaped hogan, red rock and red adobe like the ground on which it nestled. Not far from the hogan was the half-circle of brush like a dark shadow against the canyon wall—corral for sheep and goats. Farther from the hogan, in full circle, stood the horse corral made of heavy cedar branches sternly inter-locked. Chee's long thin lips curved into a smile as he passed his daughter's tiny hogan squatted like a round Pueblo oven, beside the corral. He remembered the summer day when together they sat back on their heels and plastered wet adobe all about the circling wall of rock and the woven dome of piñon twigs. How his family laughed when the Little One herded the bewildered chickens into her tiny hogan as the first snow fell.

Then the smile faded from Chee's lips and his eyes darkened as he tied his horse to a corral post and turned to the strangely empty compound. "Someone has told them," he thought, "and they are inside weeping." He passed his mother's deserted loom on the south side of the hogan and pulled the rude wooden door toward him, bowing his head, hunching his shoulders to get inside.

His mother sat sideways by the center fire, her feet drawn up under her full skirts. Her hands were busy kneading dough in the chipped white basin. With her head down, her voice was muffled when she said, "The meal will soon be ready, son."

Chee passed his father sitting against the wall, hat over his eyes as though asleep. He passed his older sister who sat turning mutton ribs on a crude wire grill over the coals, noticed tears dropping on her hands. "She cared more for my wife than I realized," he thought.

Then, because something must be said sometime, he tossed the black Stetson upon a bulging sack of wool and said, "You have heard, then." He could not shut from his mind how confidently he had set the handsome new hat on his head that very morning, slanting the wide brim over one eye: he was going to see his wife and today he would ask the doctors about bringing her home; last week she had looked so much better.

His sister nodded but did not speak. His mother sniffed and passed her vel-veteen sleeve beneath her nose. Chee sat down, leaning against the wall. "I suppose I was a fool for hoping all the time. I should have expected this. Few of our people get well from the coughing sick-ness. But *she* seemed to be getting better."

His mother was crying aloud now and blowing her nose noisily on her skirt. His father sat up, speaking gently to her.

Chee shifted his position and started a cigarette. His mind turned back to the Little One. At least she was too small to understand what had happened, the Little One who had been born three years

---

compound (KAHM pound) group of buildings

Passing By, E. Martin Hennings. The Museum of Fine Arts, Houston, TX. Gift of the Ranger Fund, National Academy of Design

before in the sanitarium where his wife was being treated for the coughing sickness, the Little One he had brought home to his mother's hogan to be nursed by his sister whose baby was a few months older. As she grew fat-cheeked and sturdy-legged, she followed him about like a shadow. Somehow her baby mind had grasped that of all those at the hogan who cared for her and played with her,

he—Chee—belonged most to her. She sat cross-legged at his elbow when he worked silver at the forge; she rode before him in the saddle when he drove the horses to water; often she lay wakeful on her sheep pelts until he stretched out for the night in the darkened hogan and she could snuggle warm against him.

Chee blew smoke slowly and some of the sadness left his dark eyes as he said,

"It is not as bad as it might be. It is not as though we are left with nothing."

Chee's sister arose, sobs catching in her throat, and rushed past him out the doorway. Chee sat upright, a terrible fear possessing him. For a moment his mouth could make no sound. Then: "The Little One! Mother, where is she?"

His mother turned her stricken face to him. "Your wife's people came after her this morning. They heard yesterday of their daughter's death through the trader at Red Sands."

Chee started to protest but his mother shook her head slowly. "I didn't expect they would want the Little One either. But there is nothing you can do. She is a girl child and belongs to her mother's people; it is custom."

Frowning, Chee got to his feet, grinding his cigarette into the dirt floor. "Custom! When did my wife's parents begin thinking about custom? Why, the hogan where they live doesn't even face the East!" He started toward the door. "Perhaps I can overtake them. Perhaps they don't realize how much we want her here with us. I'll ask them to give my daughter back to me. Surely, they won't refuse."

His mother stopped him gently with her outstretched hand. "You couldn't overtake them now. They were in the trader's car. Eat and rest, and think more about this."

"Have you forgotten how things have always been between you and your wife's people?" his father said.

That night, Chee's thoughts were troubled—half-forgotten incidents became disturbingly vivid—but early the next morning, he saddled the buckskin and set out for the settlement of Red Sands. Even though his father-in-law, Old Man Fat, might laugh, Chee knew that he must talk to him. There were some things to which Old Man Fat might listen.

Chee rode the first part of the fifteen miles to Red Sands expectantly. The sight of sandstone buttes near Cottonwood Spring reddening in the morning sun brought a song almost to his lips. He twirled his reins in salute to the small boy herding sheep toward many-colored Butterfly Mountain, watched with pleasure the feathers of smoke rising against tree-darkened western mesas from the hogans sheltered there. But as he approached the familiar settlement sprawled in mushroom growth along the highway, he began to feel as though a scene from a bad dream was becoming real.

Several cars were parked around the trading store which was built like two log hogans side by side, with red gas pumps in front and a sign across the tarpaper roofs: *Red Sands Trading Post—Groceries · Gasoline · Cold Drinks · Sandwiches · Indian Curios.* Back of the trading post, an unpainted frame house and outbuildings squatted on the drab, treeless land. Chee and the Little One's mother had lived there when they stayed with his wife's people. That was according to custom—living with one's wife's people—but

---

buttes (BYOOTS) small mountains with steep sides

Chee had never been convinced that it was custom alone which prompted Old Man Fat and his wife to insist that their daughter bring her husband to live at the trading post.

Beside the Post was a large hogan of logs, with brightly painted pseudo-Navaho designs on the roof—a hogan with smoke-smudged windows and a garish blue door which faced north to the highway. Old Man Fat had offered Chee a hogan like this one. The trader would build it if he and his wife would live there and Chee would work at his forge making silver jewelry where tourists could watch him. But Chee had asked instead for a piece of land for a cornfield and help in building a hogan far back from the highway and a corral for the sheep he had brought to this marriage.

A cold wind blowing down from the mountains began to whistle about Chee's ears. It flapped the gaudy Navaho rugs which were hung in one long bright line to attract tourists. It swayed the sign *Navaho Weaver at Work* beside the loom where Old Man Fat's wife sat hunched in her striped blanket patting the colored thread of a design into place with a wooden comb. Tourists stood watching the weaver. More tourists stood in a knot before the hogan where the sign said: *See Inside a Real Navaho Home 25¢.*

Then the knot seemed to unravel as a few people returned to their cars; some had cameras; and there against the blue door Chee saw the Little One standing uncertainly. The wind was plucking at her new purple blouse and wide green skirt; it freed truant strands of soft dark hair from the meager queue into which it had been tied with white yarn.

"Isn't she cunning!" one of the women tourists was saying as she turned away.

Chee's lips tightened as he began to look around for Old Man Fat. Finally he saw him passing among the tourists collecting coins.

Then the Little One saw Chee. The uncertainty left her face and she darted through the crowd as her father swung down from his horse. Chee lifted her in his arms, hugging her tight. While he listened to her breathless chatter, he watched Old Man Fat bearing down on them, scowling.

As his father-in-law walked heavily across the graveled lot, Chee was reminded of a statement his mother sometimes made: "When you see a fat Navaho, you see one who hasn't worked for what he has."

Old Man Fat was fattest in the middle. There was indolence in his walk even though he seemed to hurry, indolence in his cheeks so plump they made his eyes squint, eyes now smoldering with anger.

Some of the tourists were getting into their cars and driving away. The old man said belligerently to Chee, "Why do you come here? To spoil our business? To drive people away?"

---

gawdy (GAWD ee) showy; bright-colored
queue (KYOO) a braid of hair worn at the back of the neck
cunning (KUHN ing) cute
indolence (IN duh lens) laziness

"I came to talk with you," Chee answered, trying to keep his voice steady as he faced the old man.

"We have nothing to talk about," Old Man Fat blustered and did not offer to touch Chee's extended hand.

"It's about the Little One." Chee settled his daughter more comfortably against his hip as he weighed carefully all the words he had planned to say. "We are going to miss her very much. It wouldn't be so bad if we knew that *part* of each year she could be with us. That might help you too. You and your wife are no longer young people and you have no young ones here to depend upon." Chee chose his next words remembering the thriftlessness of his wife's parents, and their greed. "Perhaps we could share the care of this little one. Things are good with us. So much snow this year will make lots of grass for the sheep. We have good land for corn and melons."

Chee's words did not have the expected effect. Old Man Fat was enraged. "Farmers, all of you! Longhaired farmers! Do you think everyone must bend his back over the short-handled hoe in order

Familia India, Amado M. Pena, Jr. El Taller, Inc.

to have food to eat?" His tone changed as he began to brag a little. "We not only have all the things from cans at the trader's, but when the Pueblos come past here on their way to town we buy their salty jerked mutton, young corn for roasting, dried sweet peaches."

Chee's dark eyes surveyed the land along the highway as the old man continued to brag about being "progressive." *He no longer was tied to the land. He and his wife made money easily and could* buy *all the things they wanted.* Chee realized too late that he had stumbled into the old argument between himself and his wife's parents. They had never understood his feeling about the land—that a man took care of his land and it in turn took care of him. Old Man Fat and his wife scoffed at him, called him a Pueblo farmer, all during that summer when he planted and weeded and harvested. Yet they ate the green corn in their mutton stews, and the chili paste from the fresh ripe chilis, and the tortillas from the cornmeal his wife ground. None of this working and sweating in the sun for Old Man Fat, who talked proudly of his easy way of living—collecting money from the trader who rented this strip of land beside the highway, collecting money from the tourists.

Yet Chee had once won that argument. His wife had shared his belief in the integrity of the earth, that jobs and people might fail one but the earth never would. After that first year she had turned from her own people and gone with Chee to Little Canyon.

Old Man Fat was reaching for the Little One. "Don't be coming here with plans for my daughter's daughter," he warned. "If you try to make trouble, I'll take the case to the government man in town."

The impulse was strong in Chee to turn and ride off while he still had the Little One in his arms. But he knew his time of victory would be short. His own family would uphold the old custom of children, especially girl children, belonging to the mother's people. He would have to give his daughter up if the case were brought before the Headman of Little Canyon, and certainly he would have no better chance before a strange white man in town.

He handed the bewildered Little One to her grandfather who stood watching every movement suspiciously. Chee asked, "If I brought you a few things for the Little One, would that be making trouble? Some velvet for a blouse, or some of the jerky she likes . . . this summer's melon?"

Old Man Fat backed away from him. "Well," he hesitated, as some of the anger disappeared from his face and beads of greed shone in his eyes. "Well," he said again. Then as the Little One began to squirm in his arms and cry, he said, "No! No! Stay away from here, you and all your family."

The sense of his failure deepened as Chee rode back to Little Canyon. But it was not until he sat with his family that evening in the hogan, while the familiar

---

jerky (JUR kee) beef strips that have been dried in the sun bustle of meal preparing went on about him, that he began to doubt the wisdom of the things he'd always believed. He smelled the coffee boiling and the oily fragrance of chili powder dusted into the bubbling pot of stew; he watched his mother turning round crusty fried bread in the small black skillet. All around him was plenty—a half of mutton hanging near the door, bright strings of chili drying, corn hanging by the braided husks, cloth bags of dried peaches. Yet in his heart was nothing.

He heard the familiar sounds of the sheep outside the hogan, the splash of water as his father filled the long drinking trough from the water barrel. When his father came in, Chee could not bring himself to tell a second time of the day's happenings. He watched his wiry, soft-spoken father while his mother told the story, saw his father's queue of graying hair quiver as he nodded his head with sympathetic exclamations.

Chee's doubting, acrid thoughts kept forming: Was it wisdom his father had passed on to him or was his inheritance only the stubbornness of a longhaired Navaho resisting change? Take care of the land and it will take care of you. True, the land had always given him food, but now food was not enough. Perhaps if he had gone to school he would have learned a different kind of wisdom, something to help him now. A schoolboy might even be able to speak convincingly to this government man whom Old Man Fat threatened to call, instead of sitting here

like a clod of earth itself—Pueblo farmer indeed. What had the land to give that would restore his daughter?

In the days that followed, Chee herded sheep. He got up in the half light, drank the hot coffee his mother had ready, then started the flock moving. It was necessary to drive the sheep a long way from the hogan to find good winter forage. Sometimes Chee met friends or relatives who were on their way to town or to the road camp where they hoped to get work; then there was friendly banter and an exchange of news. But most of the days seemed endless; he could not walk far enough or fast enough from his memories of the Little One or from his bitter thoughts. Sometimes it seemed his daughter trudged beside him, so real he could almost hear her footsteps—the muffled pad-pad of little feet clad in deerhide. In the glare of a snow bank he would see her vivid face, brown eyes sparkling. Mingling with the tinkle of sheep bells he heard her laughter.

When, weary of following the small sharp hoof marks that crossed and re-crossed in the snow, he sat down in the shelter of a rock, it was only to be reminded that in his thoughts he had forsaken his brotherhood with the earth and sun and growing things. If he remembered times when he had flung himself against the earth to rest, to lie there in the sun until he could no longer feel where he left off and the earth began, it was to remember also that now he sat

---

acrid (AK rid) bitter to the tongue
forage (FAWR ij) food for animals
banter (BAN tur) good-natured teasing

like an alien against the same earth; the belonging-together was gone. The earth was one thing and he was another.

It was during the days when he herded sheep that Chee decided he must leave Little Canyon. Perhaps he would take a job silversmithing for one of the traders in town. Perhaps, even though he spoke little English, he could get a job at the road camp with his cousins; he would ask them about it.

Springtime transformed the mesas. The peach trees in the canyon were shedding fragrance and pink blossoms on the gentled wind. The sheep no longer foraged for the yellow seeds of chamiso but ranged near the hogan with the long-legged new lambs, eating tender young grass.

Chee was near the hogan on the day his cousins rode up with the message for which he waited. He had been watching with mixed emotions while his father and his sister's husband cleared the fields beside the stream.

"The boss at the camp says he needs an extra hand, but he wants to know if you'll be willing to go with the camp when they move it to the other side of the town." The tall cousin shifted his weight in the saddle.

The other cousin took up the explanation. "The work near here will last only until the new cutoff beyond Red Sands is finished. After that, the work will be too far away for you to get back here often."

That was what Chee had wanted—to get away from Little Canyon—yet he found himself not so interested in the job beyond town as in this new cutoff which was almost finished. He pulled a blade of grass, split it thoughtfully down the center as he asked questions of his cousins. Finally he said: "I need to think more about this. If I decide on this job, I'll ride over."

Before his cousins were out of sight down the canyon Chee was walking toward the fields, a bold plan shaping in his mind. As the plan began to flourish, wild and hardy as young tumbleweed, Chee added his own voice softly to the song his father was singing: ". . . In the middle of the wide field . . . Yellow Corn Boy . . . I wish to put in."

Chee walked slowly around the field, the rich red earth yielding to his footsteps. His plan depended upon this land and upon the things he remembered most about his wife's people.

Through planting time Chee worked zealously and tirelessly. He spoke little of the large new field he was planting because he felt so strongly that just now this was something between himself and the land. The first days he was ever stooping, piercing the ground with the pointed stick, placing the corn kernels there, walking around the field and through it, singing, ". . . His track leads into the ground . . . Yellow Corn Boy . . . his track leads into the ground." After that,

---

alien (AYL yun) or (AYL ee yun) foreigner; stranger
zealously (ZEHL uhs lee) eagerly; fanatically

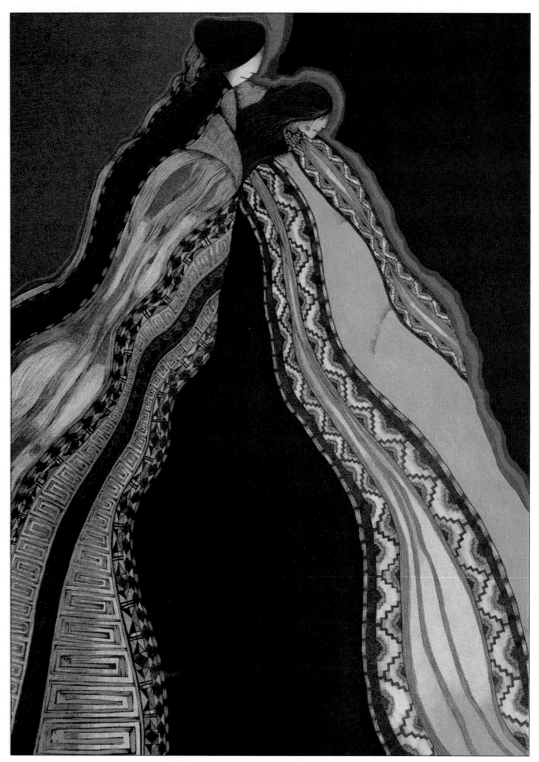

El Mercado, Amado M. Pena, Jr. El Taller, Inc.

each day Chee walked through his field watching for the tips of green to break through; first a few spikes in the center and then more and more until the corn in all parts of the field was above ground. Surely, Chee thought, if he sang the proper songs, if he cared for this land faithfully, it would not forsake him now, even though through the lonely days of winter he had betrayed the goodness of the earth in his thoughts.

Through the summer Chee worked long days, the sun hot upon his back, pulling weeds from around young corn plants; he planted squash and pumpkin; he terraced a small piece of land near his mother's hogan and planted carrots and onions and the moisture-loving chili. He was increasingly restless. Finally he told his family what he hoped the harvest from this land would bring him. Then the whole family waited with him, watching the corn: the slender graceful plants that waved green arms and bent to embrace each other as young winds wandered through the field, the maturing plants flaunting their pollen-laden tassels in the sun, the tall and sturdy parent corn with new-formed ears and a froth of purple, red, and yellow cornbeards against the dusty emerald of broad leaves.

Summer was almost over when Chee slung the bulging packs across two pack ponies. His mother helped him tie the heavy rolled pack behind the saddle of the buckskin. Chee knotted the new yellow kerchief about his neck a little tighter,

gave the broad black hat brim an extra tug, but these were only gestures of assurance and he knew it. The land had not failed him. That part was done. But this he was riding into? Who could tell?

When Chee arrived at Red Sands, it was as he had expected to find it—no cars on the highway. His cousins had told him that even the Pueblo farmers were using the new cutoff to town. The barren gravel around the Red Sands Trading Post was deserted. A sign banged against the dismantled gas pumps: *Closed until further notice.*

Old Man Fat came from the crude summer shelter built beside the log hogan from a few branches of scrub cedar and the sides of wooden crates. He seemed almost friendly when he saw Chee.

"Get down, my son," he said, eyeing the bulging packs. There was no bluster in his voice today and his face sagged, looking somewhat saddened; perhaps because his cheeks were no longer quite full enough to push his eyes upward at the corners. "You are going on a journey?"

Chee shook his head. "Our fields gave us so much this year, I thought to sell or trade this to the trader. I didn't know he was no longer here."

Old Man Fat sighed, his voice dropping to an injured tone. "He says he and his wife are going to rest this winter; then he'll after that build a place up on the new highway."

Chee moved as though to be traveling on, then jerked his head toward the pack ponies. "Anything you need?"

---

flaunting (FLAWNT ing) showing off

"I'll ask my wife," Old Man Fat said as he led the way to the shelter. "Maybe she has a little money. Things have not been too good with us since the trader closed. Only a few tourists come this way." He shrugged his shoulders. "And with the trader gone—no credit."

Chee was not deceived by his father-in-law's unexpected confidences. He recognized them as a hopeful bid for sympathy and, if possible, something for nothing. Chee made no answer. He was thinking that so far he had been right about his wife's parents: their thriftlessness had left them with no resources to last until Old Man Fat found another easy way of making a living.

Old Man Fat's wife was in the shelter working at her loom. She turned rather wearily when her husband asked with a noticeable deference if she would give him money to buy supplies. Chee surmised that the only income here was from his mother-in-law's weaving.

She peered around the corner of the shelter at the laden ponies, and then she looked at Chee. "What do you have there, my son?"

Chee smiled to himself as he turned to pull the pack from one of the ponies, dragged it to the shelter where he untied the ropes. Pumpkins and hardshelled squash tumbled out, and the ears of corn—pale yellow husks fitting firmly over plump ripe kernels, blue corn, red corn, yellow corn, many-colored corn, ears and ears of it—tumbled into every corner of the shelter.

"Yooooh," Old Man Fat's wife exclaimed as she took some of the ears in her hands. Then she glanced up at her son-in-law. "But we have no money for all this. We have sold almost everything we own—even the brass bed that stood in the hogan."

Old Man Fat's brass bed. Chee concealed his amusement as he started back for another pack. That must have been a hard parting. Then he stopped, for coming from the cool darkness of the hogan was the Little One, rubbing her eyes as though she had been asleep. She stood for a moment in the doorway and Chee saw that she was dirty, barefoot, her hair uncombed, her little blouse shorn of all its silver buttons. Then she ran toward Chee, her arms outstretched. Heedless of Old Man Fat and his wife, her father caught her in his arms, her hair falling in a dark cloud across his face, the sweetness of her laughter warm against his shoulder.

It was the haste within him to get this slow waiting game played through to the finish that made Chee speak unwisely. It was the desire to swing her before him in the saddle and ride fast to Little Canyon that prompted his words. "The money doesn't matter. You still have something. . . ."

Chee knew immediately that he had overspoken. The old woman looked from him to the corn spread before her. Unfriendliness began to harden in his father-in-law's face. All the old arguments between himself and his wife's

---

surmised (sur MYZD) supposed; made a guess

people came pushing and crowding in between them now.

Old Man Fat began kicking the ears of corn back onto the canvas as he eyed Chee angrily. "And you rode all the way over here thinking that for a little food we would give up our daughter's daughter?"

Chee did not wait for the old man to reach for the Little One. He walked dazedly to the shelter, rubbing his cheek against her soft dark hair and put her gently into her grandmother's lap. Then he turned back to the horses. He had failed. By his own haste he had failed. He swung into the saddle, his hand touching the roll behind it. Should he ride on into town?

Then he dismounted, scarcely glancing at Old Man Fat, who stood uncertainly at the corner of the shelter, listening to his wife. "Give me a hand with this other pack of corn, Grandfather," Chee said, carefully keeping the small bit of hope from his voice.

Puzzled, but willing, Old Man Fat helped carry the other pack to the shelter, opening it to find more corn as well as carrots and round, pale yellow onions. Chee went back for the roll behind the buckskin's saddle and carried it to the entrance of the shelter where he cut the ropes and gave the canvas a nudge with his toe. Tins of coffee rolled out, small plump cloth bags; jerked meat from several butcherings spilled from a flour sack, and bright red chilis splashed like flames against the dust.

"I will leave all this anyhow," Chee told them. "I would not want my daughter nor even you old people to go hungry."

Old Man Fat picked up a shiny tin of coffee, then put it down. With trembling hands he began to untie one of the cloth bags—dried sweet peaches.

The Little One had wriggled from her grandmother's lap, unheeded, and was on her knees, digging her hands into the jerked meat.

"There is almost enough food here to last all winter," Old Man Fat's wife sought the eyes of her husband.

Chee said, "I meant it to be enough. But that was when I thought you might send the Little One back with me." He looked down at his daughter noisily sucking jerky. Her mouth and both fists were full of it. "I am sorry that you feel you cannot bear to part with her."

Old Man Fat's wife brushed a straggly wisp of gray hair from her forehead as she turned to look at the Little One. Old Man Fat was looking too. And it was not a thing to see. For in that moment the Little One ceased to be their daughter's daughter and became just another mouth to feed.

"And why not?" the old woman asked wearily.

Chee was settled in the saddle, the barefooted Little One before him. He urged the buckskin faster, and his daughter clutched his shirtfront. The purpling mesas flung back the echo: ". . . My corn embrace each other. In the middle of the wide field . . . Yellow Corn Boy embrace each other."

---

straggly (STRAG lee) wandering off course

Review the Selection

UNDERSTAND THE SELECTION

Recall

1. What event has just taken place in Chee's life?

2. What does Chee find out at home after his wife's death?

3. What does Chee decide to do about it?

Infer

4. Why did Old Man Fat think he was superior to Chee?

5. What trait in his father-in-law did Chee hope would work to his advantage?

6. Why did Chee suspect that his father-in-law's fortunes would worsen?

7. Why did Chee empty all the bundles of food on the floor before he left?

Apply

8. Select details in the story that show how Chee's in-laws have gone from prosperity to poverty.

9. Do you agree with Chee that "jobs and people might fail one, but the earth never would"?

10. What might have happened if Chee had taken the job offered by his cousins?

Respond to Literature

What discoveries did Chee make in the course of the story? What did he finally discover about his own values?

WRITE ABOUT THE SELECTION

In the short story "Chee's Daughter," several characters are important to the story's development. There is Chee himself, the Little One, Old Man Fat, and Old Man Fat's wife. How do you feel about each of these characters? Do you admire Chee? Do you agree with Old Man Fat's values and actions? Do you feel sorry for the Little One? Do you like or dislike Old Man Fat's wife? Explain why.

Prewriting   Make a chart of the four characters. List your feelings about each character, both positive and negative. Then decide which character you feel most strongly about. That will be the subject of your paragraph.

Writing   Use the ideas in your list to write a paragraph that describes your reaction to a character in "Chee's Daughter."

Revising   To revise your paragraph, think of adding a sentence that reflects an opinion different from yours. For example, if you disliked Old Man Fat, you might add the sentence: "I did not like Old Man Fat, but some people might admire him because he did what was most practical in the situation." Be sure to use evidence from the story to support your opinion and the opposing opinion.

Proofreading   Check your paper for mistakes in spelling, usage, and mechanics. Be sure you have used commas before the conjunctions in compound sentences.

THINK ABOUT SYMBOLISM

A symbol links a specific thing with a certain idea, value, people, or way of life. A symbol points to something beyond itself, to a greater meaning.

1. What object is used as a symbol in the opening of "Chee's Daughter"?

2. What does this symbol tell you about Chee's mood?

3. What symbol do the authors use to represent the land?

4. In what way is this symbol woven into the story?

5. Explain why the authors end the story with this symbol.

READING FOCUS

Make Inferences To understand the characters' feelings and actions in "Chee's Daughter," you often had to make inferences from statements by and about the characters. What can you infer about Chee's mood at the beginning of the story? at the end of the story? On what details are your inferences based?

DEVELOP YOUR VOCABULARY

An **adjective** is a word that modifies or describes a noun. For example, the word *fat* is an adjective because it can describe nouns such as *man*, *dog*, *baby*, or *face*: fat man, fat dog, fat baby, fat face.

An **adverb** is a word that modifies or describes a verb. An adverb tells how an action takes place. For example, the word *fast* is an adverb. *Fast* can be used to describe the way a person runs (he runs fast), thinks (she thinks fast), or talks (the teacher talks fast).

Review the meaning of each of these words from "Chee's Daughter." Decide whether each word is an adjective or an adverb. Then use each word in an original sentence. In your sentences, underline the noun or verb that the adjective or adverb modifies.

1. rakish
2. zealously
3. straggly
4. gaudy
5. acrid

SYMBOLISM IN POETRY

A **symbol** is an object that represents a larger idea. Symbolism is often used in poetry because it can express a great deal of meaning in the space of a few words.

In the story "Chee's Daughter," the land is very important to Chee. Throughout the story, fragments of a Navaho song about the Corn Boy run through Chee's mind. This song—and the corn itself—are symbols of Chee's deep connection to the land. The Navaho Chant that you are about to read is part of the song that Chee sings,

In the poem "Navaho Chant," there are many symbols. As you read the poem, ask yourself:

1. Who is speaking in the poem?
2. What does the symbol "home" represent?

WRITING CONNECTION

Native American writers and others often use objects from nature as symbols. Think of something in nature that is meaningful to you. For example, perhaps you find special meaning in sunsets, the ocean, clouds, snow, or a certain kind of tree. Write a short poem or paragraph in which this object from nature is used as a symbol of a larger idea.

READING FOCUS

Identify Fact and Opinion A fact is a statement that can be measured or proven. An opinion is a statement that tells what a person believes. "This poem has sixteen lines" is a fact. "This chant is very interesting to me" is an opinion. Facts and opinions can occur side by side in any type of writing.

As you read "Navaho Chant," note the statements you think are opinions of the speaker and which you think are facts.

Corn Ceremony, Narciso Abeyta (Ha-So-De), Navaho,
Courtesy, Alice G. Howland

NAVAHO CHANT

Traditional Navaho Song

I am the White Corn Boy.
I walk in sight of my home.
I walk in plain sight of my home.
I walk on the straight path which is towards my home.
5 I walk to the entrance of my home.
I arrive at the beautiful goods curtain which hangs at the doorway.
I arrive at the entrance of my home.
I am in the middle of my home.
I am at the back of my home.
10 I am on top of the pollen seed footprint.
I am like the Most High Power Whose Ways Are Beautiful.
Before me it is beautiful,
Behind me it is beautiful,
Under me it is beautiful,
15 Above me it is beautiful,
All around me it is beautiful.

Review the Selection

UNDERSTAND THE SELECTION

Recall

1. Who is speaking in the poem?

2. Where is the speaker going?

3. To whom does the speaker liken himself?

Infer

4. What is the meaning of the word "home" in the poem?

5. What might the "straight path" refer to?

6. What is the "pollen seed footprint"?

7. What is the speaker's feeling at the end of the poem?

Apply

8. Compare the feeling of the poem to Chee's feeling at the end of "Chee's Daughter."

9. Select a word that is used repeatedly throughout the poem. Explain the importance of the word.

10. Explain how this poem might be dramatized in movement.

Respond to Literature

The speaker in the poem completes a kind of journey and, as a result, discovers certain feelings. What feelings have you discovered in yourself after completing a journey or reaching a goal?

WRITE ABOUT THE SELECTION

The poem "Navaho Chant" is written from the Corn Boy's point of view. How might the same poem be written from another point of view? Your task is to write a paragraph in which a person, animal, or object in nature views the Corn Boy.

Prewriting Make a list of possible points of view. For example, the corn could be seen by a bird, an old person, a child, an insect, or the earth itself. Decide which viewpoint you find most interesting; then let this be the point of view of your paragraph. Jot down as many ideas as you can think of about how the corn would look from the viewpoint you have chosen.

Writing Use the ideas from your notes to write a paragraph that describes the corn from another point of view. Your paragraph should make it clear who or what is viewing the corn. Do you want to use first person (*I*) or third person (*he, she, it, they*)?

Revising Try writing all or part of your paragraph in a chant style similar to the poem itself. It is often helpful to read aloud what you have written to see if it really has the sound of a chant or song.

Consider adding or eliminating details to make your paragraph more descriptive.

Proofreading Check for errors in spelling, usage, and mechanics. Remember to capitalize the first word in each line if you wrote your paragraph as a chant.

THINK ABOUT SYMBOLISM

Symbolism is a form of figurative language. **Figurative language** expresses meaning that is more than just the dictionary definition of the words themselves. A symbol is something that has meaning in itself but also stands for something else. The special meaning of a symbol depends on the poem or story in which it appears.

1. What is the special meaning of the word *home* in "Navaho Chant"?

2. Why do you think the author of the poem chose to use this word?

3. What choice of words describes the movement of the corn as it grows?

4. How does the poem make the corn seem like a person?

5. What is the Most High Power Whose Ways Are Beautiful?

READING FOCUS

Identify Fact and Opinion Create a fact and opinion chart for "Navaho Chant." Divide a sheet of paper in half. On the left, write the lines of the poem that state opinions. On the right, write the lines that state facts. Then write a paragraph about your impression of the poem. Use supporting details from your chart.

DEVELOP YOUR VOCABULARY

A **preposition** can be used to describe the relationship between two words or phrases. For example, in the sentence, "The ground is under the corn," the preposition *under* describes the relationship between the corn and the ground.

In "Navaho Chant," prepositions are important to the meaning of the poem. Explain how each of the prepositions listed below is used in the poem to describe a relationship. Then use each preposition in an original sentence.

1. on	**5.** behind
2. to	**6.** under
3. at	**7.** above
4. before	**8.** around

Learn About

CHARACTER TRAITS

In literature, a character is a person who the author invents through words. An author creates a character by describing the character and by having the character say and do certain things. An author also creates a character by commenting on the character's thoughts and feelings.

Characters in stories can usually be classified as either flat or round. **Flat characters** are stereotypes: the crazy teenager, the greedy businessman, the crabby old lady. **Round characters** come across as real people. They have many facets, or parts, to their personalities.

The story "The Gold Medal" contains both flat and round characters. As you read the story, ask yourself:

1. Is Amanda a flat or a round character?
2. What stereotypes exist among the other characters?

WRITING CONNECTION

Think of a person you meet almost every day. If you were writing a story about yourself, would this person appear as a flat or a round character? Write a paragraph in which you describe this person.

READING FOCUS

Use Connotations Many words have connotations; that is, they suggest certain feelings. These feelings may be positive or negative. For example, the word *skinny* has a negative connotation, while the word *slender* has a more positive connotation. Writers pay close attention to the connotations of the words they use. By noticing these connotations, you can make inferences about the characters' attitudes and opinions.

THE
GOLD
MEDAL

by Nan Gilbert

The day had been too much for Amanda. It had started out bad and got no better, one thing piling on another all day long.

"That skirt is too short," her mother had frowned during this morning's last minute inspection. "Did you scrub your teeth? Are your fingernails clean?"

"Mom, I'm not a *baby*!" Amanda had let out a hopeless squawk and fled. It was no use. When her mother looked at her, she didn't see Amanda—not really. She saw an Example to help show their new neighbors that the Dawsons were as clean and quiet and well-mannered as any family on the block.

"I'm not an Example!" grumbled Amanda rebelliously. "I'm *me*!"

Amanda Dawson—tall for her years, a little thin, leggy as a newborn colt. Flopping short black ponytail, jutting elbows, springy knees. Long feet that could trip her up—and frequently did. Face plain and unremarkable except for large, liquid, chocolate-brown eyes, just one shade darker than her scrubbed, shining skin.

What did her mother see, if she didn't see Amanda? Amanda's quick imagination leaped to present her with the picture of a Proper Example: a spotlessly clean, tidy creature who kept her elbows in and her knees hidden . . . whose hair never worked loose from its tight rubberband . . . who didn't run or shout or use slang . . . whose name was always on the honor roll. . . .

"You there—shoo! Don't trespass! Keep to the sidewalk!"

Absorbed in her picture-making, Amanda had unthinkingly taken the shortcut across Mrs. Hawthorne's corner

---

rebelliously (rih BEL yus lee) resisting authority
jutting (JUHT ing) sticking out sharply
absorbed (ab SAWRBD) deeply interested

lot. Now the old lady had popped from her house like a cuckoo from a clock.

"Oh, woe!" muttered Amanda, retreating quickly. "Here we go again!"

The first time this had happened, Amanda had felt bewildered. The short-cut was worn bare by years of school-children's feet, and others seemed to be using it freely.

"I'm not hurting anything," she had said.

Her protest roused the old lady to a flurry of shrill bird-like cries. "This is private property—I have my rights!"

Now, loping back to the sidewalk, pursued by indignant chirps, Amanda told herself resignedly, "Mrs. Hawthorne doesn't see me either." When the old lady looked at Amanda, it was as though she saw not just one girl, but a whole regiment of Amandas, marching across her lot, crushing flowers and shrubs!

Amanda sighed. How did you make someone really *see* you? So they'd know you were *you*? Not a Regiment. Not an Example.

Not a Gang of Hoodlums, either! That's what Mr. Grogan always saw when he looked at her, Amanda decided. By the time Amanda entered Mr. Grogan's store to buy a candy bar, her imagination was growing livelier by the minute.

Mr. Grogan was all smiles and jokes—"Well, well, what's it going to be this time? A nice big box of chocolates, maybe?" he asked.

But he watched Amanda carefully as she lingered over the candy display. When she brought her purchase to the counter, he made an excuse to peek into her lunch sack—"My, my, won't get any fatter on a diet like that!"

No need to look—I didn't steal anything! For a second, Amanda was afraid she had said the words out loud. Mom would split a seam if she even suspected Amanda of speaking up like that, pert and sassy! Hastily, Amanda grabbed her sack and ducked out of the store. Until she had her imagination under control, she'd better keep a close guard on her tongue!

Head down, Amanda scuffed slowly toward school. The day had hardly begun and already it rested heavily on her shoulders. Nor did she expect anything inside the walls of Jefferson School to lighten the load.

School was Amanda's greatest trial this fall. Instead of a familiar building filled with old friends, her family's move to a new home had made Amanda a stranger among strangers. As yet she had made no real friends to replace those she had lost.

---

bewildered (bih WIL durd) confused; puzzled
flurry (FLUR ee) noisy confusion
indignant (in DIG nunt) angry
resignedly (rih ZYN id lee) without a struggle
regiment (REJ uh ment) a military unit
pert (PURT) bold speech or behavior

Though some of the girls were cordial and kind, nobody asked her home after school or stopped at Amanda's house for cookies and pop. And she knew there were others—or maybe it was their parents—who didn't like her being at Jefferson at all. This thought added to the day's accumulating weight of gloom.

During the noon break, Amanda avoided the lunchroom. She took her sack-lunch outside to a sheltered corner of the building. For some reason, today the sunny nook seemed lonely. Each bite Amanda swallowed had to fight its way past a great lump that unexpectedly blocked her throat.

When the bell summoned her back to class, Amanda reluctantly joined the hurrying, chattering crowds in the hall. Her next class was science, taught by Mr. Moore. Amanda thought Mr. Moore the nicest of all the teachers; for him she tried extra hard to do good work. Her first lonely, awkward day in Jefferson, Mr. Moore had welcomed her with genuine warmth. And he was always generous with his after-school time, ready to help her if there was something she didn't understand.

But now, slumped low in her backrow seat, with the lump still big in her throat and a growing heaviness in her heart,

Amanda thought, "He doesn't see me either. He'd treat *any* black kid the same way." Because he's kindhearted. Because he truly wants to help a black child fit into a white world. For him, she was the symbol of a cause he believed in. She wasn't herself at all.

Mr. Moore had to call her name twice before she realized he had asked her a question. Amanda stared at him somberly.

"I don't know," she said.

"Oh, come now, Amanda, of course you do. Remember, it's what we talked about yesterday—"

"I don't know!" The lump in Amanda's throat broke suddenly into a loud, dismaying sob. "Why is it so awful if *I* don't know? Lots of times *they* don't know, and you never look so—so—" It was Mr. Moore's look of hurt surprise that sent her dashing out of the room, that and the new and louder sob rising in her throat.

From the doorway she turned to face him. "I don't care—it's true!—I've got as much right to be st-stupid as anybody!" The second sob got away from her before she could slam the door. Humiliated, she pelted down the hall and out of the building.

The day was too lovely for gloom— an Indian summer afternoon, with rich

---

cordial (KAWR jul) warm, friendly
reluctantly (rih LUK tunt lee) unwillingly; slowly
genuine (JEN yoo in) real, authentic
somberly (SOM bur lee) sadly; unhappily
dismaying (dis MAY ing) losing courage or confidence
pelt (PELT) to hurry or rush

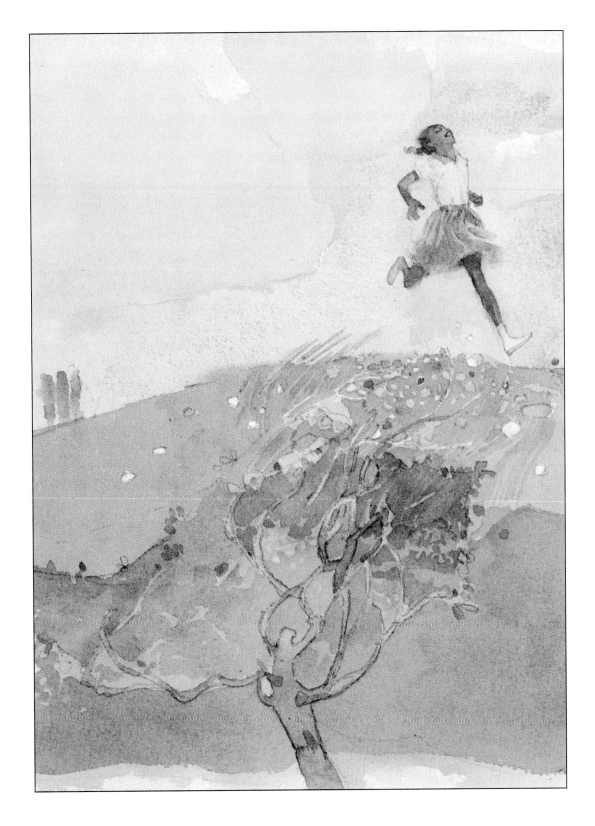

golden warmth spread over the fields and hills like an eiderdown quilt. In spite of herself, her bowed shoulders lifted, her heart lightened. . . .

And she began to run. Running, to Amanda, was like flying. There was special joy in the clean rush of air against her upraised face, the pounding blood in her veins. When Amanda ran, she left all her coltish awkwardness behind. Her stride lengthened; her arms pumped; her long feet—that could trip her up when she walked—barely skimmed the ground.

Down the road she flew, and across a pasture where horses pricked their ears at her in mild amazement. She had to stop for breath—panting, laughing, giddy with this supercharge of oxygen—then she was off again. Up and over a gentle slope where a giant cottonwood offered an oasis of cool green shade she flew.

Too late Amanda saw the high heap of overturned earth below the tree. The springs in her tiring legs coiled and propelled her upward. Arms and legs stretched wide in a split. Thin body bent flat over her forward knee, Amanda cleared the pile of dirt—

But not the excavation behind it. Arms flailing, legs treading the air, she lunged for the far side, then fell back ingloriously into the hole.

"You hurt?" a voice asked with quavery concern.

Amanda sat up, dazed, and brushed dirt from her hands and skirt. Her startled brown eyes, almost level with the rim of hollowed-out earth, saw for the first time the bent figure of an old man under the tree.

"N-no," she said.

"That was mighty pretty running," the old man said with approval, "and as nice a hurdle as ever I've seen. I'm glad you didn't hurt yourself." After a moment, he added, "That's a grave you're settin' in."

Amanda squeaked and scrambled out onto the grass. "A—a *grave*?"

"Yep, for Chief. Chief's my dog."

"Oh—" Amanda cast about for words. "I—I'm sorry he's dead."

"He isn't. Not yet anyway." The old man struggled to his feet. He leaned heavily on his spade as he surveyed his handiwork. "Just about ready. Yep, a few more days and it'll be done. Wouldn't want anyone else to dig it—not for Chief. But if I was to do it, I figured I'd better get started. Can't turn more'n a few spadefuls a day."

Amanda looked at the excavation

---

eiderdown quilt (EYE dur doun KWILT) a comforter filled with soft duck feathers
giddy (GID ee) dizzy, lightheaded
cottonwood (KOT un wuud) kind of wide-spreading tree
propel (pruh PEL) to drive forward
excavation (eks kuh VAY shun) hole made by digging
flailing (FLAYL ing) waving wildly
treading (TRED ing) stepping on
ingloriously (in GLAWR ee us lee) disgracefully
quavery (KWAY vur ee) trembling; shaking

over which the old man was now pulling a piece of tarpaulin. "He—must be a big dog."

"He's that, all right. Used to be, anyway." The old man weighted the tarpaulin with a rock at each corner, then straightened slowly. "Kinda thin now, poor old boy. You want to come meet him? Chief was a runner, too, in his day—and his day lasted a lot longer than most."

Taking her consent for granted, he started down the other side of the slope toward a small house almost hidden behind a tangle of vines and shrubbery. Amanda looked a little wildly toward town, but an emotion much stronger than her alarm tugged her in the opposite direction. A runner, the old man had said—just like that. Here was someone who had looked at her and seen—not a Black Child or an Example or a Black Regiment, but Amanda herself—a runner. Wordless with upswelling gratitude, she followed the old man through a door. When Amanda's eyes adjusted to the dim light inside, she made out the form of a big black dog sprawled near the window in a dappling of green-filtered sunlight. Except for a single thump of tail, he didn't move. The old man stooped low, patted the black head and scratched gently behind long velvety ears.

Cautiously, Amanda went nearer. She didn't know much about dogs; she was uncertain how to treat one that seemed so barely alive. "Is he—uh—pretty old?"

"Sixteen," the old man said. "Yep, that's pretty old for a dog. 'Specially a hunter like Chief . . . we've had some high times together, haven't we, old boy?"

The tail thumped once again. Amanda knelt gingerly and stroked the black coat; it was silky soft, but there seemed nothing between it and the bones beneath. To cover her dismay, she said hurriedly, "I guess a dog is a pretty good friend, isn't he?"

"The right kind of dog—yep, no better."

"You mean, like a hunter maybe?"

The old man snorted, "Breed's the least of it! Line up a hundred Labradors and, chances are, you wouldn't find another like Chief. Wasn't another in his own litter like him. I know—I had the pick of the litter."

Grunting a little with the effort, he straightened and moved to a chair by an ancient roll-top desk. "My friend couldn't figure why I took the pup I did. 'Sam,' he says, 'that's the runt of the lot! Look here—see how lively this one is!' But I held to my choice—yes siree, I knew I had a winner."

"How?" asked Amanda, fascinated.

---

tarpaulin (tahr PAW lin) a waterproof sheet used to protect
dappling (DAP ling) group, or bunch of spots
gingerly (JIN jur lee) very carefully
Labradors (LAB ruh dawrz) breed of big dogs
litter (LIT ur) young animals born at one time

"By the look in his eyes. There he sat, all paws and floppy head, as forlorn a pup as you'd see by any ash can, but those eyes were watching me. 'Believe in me,' they said, 'and I can do anything.'" The old man laughed. "Guess you think I'm a little foolish—well, maybe so. But I wasn't wrong about Chief, no sir! This proves it."

The old desk creaked as he rolled up the cover. In every pigeonhole within there was a ribbon—red ribbons, blue ribbons, purple ribbons, and a single gold medal. "Won 'em all, Chief did," the old man said proudly. He touched one after another. "Best working dog . . . best in class . . . best of show . . ."

Out of curiosity, Amanda reached for the gold medal. "Why, it's a *runner's* medal!" she cried.

The old man took the medal from her and studied it fondly. "Yep, this was his first—bought it myself. Chief cried his heart out that day, wanted to do miracles for me but he just didn't have the know-how yet. 'Never you mind,' I told him. 'I know you're a champion.' Next time I went to town, I bought him a medal to wear till he'd proved himself to everyone else."

As if he had followed their conversation, the black dog thumped his tail once more, and fleetingly raised his head. The old man nodded. "Yep, you're right, Chief. You showed 'em. Don't need this one anymore."

Unexpectedly, he extended it to Amanda. "*You* wear it, Sis. You got the look—just like Chief had. Wear it till you win your own."

Amanda gulped. She sniffed back tears and had to rub her nose childishly. "They look at me—" she sobbed, "but they don't *see* me!"

"You see yourself, don't you?" the old man asked mildly. "Well, then, what more do you need? A dream, and the ambition to work for it—enough for anybody." Gently he closed her fingers over the medal.

---

forlorn (fur LAWRN) miserable
pigeonhole (PIJ un hohl) small compartment in a desk

Review the Selection

UNDERSTAND THE SELECTION

Recall

1. What is Amanda's mood at first?

2. What happens to Amanda in class?

3. What does Amanda do after she leaves school?

Infer

4. Why is Amanda's mother so eager for her to be an example?

5. According to Amanda, why is Mr. Moore always nice to her?

6. Would you guess that Amanda's school and neighborhood are racially mixed, mostly African American, or mostly white?

7. In what ways does the old man think that Amanda and Chief are alike?

Apply

8. How do you think receiving the gold medal will affect Amanda?

9. What do you think would have happened to Amanda that day if she had not met the old man?

10. You are Mr. Moore. How did you feel when Amanda left class?

Respond to Literature

How did the old man help Amanda discover herself? In what ways was he different from the other adults in Amanda's life?

WRITE ABOUT THE SELECTION

At the end of the story, Amanda is still with the old man. What do you think will happen to Amanda when she reenters her everyday world of home and school? Write a paragraph that describes something that happens to Amanda within the next 24 hours after the story ends.

Prewriting Make a list of the situations that Amanda will probably have to face. For example, how will Amanda explain her muddy clothes to her mother? Will she get in trouble for leaving school early? What will she say to Mr. Moore? Choose the situation that most interests you and let this be the subject of your paragraph. Then jot down some of the details that you wish to include.

Writing As you write your paragraph, ask yourself these questions: Which characters are involved in this situation? What do they say and do? How does Amanda feel about this situation? Has her experience with the gold medal changed her feelings and attitudes? What is the outcome of the situation?

Revising Rewrite your paragraph so that it flows easily after the last paragraph of the story. See if you can make the tone and style of your paragraph similar to that of the author.

Proofreading Check your paragraph for mistakes in spelling, usage, and mechanics. Be sure to use question marks if you use questions in your paper.

THINK ABOUT CHARACTER

Round characters tend to develop and change as a story progresses. Flat characters, on the other hand, tend to stay the same. Often the flat characters form a kind of background for the main character's story.

1. Explain why you think Amanda is a flat or a round character.

2. How do other characters in the story see Amanda—as flat or round?

3. Identify three flat characters in the story and their stereotypes.

4. Based on what you know about Amanda's mother, how do you think she would react if Amanda were to pursue running as a sport or career?

5. Would you say that the animal character in the story is flat or round?

DEVELOP YOUR VOCABULARY

Many adverbs are formed by adding -ly to an adjective. For example, the adverb *quickly* is formed by adding -ly to the adjective *quick*. If you are not sure of the meaning of an adverb that ends in -ly, try to figure out the meaning of the adjective from which it has been formed. The adverb should have a similar meaning. For example, a quick (adjective) runner will run quickly (adverb).

Review the meanings of these adverbs from "The Gold Medal." Underline the adjective from which each is formed. Then use each adverb in an original sentence.

1. rebelliously
2. frequently
3. unthinkingly
4. resignedly
5. reluctantly
6. unexpectedly
7. somberly
8. childishly
9. mildly
10. fleetingly

READING FOCUS

Use Connotations On your own, choose a word (an adjective) that sums up your opinion of "The Gold Medal." Avoid the words *good* or *bad*. Then, as a class, draw a long horizontal line on the chalkboard to represent a scale. Mark the center of the scale with a zero. Label one end of the scale "very positive" and the other "very negative." Take turns recording the words you chose on the scale. Write your word at the appropriate place on the scale depending on its connotation and how strong it is.

Learn About

SPEAKER

The **speaker** in a poem is a person, animal, or object that relates what is happening. A speaker is another term for the narrator. Sometimes the poet and the speaker are the same. Sometimes they are not. For example, in "Navaho Chant," you may remember that the speaker is the corn.

A poem can be written in the first, second, or third person. A poem written in the **first person** uses the pronouns *I* and *me*. A poem written in the **second person** speaks directly to the reader or to some real or imaginary person or object. This type of poem uses the pronoun *you*. A poem written in the **third person** uses the pronouns *he*, *she*, or *it*.

As you read the poem, ask yourself:
1. Who is the speaker?
2. In what person is the poem written? How can you tell?

WRITING CONNECTION

Think of an idea or feeling about a day's event that you would like to communicate. Write a short poem or paragraph in which you create a speaker to voice your idea. For example, write a poem about students from a locker's point of view.

READING FOCUS

Identify Main Idea Poets usually express the main idea of a poem indirectly. One way to find the main idea in a poem is to first think about what the different parts of the poem mean. Try pausing briefly after each paragraph of "Four Skinny Trees." Then restate each paragraph in your own words. What is the main idea the poet is trying to express?

Four Skinny Trees

by Sandra Cisneros

They are the only ones who understand me. I am the only one who understands them. Four skinny trees with skinny necks and pointy elbows like mine. Four who do not belong here but are here. Four raggedy excuses planted by the city. From our room we can hear them, but Nenny just sleeps and doesn't appreciate things.

Their strength is secret. They send ferocious roots beneath the ground. They grow up and they grow down and grab the earth between their hairy toes and bite the sky with violent teeth and never quit their anger. This is how they keep.

Let one forget his reason for being, they'd all droop like tulips in a glass, each with their arms around the other. Keep, keep, keep, trees say when I sleep. They teach.

When I am too sad and too skinny to keep keeping, when I am a tiny thing against so many bricks, then it is I look at the trees. When there is nothing left to look at on this street. Four who grew despite concrete. Four who reach and do not forget to reach. Four whose only reason is to be and be.

---

raggedy (RAG ih dee) tattered, frayed, or torn like a rag
ferocious (fuh ROH shus) very cruel; savage
despite (dih SPYT) in spite of

Review the Selection

Recall

1. How are the trees like the speaker?

2. Who shares a room with the speaker?

3. What physical traits do the trees have that keep them alive?

Infer

4. How does the speaker feel about the city?

5. Is the speaker a happy person? Explain.

6. What can you infer about Nenny from the poem?

7. Why does the speaker feel like giving up sometimes?

Apply

8. When the speaker sees that the trees grow "despite concrete" and they "do not forget to reach," how does this help her?

9. If you were sad, what would you think about for encouragement?

10. What object, other than a tree, could you compare yourself to? What features of the object are similar to your features or behaviors?

Respond to Literature

If you could see the speaker of "Four Skinny Trees" in ten years, would you expect her to have succeeded? Explain.

WRITE ABOUT THE SELECTION

The speaker in "Four Skinny Trees" was inspired by the view from her room. Write a paragraph or short poem that describes what you can see from the window of a room where you live.

Prewriting Visualize yourself looking out the window. What would you see? Make a rough sketch of the view, and then use your sketch as a guide to list what you will describe. Jot down some details about each part of the view, such as its size, shape, color, or purpose.

Writing Describe the images in your sketch from left to right or right to left. Remember to give as many details as you can to help the reader picture your description.

Revising You might ask a partner to read and respond to your description. Ask if you should use more descriptive words or details and whether the reader can imagine the scene. Use your partner's comments to revise and clarify your description.

Proofreading Check for errors in spelling, usage, and mechanics. Remove any unnecessary commas and make sure that all your sentences have ending marks.

The **speaker** in a poem is like the narrator in a story. The speaker in a poem can be a real or imaginary person, animal, or object. Sometimes a poem will have more than one speaker. However, the poem is usually told from one main point of view.

1. Do you think the poet is the speaker? Explain.

2. From what point of view is the poem told?

3. What characteristics do the trees and the speaker share?

4. The speaker says that she can "hear" the trees from her room. What does this show about her feelings for the trees?

READING FOCUS

Identify Main Idea As you read the poem, you analyzed each paragraph to determine its main idea. Now state the main idea of the entire poem in a sentence.

DEVELOP YOUR VOCABULARY

In English, many words do not sound the way they are spelled. For example, in the word *often*, the *t* is silent.

You can find out how to pronounce a word by looking it up in the dictionary. Following the entry word, you will find the pronunciation of the word in parenthesis. The symbols and letters that tell you how to pronounce the word are called **diacritical marks**. For example, the diacritical marks that show the pronunciation for the word *often* are (ôf´ən). The key to these marks can be found at the bottom of the dictionary page.

Look in the dictionary for each of these words from "Four Skinny Trees." Write the diacritical marks for each word and practice saying the word aloud. Then read the entire poem aloud.

1. excuses
2. appreciate
3. ferocious
4. concrete

Learn About

Detail of a hide painting depicting a buffalo hunt,
Plains Indian, Shoshoni, c.1875. Werner Forman
Archive, H.W. Read Collection, Plains Indian Museum,
Buffalo Bill Historical Center, Cody, Wyoming

READING FOCUS

Recognize Facts That Support Opinions
Opinions carry more weight when they
are backed up with facts. Opinions
occur in many kinds of writing, from ads
and newspaper editorials to short stories
and poems.

When a writer gives facts to support
an opinion, you should examine them
closely. Ask yourself: Do they really
relate to the writer's point? Likewise,
when you express an opinion about a
character or story, you should select facts
from the story or from your experience
to support your opinion.

AUTOBIOGRAPHY

An **autobiography** is the story of a person's life written by that person. Because
the author is writing about himself or
herself, an autobiography is usually written in the first person.

An autobiography may tell about a
person's entire life, or it may focus on just
part of it. Short stories that are autobio-
graphical usually tell about a particular
event or incident in the author's life.

From an autobiography you learn
about the author as a person. You also
learn about the circumstances of the
author's life. As you read "Ta-Na-E-Ka,"
ask yourself:

1. What situation in Mary Whitebird's
   life is described in the story?
2. What do you learn about the
   author from the way she handles
   the situation?

WRITING CONNECTION

Choose an interesting or amusing incident that has happened to you during
the past several weeks. Write a paragraph
in which you recount the incident as
if you were writing your autobiography.
Be sure to include not only the facts,
but also your feelings about the incident.

TA-NA-E-KA

ADAPTED

by Mary Whitebird

As my birthday drew closer, I had awful nightmares about it. I was reaching the age at which all Kaw Indians had to take part in Ta-Na-E-Ka. Well, not all Kaws. Many of the younger families on the reservation were beginning to give up the old customs. But my grandfather, Amos Deer Leg, stood by the old traditions. He still wore handmade beaded moccasins instead of shoes. He kept his iron-gray hair in tight braids. He could speak English, but he spoke it only with white men. With his family he used a Sioux dialect.

Grandfather was one of the last living Indians who actually fought against the U.S. Cavalry. Not only did he fight, he was wounded in a skirmish at Rosebud Creek. This was the famous battle in which the well-known Kaw chief Flat Nose lost his life. At the time, my grandfather was only eleven years old.

Eleven was a magic word among the Kaws. It was the time of Ta-Na-E-Ka, which means "flowering of adulthood."

My grandfather had told us about it hundreds of times. It was the age, he said, "when a boy could prove himself to be a warrior. And a girl can take the first steps to womanhood."

"I don't want to be a warrior," my cousin, Roger Deer Leg, confided to me. "I'm going to become an accountant."

"None of the other tribes make girls go through the survival ritual," I complained to my mother.

"It won't be as bad as you think, Mary," my mother said. "Once you've gone through it, you'll never forget it. You'll be proud."

I even complained to my teacher, Mrs. Richardson. I felt that, as a white woman, she would side with me.

She didn't. "All of us have rituals of one kind or another," Mrs. Richardson said. "And look at it this way: How many girls have the chance to compete on equal terms with boys? Don't look down on your heritage."

---

dialect (DY uh lekt) local manner of speaking
skirmish (SKUR mish) minor battle in a war
confide (kun FYD) tell as a secret
ritual (RICH oo ul) ceremony; tradition
heritage (HER ih tij) what is handed down to a person from ancestors

Heritage, indeed! I didn't plan to live on a reservation for the rest of my life. I was a good student. I loved school. My favorite stories were about knights in armor and fair ladies and dragons. I had never once thought that being Indian was exciting.

But I've always thought that equal rights for women started with the Kaw. No other Indian tribe treated women more "equally" than the Kaw. Unlike most other Sioux tribes, the Kaw allowed men and women to eat together. And hundreds of years ago, a Kaw woman had the right to reject a man chosen for her—even if her father had arranged a marriage.

The wisest women (usually the old ones) often sat in tribal councils. Furthermore, most Kaw legends are about "Good Woman," a kind of super person. Good Woman led Kaw warriors into battle after battle, which they always seemed to win.

And girls as well as boys were required to go through Ta-Na-E-Ka.

The actual ceremony varied from tribe to tribe. But since the Indians' life on the plains depended on survival, Ta-Na-E-Ka was a test of survival.

"Endurance is the highest virtue of the Indian," my grandfather explained. "To survive, we must endure. When I was a boy, Ta-Na-E-Ka was more than just the symbol it is now. We were painted white with the juice of a sacred herb. Then we were sent naked into the wilderness, without so much as a knife. We couldn't return until the white had worn off. It wouldn't wash off. It took almost eighteen days.

"During that time," he went on, "we had to stay alive. We did it by trapping food, eating insects and roots and berries, and watching out for enemies. And we did have enemies—both the white soldiers and the Omaha warriors. They were always trying to capture Kaw boys and girls going through their endurance tests. It was an exciting time."

"What happened if you couldn't make it?" Roger asked. He was born only three days after I was, and we were being trained for Ta-Na-E-Ka together. I was happy to know he was frightened, too.

"Many didn't return," Grandfather said. "Only the strongest and shrewdest. Mothers were not allowed to weep over those who didn't return. If a Kaw couldn't survive, he or she wasn't worth weeping over. It was our way."

"What a lot of hooey," Roger whispered. "I'd give anything to get out of it."

"I don't see how we have any choice," I replied.

Roger gave my arm a little squeeze. "Well, it's only five days."

Five days! Maybe it was better than being painted white and sent out naked for eighteen days. But not much better.

We were to be sent, barefoot and in bathing suits, into the woods. Even our very traditional parents put their foot

---

endurance (en DUUR uns) ability to withstand hardship; survival
virtue (VUR choo) good quality
shrewdest (SHROOD ist) cleverest
traditional (truh DISH uh nul) following old customs

T.C. and Me: Revisited, Amado M. Pena, Jr. El Taller, Inc.

down when Grandfather suggested we go naked. For five days we'd have to live off the land. We'd have to keep warm as best we could and get food where we could. It was May. But on the northernmost shores of the Missouri River, the days were still chilly and the nights fiercely cold.

Grandfather was in charge of the month's training for Ta-Na-E-Ka. One day he caught a grasshopper. Then he showed us how to pull its legs and wings off in one flick of the fingers. And

how to swallow it.

I felt sick, and Roger turned green. "It's a darn good thing it's 1947," I told Roger teasingly. "You'd make a terrible warrior." Roger just made a face.

I knew one thing. This was one Kaw Indian girl who wasn't going to swallow a grasshopper—no matter how hungry she got. And then I had an idea. Why hadn't I thought of it before? It would have saved nights of bad dreams about squooshy grasshoppers.

I headed straight for my teacher's house. "Mrs. Richardson," I said, "would you lend me five dollars?"

"Five dollars!" she exclaimed. "What for?"

"You remember the ceremony I talked about?"

"Ta-Na-E-Ka. Of course. Your parents have written and asked me to excuse you from school so you can take part in it."

"Well, I need some things for the ceremony," I said, in a half-truth. "I don't want to ask my parents for the money."

"It's not a crime to borrow money, Mary. But how can you pay it back?"

"I'll baby-sit for you ten times."

"That's more than fair," she said. She went to her purse and handed me a crisp, new five-dollar bill. I'd never had that much money at once.

"I'm happy to know the money's going to be put to a good use," Mrs. Richardson said.

A few days later, Ta-Na-E-Ka began. First came a long speech from my grandfather. It was all about how we had reached the age of decision, how we now had to take care of ourselves. We had to prove that we could survive the most horrendous of ordeals.

All the friends and relatives gathered at our house for dinner and made jokes about their own Ta-Na-E-Kas. They all advised us to fill up now, since for the next five days we'd be eating crickets. Neither Roger nor I was very hungry.

"I'll probably laugh about this when I'm an accountant," Roger said, trembling.

"Are you trembling?" I asked.

"What do you think?"

"I'm happy to know boys tremble, too," I said.

At six the next morning, we kissed our parents and went off to the woods. "Which side do you want?" Roger asked. According to the rules, Roger and I would stake out "territories" in separate areas of the woods. We weren't to communicate during the whole ordeal.

"I'll go toward the river, if it's okay with you," I said.

"Sure," Roger answered. "What difference does it make?"

To me, it made a lot of difference. There was a marina a few miles up the river, and there were boats anchored there. At least I hoped so. I figured that a boat was a better place to sleep than under a pile of leaves.

"Why do you keep holding your head?" Roger asked.

"Oh, nothing. Just nervous," I told him. Actually, I was afraid I'd lose the five-dollar bill, which I had tucked into my hair with a bobby pin. As we came to a fork in the trail, Roger shook my hand. "Good luck, Mary."

"N'ko-n'ta," I said. It was the Kaw word for *courage*.

---

horrendous (haw REN dus) horrible; awful
ordeal (awr DEEL) severe test; harsh experience
stake out (STAYK out) mark the limits of
marina (muh REE nuh) large area set up for docking boats

The sun was shining and it was warm. But my bare feet began to hurt right away. I saw one of the berry bushes Grandfather had told us about. "You're lucky," he had said. "The berries are ripe in the spring, and they are delicious and nourishing." They were orange and fat and I popped one into my mouth.

Argh! I spat it out. It was awful and bitter. Even grasshoppers were probably better tasting. However, I never intended to find out.

I sat down to rest my feet. A rabbit hopped out from under the berry bush. He nuzzled the berry I'd spat out and ate it. He picked another one and ate that, too. He liked them. He looked at me, twitching his nose. Then I watched a red-headed woodpecker tap on an elm tree. I caught a glimpse of a skunk waddling through some twigs. All of a sudden, I realized I was no longer frightened. Ta-Na-E-Ka might be more fun than I'd expected. I got up and headed toward the marina.

"Not one boat," I said to myself, depressed. But the restaurant on the shore, "Ernie's Riverside," was open. I walked in, feeling silly in my bathing suit. The man at the counter was big and tough-looking. He wore a sweat-shirt with the words "Fort Sheridan, 1944," and he had only three fingers on one of his hands. He asked me what I wanted.

"A hamburger and a milk shake," I said. I held the five-dollar bill in my hand so he'd know I had money

"That's a pretty heavy breakfast, honey," he said.

"That's what I always have for breakfast," I lied.

"Forty-five cents," he said, bringing me the food. (Back in 1947, hamburgers were twenty-five cents and milk shakes were twenty cents.) "Delicious," I thought. "Better'n grasshoppers. And Grandfather never once said that I couldn't eat hamburgers."

While I was eating, I had a grand idea. Why not sleep in the restaurant? I went to the ladies' room and made sure the window was unlocked. Then I went back outside and played along the riverbank. I watched the water birds, trying to identify each one. I planned to look for a beaver dam the next day.

The restaurant closed at sunset, and I watched the three-fingered man drive away. Then I climbed in the unlocked window. There was a night light on, so I didn't turn on any lights. But there was a radio on the counter. I turned it on to a music program.

It was warm in the restaurant, and I was hungry. I helped myself to a glass of milk and a piece of pie. But I meant to keep a list of what I'd eaten, so I could leave money. I also meant to get up early. Then I could sneak out through the window and head for the woods before the three-fingered man returned. I turned off the radio. I wrapped myself in the man's apron. And, in spite of the hardness of the floor, I fell asleep.

---

nuzzle (NUZ ul) nudge with the nose

"What the heck are you doing here, kid?"

It was the man's voice.

It was morning. I'd overslept. I was scared.

"Hold it, kid. I just wanna know what you're doing here. You lost? You must be from the reservation. Your folks must be worried sick about you. Do they have a phone?"

"Yes, yes," I answered. "But don't call them."

I was shivering. The man, who told me his name was Ernie, made me a cup of hot chocolate. Meanwhile, I explained about Ta-Na-E-Ka.

"Darndest thing I ever heard," he said, when I was through. "Lived next to the reservation all my life, and this is the first I've heard of Ta-Na whatever-you-call-it." He looked at me, all goose bumps in my bathing suit. "Pretty silly thing to do to a kid," he muttered.

That was just what I'd been thinking for months. But when Ernie said it, I became angry. "No, it isn't silly. It's a custom of the Kaw. We've been doing this for hundreds of years. My mother and my grandfather and everybody in my family went through this ceremony. It's why the Kaw are great warriors."

"Okay, great warrior," Ernie chuckled, "suit yourself. And if you want to stick around, it's okay with me." Ernie went to the broom closet and tossed me a bundle. "That's the lost-and-found closet," he said. "Stuff people left on boats. Maybe there's something to keep you warm."

The sweater fitted loosely, but it felt good. I felt good. And I'd found a new friend. Most important, I was surviving Ta-Na-E-Ka.

My grandfather had said Ta-Na-E-Ka would be filled with adventure. I was certainly having my fill. And Grandfather had never said we couldn't accept hospitality.

I stayed at Ernie's Riverside for the whole five days. In the mornings, I went into the woods. There I watched the animals and picked flowers for each of the tables in Ernie's. I had never felt better. I was up early enough to watch the sun rise on the Missouri, and I went to bed after it set. I ate everything I wanted—insisting that Ernie take all my money for the food.

"I'll keep this in trust for you, Mary," Ernie promised. "In case you are ever desperate for five dollars."

I was sorry when the five days were over. I'd enjoyed every minute with Ernie. He taught me how to make western omelets and Chili Ernie Style. (That's still one of my favorite dishes.) And I told Ernie all about the legends of the Kaw. I hadn't realized I knew so much about my people.

But Ta-Na-E-Ka was over. As I neared my house, at about nine-thirty in the evening, I became nervous all over again. What if Grandfather asked me about the berries and the grasshoppers? And my feet were hardly cut. I hadn't lost a pound, and my hair was combed.

---

omelet (OM lut) eggs beaten up, fried, and folded in half when done

"They'll be so happy to see me," I told myself hopefully, "that they won't ask too many questions."

I opened the door. My grandfather was in the front room. He was wearing the ceremonial beaded deerskin shirt which had belonged to *his* grandfather.

"N'g'da'ma," he said. "Welcome back."

I hugged my parents warmly. Then I let go when I saw my cousin Roger sprawled on the couch. His eyes were red and swollen. He'd lost weight. His feet were an unsightly mass of blood and blisters. And he was moaning: "I made it, see, I made it. I'm a warrior. A warrior."

My grandfather looked at me strangely. I looked clean, well fed, and radiantly healthy. My parents got the message. My uncle and aunt gazed at me with hostility.

Finally my grandfather asked, "What did you eat to keep you so well?"

I sucked in my breath and blurted out the truth: "Hamburgers and milk shakes."

"Hamburgers!" my grandfather growled.

"Milk shakes!" Roger moaned.

"You didn't say we *had* to eat grasshoppers," I said meekly.

"Tell us about your Ta-Na-E-Ka," my grandfather commanded.

I told them everything, from borrowing the five dollars, to Ernie's kindness, to watching the beaver.

"That's not what I trained you for," my grandfather said sadly.

I stood up. "Grandfather, I learned that Ta-Na-E-Ka *is* important. I didn't think so during training. I was scared stiff of it.

I handled it my way. And I learned I had nothing to be afraid of. There's no reason in 1947 to eat grasshoppers when you can eat a hamburger."

Inside, I was shocked at my own boldness. But I liked it. "Grandfather, I'll bet you never ate one of those rotten berries yourself."

Grandfather laughed! He laughed aloud! My mother and father and aunt and uncle were all dumbfounded. Grandfather never laughed. Never.

"Those berries—they are terrible," Grandfather admitted. "I could never swallow them. On the first day of my Ta-Na-E-Ka, I found a dead deer—shot by a soldier, probably. It kept my belly full for the entire period of the test!"

Grandfather stopped laughing. "We should send you out again," he said.

I looked at Roger. "You're pretty smart, Mary," Roger groaned. "I'd never have thought of what you did."

"Accountants just have to be good at arithmetic," I said comfortingly. "I'm terrible at arithmetic."

Roger tried to smile, but couldn't. My grandfather called me to him. "You should have done what your cousin did. But I think you are more aware of what is happening to our people today than we are. I think you would have passed the test under any circumstances, in any time. Somehow, you know how to live in a world that wasn't made for Indians. I don't think you're going to have any trouble surviving."

Grandfather wasn't entirely right. But I'll tell about that another time.

Review the Selection

UNDERSTAND THE SELECTION

Recall

1. What is Ta-Na-E-Ka?

2. Who else goes through Ta-Na-E-Ka with Mary?

3. Where does Mary spend Ta-Na-E-Ka?

Infer

4. What can you infer about what is happening in the Kaw culture?

5. Why does Roger object to Ta-Na-E-Ka?

6. What was unusual about the way Kaws treated women?

7. Why were Mary's relatives hostile toward her when she returned?

Apply

8. How do you think Mary Whitebird felt when she saw Roger after Ta-Na-E-Ka?

9. Predict what would have happened if Mary Whitebird had stayed in the woods the way her cousin did.

10. Why does Grandfather say that Ta-Na-E-Ka is just a symbol today?

Respond to Literature

Do you agree or disagree with the following statement? Why?

"Mary Whitebird made some important discoveries during the Ta-Na-E-Ka, but not the ones her grandfather expected her to make."

WRITE ABOUT THE SELECTION

At the conclusion of the story, Mary Whitebird's grandfather says, "Somehow, you know how to live in a world that wasn't made for Indians. I don't think you're going to have any trouble surviving." Then the author comments, "Grandfather wasn't entirely right. But I'll tell about that another time."

What do you think may have happened to Mary later in life to cause her to make this comment? Write a paragraph in which you describe an event in Mary's life that happens after Ta-Na-E-Ka.

Prewriting Make a list of possible situations that could challenge Mary's ability to survive. Write what the outcome might be.

Writing Choose a situation from your list and let this be the subject of your paragraph. Make it clear in your paragraph how much time has elapsed since the end of "Ta-Na-E-Ka." For example, you might be writing about the day that Mary Whitebird enters college. This event would take place about nine years after the Ta-Na-E-Ka ritual.

Revising Read your paragraph and note any sentences that seem too long or too choppy. Make run-ons into separate sentences. Combine short sentences to make more sophisticated compound or complex ones. Rewrite these sentences.

Proofreading Check your paper for errors in spelling, usage, and mechanics. Be sure you have used abbreviations correctly.

THINK ABOUT AUTOBIOGRAPHY

When you read an autobiography, you see the author's world through his or her eyes. You learn how the author views the times, the social conditions, and the geographic location in which he or she lives. In this way, autobiographies provide valuable historical information.

1. What is the setting for "Ta-Na-E-Ka"?

2. How old is Mary when "Ta-Na-E-Ka" takes place? Why is this age important?

3. If Mary Whitebird's autobiography were cataloged in the library as a social studies book, under what subject might it be classified?

4. Why is Grandfather a significant character in this story?

5. What do Mrs. Richardson's comments about Ta-Na-E-Ka add to the story?

READING FOCUS

Recognize Facts That Support Opinions
Respond to this opinion: Roger benefited as much from his experience as Mary did from hers during Ta-Na-E-Ka. Cite several facts to support this opinion. These facts should come from the story, as well as from challenging experiences you have had.

DEVELOP YOUR VOCABULARY

A **contraction** is a shortened form of two words. The two words are joined together by leaving out one or more letters. An apostrophe takes the place of the missing letter or letters. For example, the contraction *isn't* is a combination of the words *is not*. In the story "Ta-Na-E-Ka," the author uses many contractions. She does this in order to give the story a natural, informal tone.

Write the two words that have been combined to form each contraction.

1. I don't want to be a warrior.

2. Once you've gone through it, you'll never forget it.

3. Many didn't return.

4. We couldn't return until the white had worn off.

5. You'd make a terrible warrior.

Focus ON NONFICTION

*N*onfiction is literature that tells about real life, real people, and events that actually happened. Autobiographies, biographies, and essays are all nonfictional accounts. Autobiographies and biographies tell stories, or narratives, about real people. Essays express writers' thoughts and opinions on a topic. You can better understand these narratives by thinking about the four main parts, or elements, of nonfiction: plot, point of view, tone, and theme.

Plot The plot is a series of events that make up a narrative, such as a nonfictional account. In nonfiction, the plot describes both the things that happen to the characters and the things that the characters do. As the plot unfolds, you learn what happens and why it happens. An important part of the plot is **conflict**. Usually the central character is presented with a set of problems that he or she must overcome. These problems will force the main character to struggle with another character or group of characters, an object, or nature. Sometimes the struggle is within the main character's own self.

As you read a nonfictional account, you can identify three main parts: introduction, body, and conclusion. The **introduction** sets the stage and draws you into the world of the characters. A good introduction will spark your curiosity and make you ask questions such as: "What is this account about? Who is telling it? What has happened? What is going to happen?" In the **body**, the plot unfolds. You follow the main character's struggles and conflicts until you reach the outcome or climax. When the entire account has been told, the author brings it to a **conclusion**. The conclusion may sum up the events or it may offer a comment on the value or importance of the account. In some cases, the author may hint at what happens next in the characters' lives. For example, in "Ta-Na-E-Ka," Mary Whitebird indicates that, later in life, she did not always cope so well with the world as she did during her Ta-Na-E-Ka.

Point of View   Every narrative must be written from a certain point of view. That is, someone must tell what is happening. Usually a nonfictional account is told from either a first-person or a third-person point of view.

When a narrative is told in the **first person**, the narrator is usually a character in the story. You can tell when a narrative is told in the first person because the narrator refers to himself or herself as *I* and *me*. A first-person narrator can be a major character or a minor character. An important point to remember in first-person narration is that the information given is limited to what the narrator can see, hear, think, know, and feel. Most autobiographies are written in the first person.

A **third-person** narrator stands outside the story. The narrator refers to each character as *he* or *she*. A third-person narrator is not limited by what one person can see, hear, or know, but is free to comment on any aspect of the narrative. Biographies usually have a third-person point of view.

Tone   The tone communicates the author's feelings about the subject of his or her account. The tone can be serious or humorous, personal or detached, lighthearted or somber, casual, formal, or any combination of these. For example, in "Ta-Na-E-Ka," Mary Whitebird's narration is serious but also somewhat lighthearted, reflecting an 11-year-old girl's thinking.

Theme   A person writes a nonfictional account because he or she has something to say. The message the writer wants to send to the reader is the theme, or main idea of the account. Some nonfiction accounts state the theme clearly, while others ask you to figure it out for yourself.

As you read "Dead at Seventeen," discover the elements of nonfiction that are present. Ask yourself these questions:

1. What is the point of view?
2. How is this point of view unusual?

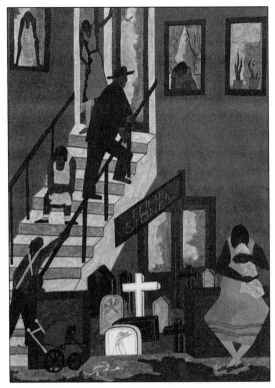

Tombstones, Jacob Lawrence. Collection of the Whitney Museum of American Art

Dead at Seventeen

from Ann Landers

Dear Readers: Today's column is dedicated to that beautiful guy, Paul "Bear" Bryant, the "winningest coach" from the University of Alabama. The Bear, who died last Jan. 26, used to read this column to every freshman class on opening day.

It would be lovely if Ray Perkins, the Bear's successor, carried on the tradition. Bryant loved his kids and he wanted them to stay alive.

FOCUS ON NONFICTION STUDY HINTS

The introduction sets the tone for the selection. How does the introduction draw you into the account?

Agony claws my mind. I am a statistic. When I first got here I felt very much alone. I was overwhelmed with grief, and I expected to find sympathy.

I found no sympathy. I saw only thousands of others whose bodies were as badly mangled as mine. I was given a number and placed in a category. The category was called "Traffic Fatalities."

Notice the point of view. How is this point of view effective?

The day I died was an ordinary school day. How I wish I had taken the bus! But I was too cool for the bus. I remember how I wheedled the car out of Mom. "Special favor," I pleaded. "All the kids drive." When the 2:50 bell rang, I threw my books in the locker . . . free until tomorrow morning! I ran to the parking lot, excited at the thought of driving a car and being my own boss.

The body text in the next five paragraphs contains the plot of the account. You learn what happened to the narrator and how he felt.

It doesn't matter how the accident happened. I was goofing off—going too fast, taking crazy chances. But I was enjoying my freedom and having fun. The last thing I remember was passing an old lady who seemed to be going awfully slow. I heard a crash and felt a terrific jolt. Glass and steel flew everywhere. My whole body seemed to be turning inside out. I heard myself scream.

Suddenly, I awakened. It was very quiet. A police officer was standing over me. I saw a doctor. My body was mangled. I was saturated with blood. Pieces of jagged glass were sticking out all over. Strange that I couldn't feel anything. Hey, don't pull that sheet over my head. I can't be dead. I'm only 17. I've got a date tonight. I'm supposed to have a wonderful life ahead of me. I haven't lived yet. I can't be dead.

Later I was placed in a drawer. My folks came to identify me. Why did they have to see me like this? Why did I have to look at Mom's eyes when she faced the most terrible ordeal of her life? Dad suddenly looked very old. He told the man in charge, "Yes, he's our son."

The funeral was weird. I saw all my relatives and friends walk toward the casket. They looked at me with the saddest eyes I've ever seen. Some of my buddies were crying. A few of the girls touched my hand and sobbed as they walked by.

As the conclusion begins, notice that you are back to where the narrator is now.

Please somebody—wake me up! Get me out of here. I can't bear to see Mom and Dad in such pain. My grandparents are so weak from grief they can barely walk. My brother and sister are like zombies. They move like robots. In a daze. Everybody. No one can believe this. I can't believe it, either.

The author's purpose for writing the story is clear. This is the theme of the account.

Please, don't bury me! I'm not dead! I have a lot of living to do! I want to laugh and run again. I want to sing and dance. Please don't put me in the ground! I promise if you give me just one more chance, God, I'll be the most careful driver in the whole world. All I want is one more chance. Please, God, I'm only 17.

Paul "Bear" Bryant

Review the Selection

Recall

1. Who is telling this account?

2. Where is the narrator?

3. What has happened to him?

Infer

4. Describe the narrator's mood as he leaves school at the end of the day.

5. In what state was the narrator when he "awakened"?

6. Explain the meaning of the phrase "placed in a drawer."

7. How does the narrator feel about his parents, relatives, and friends?

Apply

8. What kind of bargain does the narrator wish to make with God?

9. How do you think this boy's mother felt after loaning him the car?

10. Suppose you had been a passenger in the narrator's car. How would you feel if you had lived?

Respond to Literature

How is this boy's discovery different from or similar to discoveries you have made in your own life? Have you ever discovered something too late?

WRITE ABOUT THE SELECTION

The selection "Dead at Seventeen" originally appeared in an Ann Landers column. Landers wrote that there was a coach at the University of Alabama who used to read this story to every freshman class on opening day. She said that he loved his kids and wanted them to stay alive.

Write a paragraph in which you express your reaction to this selection. Is it one that you will remember? How might it influence you in the future?

Prewriting Read the selection again and write down any thoughts and feelings that come to mind. Try to relate the selection to your own life and experience. Have you ever been involved in a car accident? Have you ever known anyone who was killed in an accident? Have you ever ridden with someone who was driving carelessly? How did you feel?

Writing Use your notes to write a response to "Dead at Seventeen." Include in your paragraph your overall feeling about the selection.

Revising Imagine that you are writing this paragraph in a letter to a friend. Add a sentence about why you think your friend should read the selection.

Proofreading Check your paragraph for errors in spelling, usage, and mechanics. Correct any sentence fragments by making them into complete sentences.

THINK ABOUT NONFICTION

A nonfiction story tells about real people and events. The four main parts of a nonfictional account are plot, point of view, tone, and theme. A narrative also has a recognizable introduction, body, and conclusion.

1. What is the tone of "Dead at Seventeen"?

2. What is the account's point of view? Is the narrator the person to whom the events actually happened? Why or why not?

3. How does the introduction draw you into the account?

4. Briefly summarize the series of events that take place.

5. What is the message of the account? Why do you think the author wrote it?

DEVELOP YOUR VOCABULARY

Slang is nonstandard language that is used in casual speech. Slang expressions are often popular with teenagers. For example, the author of "Dead at Seventeen" uses slang expressions in order to make the voice of the seventeen-year-old storyteller seem more real and believable.

Slang tends to change with time. For example, teenagers in the 1950s referred to something really great as "keen." When slang expressions are used over a period of time by a large number of people, they often become entry words in the dictionary.

Identify the slang expression in each of the following sentences. Then rewrite each sentence using standard language to express the same idea.

1. I was too cool to take the bus.

2. That's a sharp dress you have on.

3. You're so dense.

4. I blew it.

5. Somebody ripped off my pen.

Learn About

THEME

A **theme** is an idea or message in a story, play, or poem. It is possible for a piece of literature to have several themes. Only one of these, however, will be the main theme. For example, in the story "The Gold Medal," the main theme is Amanda's discovery of her true self apart from the roles people tried to impose on her. A less important theme, or **subtheme**, is the dilemma of an African American girl in a society that is made up mostly of white people.

You can often recognize the theme of a story by thinking, "Why did the author write this story, play, or poem?" As you read "Thank You, M'am," ask yourself:

1. What message does Langston Hughes wish to convey?
2. How does the story communicate this message?

READING FOCUS

Make Predictions When you make predictions, you try to guess what will happen in a story before it actually happens. Confirming your predictions is one way to measure how well you understand the story. Revising predictions helps you summarize what has happened so far and adds to your enjoyment. Your own experience can help you make predictions about a story. Jot down your predictions. Compare them to what happens in the story. Then make new predictions based on what you have read.

WRITING CONNECTION

Imagine that you are a short-story writer. What kind of a theme might you choose? Write a paragraph in which you describe a theme that is meaningful to you. (For example, you might want to write about standing up for someone who is being teased.) Discuss how you would handle the theme and the message you would communicate.

THANK YOU, M'AM

by Langston Hughes

She was a large woman with a large purse that had everything in it but hammer and nails. It had a long strap, and she carried it slung across her shoulder. It was about eleven o'clock at night, and she was walking alone, when a boy ran up behind her and tried to snatch her purse. The strap broke with the sudden single tug the boy gave it from behind. But the boy's weight and the weight of the purse combined caused him to lose his balance.

---

slung (SLUNG) hung; made to swing loosely

Instead of taking off full blast as he had hoped, the boy fell on his back on the sidewalk, and his legs flew up. The large woman simply turned around and kicked him right square in his blue-jeaned sitter. Then she reached down, picked the boy up by his shirt front, and shook him until his teeth rattled.

After that the woman said, "Pick up my pocketbook, boy, and give it here."

She still held him tightly. But she bent down enough to permit him to stoop and pick up her purse. Then she said, "Now ain't you ashamed of yourself?"

Firmly gripped by his shirt front, the boy said, "Yes'm."

The woman said, "What did you want to do it for?"

The boy said, "I didn't aim to."

She said, "You a lie!"

By that time two or three people passed, stopped, turned to look, and some stood watching.

"If I turn you loose, will you run?" asked the woman.

"Yes'm," said the boy.

"Then I won't turn you loose," said the woman. She did not release him.

"Lady, I'm sorry," whispered the boy.

"Um-hum! Your face is dirty. I got a great mind to wash your face for you. Ain't you got nobody home to tell you to wash your face?"

"No'm," said the boy.

"Then it will get washed this evening," said the large woman, starting up the street, dragging the frightened boy behind her.

He looked as if he were fourteen or fifteen, frail and willow-wild, in tennis shoes and blue jeans.

The woman said, "You ought to be my son. I would teach you right from wrong. Least I can do right now is to wash your face. Are you hungry?"

"No'm," said the being-dragged boy. "I just want you to turn me loose."

"Was I bothering *you* when I turned that corner?" asked the woman.

"No'm."

"But you put yourself in contact with *me*," said the woman.

---

frail (FRAYL) weak

"If you think that that contact is not going to last awhile, you got another thought coming. When I get through with you, sir, you are going to remember Mrs. Luella Bates Washington Jones."

Sweat popped out on the boy's face and he began to struggle. Mrs. Jones stopped, jerked him around in front of her, put a half nelson about his neck, and continued to drag him up the street. When she got to her door, she dragged the boy inside, down a hall, and into a large kitchenette-furnished room at the rear of the house. She switched on the light and left the door open. The boy could hear other roomers laughing and talking in the large house. Some of their doors were open, too, so he knew he and the woman were not alone. The woman still had him by the neck in the middle of her room.

She said, "What is your name?"

"Roger," answered the boy.

"Then, Roger, you go to that sink and wash your face," said the woman, whereupon she turned him loose—at last. Roger looked at the door—looked at the woman—looked at the door—*and went to the sink.*

"Let the water run until it gets warm," she said. "Here's a clean towel."

"You gonna take me to jail?" asked the boy, bending over the sink.

"Not with that face, I would not take you nowhere," said the woman. "Here I am trying to get home to cook me a bite to eat, and you snatch my pocketbook! Maybe you ain't been to your supper either, late as it be. Have you?"

"There's nobody home at my house," said the boy.

"Then we'll eat," said the woman. "I believe you're hungry— or been hungry—to try to snatch my pocketbook!"

"I want a pair of blue suede shoes," said the boy.

"Well, you didn't have to snatch *my* pocketbook to get some suede shoes," said Mrs. Luella Bates Washington Jones. "You could of asked me."

"M'am? "

The water dripping from his face, the boy looked at her. There

---

half nelson (HAF NEL sun) wrestling hold on back of neck
whereupon (HWAIR uh pon) after which
suede (SWAYD) soft leather with a velvet-like surface

was a long pause. A very long pause. After he had dried his face, and not knowing what else to do, dried it again, the boy turned around, wondering what next. The door was open. He could make a dash for it down the hall. He could run, run, run, *run*!

The woman was sitting on the daybed. After a while she said, "I were young once and I wanted things I could not get."

There was another long pause. The boy's mouth opened. Then he frowned, not knowing he frowned.

The woman said, "Um-hum! You thought I was going to say *but*, didn't you? You thought I was going to say, *but I didn't snatch people's pocketbooks.* Well, I wasn't going to say that." Pause. Silence. "I have done things, too, which I would not tell you, son—neither tell God, if He didn't already know. Everybody's got something in common. So you set down while I fix us something to eat. You might run that comb through your hair so you will look presentable."

In another corner of the room behind a screen was a gas plate and an icebox. Mrs. Jones got up and went behind the screen. The woman did not watch the boy to see if he was going to run now, nor did she watch her purse, which she left behind her on the daybed. But the boy took care to sit on the far side of the room, away from the purse, where he thought she could easily see him out of the corner of her eye if she wanted to. He did not trust the woman *not* to trust him. And he did not want to be mistrusted now.

"Do you need somebody to go to the store," asked the boy, "maybe to get some milk or something?"

"Don't believe I do," said the woman, "unless you just want sweet milk yourself. I was going to make cocoa out of this canned milk I got here."

"That will be fine," said the boy.

She heated some lima beans and ham she had in the icebox, made the cocoa, and set the table. The woman did not ask the boy anything about where he lived, or his folks, or anything else that would embarrass him. Instead, as they ate, she told him about her job in a hotel beauty shop that stayed open late, what the work was like, and how all kinds of women came in and out, blondes, redheads, and Spanish. Then she cut him a half of her ten-cent cake.

---

plate (PLAYT) small burner for cooking

"Eat some more, son," she said.

When they were finished eating, she got up and said, "Now here, take this ten dollars and buy yourself some blue suede shoes. And next time, do not make the mistake of latching onto *my* pocketbook *nor nobody else's*—because shoes got by devilish ways will burn your feet. I got to get my rest now. But from here on in, son, I hope you will behave yourself."

She led him down the hall to the front door and opened it. "Good night! Behave yourself, boy!" she said, looking out into the street as he went down the steps.

The boy wanted to say something else other than, "Thank you, m'am," to Mrs. Luella Bates Washington Jones, but although his lips moved, he couldn't even say that as he turned at the foot of the barren stoop and looked up at the large woman in the door. Then she shut the door.

---

barren (BAR un) dull; uninteresting
stoop (STOOP) front step

Review the Selection

UNDERSTAND THE SELECTION

Recall

1. What is the opening incident?

2. Where does Mrs. Jones take the boy?

3. What does Mrs. Jones give the boy at the end of the story?

Infer

4. What can you infer about the boy's parents?

5. What argument does Mrs. Jones use when the boy begs her to turn him loose?

6. In what kind of house does Mrs. Jones live?

7. What hint in the story tells you that Mrs. Jones did not always behave herself when she was young?

Apply

8. Why do you think the boy does not run from Mrs. Jones's house when he has the chance?

9. What will the boy do with the money?

10. Predict whether or not you think the boy will behave himself from now on.

Respond to Literature

What do Mrs. Jones and the boy discover about each other? Do you think discoveries like this can happen in real life?

WRITE ABOUT THE SELECTION

Suppose that many years have passed and that the boy in "Thank You, M'am" is an adult. How do you think he would remember his encounter with Luella Bates Washington Jones? Write a paragraph in which the boy (now grown up) tells about Mrs. Jones.

Prewriting   Take a few minutes to brainstorm about the details you want to include in your paragraph. Decide how old you want the boy to be and what the circumstances of his life are (such as rich, poor, successful, in jail).

Writing   Use the ideas from your brainstorming session to write a paragraph from the adult boy's point of view. Be sure to make clear the boy's feelings about Mrs. Jones and the incident with the purse. Also, make clear what effect, if any, the incident had on the boy as he grew older. Base your paragraph on Langston Hughes's message to the readers in the story.

Revising   You can make your paragraph more effective by adding specific details from the story as seen from the boy's point of view. Rearrange phrases and eliminate boring words to make your story come alive.

Proofreading   Check your paragraph for errors in spelling, usage, and mechanics. Add periods or other end marks to correct run on sentences. Make sure that every sentence ends with a period, question mark, or exclamation mark.

THINK ABOUT THEME

When thinking about the theme of a story, it is important not to confuse theme with plot. The **plot** of a story is what happens in the story, while the **theme** is the message or main idea of the story. Stories with different plots might have the same theme.

1. What is the theme of "Thank You, M'am"?

2. Do you agree with the message of the story?

3. Why do you think Mrs. Jones treated the boy the way she did?

4. What did Mrs. Jones hope her encounter with the boy would accomplish?

5. In general, do you think that people like Mrs. Jones tend to make other people better or that others just take advantage of them?

READING FOCUS

Make Predictions As you read "Thank You, M'am," you were able to make, confirm, and revise predictions. How were your predictions about the title and the characters confirmed? Did you have to revise any of your other predictions? If so, how?

DEVELOP YOUR VOCABULARY

A **synonym** is a word that has the same or almost the same meaning as another word. For example, the boy in "Thank You, M'am" tries to *snatch* Mrs. Jones's purse. Two words that are synonyms for *snatch* are the words *take* and *grab*.

Review these words from "Thank You, M'am" and other stories in this unit. Write at least one synonym for each word. Then write an original paragraph that uses the words from the list.

1. slung
2. frail
3. barren
4. gingerly
5. quaver
6. zealously
7. surmised
8. acrid
9. shrewdest
10. horrendous

HAIKU

Haiku is a form of poetry that has been popular in Japan for over 300 years. A **haiku** consists of 17 syllables arranged in three lines. Haiku often has a 5-7-5 pattern of syllables (the first line has five syllables, the second line has seven, and the third line has five). Sometimes, when haiku are translated into English, they do not follow this pattern. All haiku strives to say much in as few words as possible.

Usually a haiku refers to or describes something in nature. A haiku may also have some symbolic meaning. You will also notice that the last selection about a bee is too long to be a haiku. But, like haiku, it uses the world of nature as a symbol for something else.

As you read the four haiku that follow, ask yourself:

1. What do these poems say about the objects they are describing?
2. What do these poems say about people and life?

WRITING CONNECTION

Think of an object in nature that interests you: perhaps an animal, insect, flower, or tree. Write a description of the object in haiku form, using three lines in a 5-7-5 pattern of syllables.

READING FOCUS

Identify Fact and Opinion Haiku and many others forms of poetry are descriptive. The speaker makes factual observations about the world. However, the overall tone of the poem may express an opinion, or point of view, about the thing that the speaker observes. As you read the poems, notice how each speaker conveys an opinion by the way he or she states facts.

Shadows of Evening, Rockwell Kent. Collection of the Whitney Museum of American Art

Four Haiku

1

Here . . . there. . .
the sound of waterfall is heard—
young leaves, everywhere.   *—Buson*

2

Friend, that open mouth
reveals your whole interior. . .
Silly hollow frog!   *—Anonymous*

3

Make up your mind snail!
You are half inside your house
and halfway out!   *—Richard Wright*

4

Insects, why cry?
We all go
that way.   *—Issa*

A bee thumps

5

A bee thumps against the dusty window
falls to the sill,
climbs back up, buzzing;
falls again;
and does this over and over.
If only he would climb higher!
The top half of the window is
open.   *—Robert Sund*

Review the Selection

UNDERSTAND THE SELECTION

Recall

1. What is the setting for the first haiku?

2. What animal is described in the second haiku?

3. What is the bee doing in the last poem?

Infer

4. What time of year does the first haiku describe?

5. What human quality might be symbolized by the animal in the second haiku?

6. In what ways is the last poem similar to a haiku?

7. What human predicament might the bee symbolize?

Apply

8. How might the title "Indecision" apply to the haiku about the snail?

9. What is the meaning of the haiku about insects?

10. What is the meaning of the word "house" in the poem about the snail?

Respond to Literature

What images do these five poems bring to mind? Do the images relate only to nature, or do they relate to human life as well?

WRITE ABOUT THE SELECTION

Several of the poems in this selection symbolize human qualities that are represented by animals. Think of a person you know (it might be you!) who has a characteristic that might be presented in a haiku about an animal. Then write a haiku or poem describing this person.

Prewriting Make a chart of several animals that lend themselves to this assignment. (For convenience, you can use the animals in the haiku you studied, such as "Frog" or "Snail.") Under each title you list, write down the human characteristic that is symbolized. Then write down the names of people you know who have this characteristic.

Writing Decide which name on your list would make the best subject for your haiku or poem. Then describe this person with words that you could use in the poem. Try to include a specific incident involving the person that illustrates the characteristic you are writing about.

Revising The use of adjectives is important in a description. Reread your poem and add or substitute at least three adjectives that make the picture of the person you are writing about more vivid.

Proofreading Check for mistakes in spelling, usage, and mechanics. Be sure to use apostrophes to make nouns possessive.

THINK ABOUT HAIKU

A **haiku** paints a picture in words. The subject of the haiku is usually an object in nature. Very often, the meaning of a haiku goes beyond its subject. The subject becomes a symbol of a human characteristic or an aspect of human life.

1. In the second poem, how is the interior of the frog described?

2. How does this description comment on a person who is like the frog?

3. In the poem about the bee, what does the bee not realize?

4. How does this poem apply to someone who keeps making the same mistake over and over?

5. Describe the picture that is painted in the first haiku.

READING FOCUS

Identify Fact and Opinion Tell what is being described in each poem. Then write the opinion that the words or tone convey. Tell how the speaker feels or what the speaker believes about the thing he or she is describing.

DEVELOP YOUR VOCABULARY

A **thesaurus** is a dictionary of synonyms. When you look up a word in a thesaurus, you will find a list of words that have meanings that are similar to the meaning of that word.

The words in a thesaurus can be very helpful when writing a poem, story, or essay. Suppose you are writing a haiku and you need a one-syllable word that means ocean. If you look up the word *ocean* in a thesaurus, you will find the word *sea* which has the same meaning.

Look up the following words in a thesaurus, and find at least two synonyms for each word. Then use each word in an original sentence.

1. interior   4. sound
2. hollow   5. fall
3. house   6. window

Portage in the Hoarfrost River, Canada, Sir George Back. Royal Geographical Society, London, UK/Bridgeman Art Library

READING FOCUS

Summarize When you summarize a piece of writing, you state only the main ideas or events that are presented. Stories can usually be divided into a beginning, middle, and end. When you read a longer story, try pausing at the end of each part to summarize what has happened. Summarizing the action in your own words can help you remember and understand the story. A summary should always be simpler and shorter than the piece you are summarizing.

CONFLICT

An important ingredient in the plot of a story is **conflict**. A conflict is a meeting of two opposing forces. Often the central character in a story is involved in a struggle with another character. In some stories, however, the struggle is between the main character and nature, or between the main character and some other thing. It is also possible for the conflict to be within a person.

A story begins to develop once a conflict is established. As you read "Starvation Wilderness," ask yourself:

1. What is the conflict in this story?
2. What is the outcome of the conflict?

WRITING CONNECTION

Think of a conflict that you have been involved in recently. It may have been a confrontation with another person, or it may have been a difficult set of circumstances or a conflict within your own mind. Write a short paragraph in which you describe the nature of the conflict and the way it was handled. Also, indicate the outcome of the conflict.

STARVATION WILDERNESS

ADAPTED   *by Olive A. Fredrickson*

Our scow was heavy. It was an old 30-footer that we had bought at Fort Fitzgerald. But with only two grown-ups, a baby, and a pair of sled dogs on board, it rode high. The steady current of the Slave River pushed us north far faster than anyone could have walked on shore.

We had oars, and now and then my young husband, Walter, used them for a short distance. But there was no need for it. Mostly he just steered. We watched the early-fall scenery slip past or played with our six-month-old daughter, Olive. When we weren't cuddling her, she slept as contented as a kitten in the small cardboard box that was her crib.

Muskrat sign was plentiful along the river. Wherever there was green grass along the shore, snow geese pastured by the hundreds. We were rarely out of hearing of their wild voices. We had come to a land of plenty, Walter and I agreed. It was a dream country for a young trapper and his wife.

The time was late August of 1922. The trip had come about when Walter met two trappers, Nels Nelson and Pete Anderson, at Fort Fitzgerald. They had trapped the fall before down the Slave in Northwest Territories. They had come out before Christmas, they said, with 1,600 muskrat skins that brought $1.50 apiece. There were lakes all over the country, they told Walter, and every one of those lakes crawled with marsh rats.

My husband was a trapper at heart, above everything else. For him stories of that kind were like wild tales of gold to other men. He gave up then and there all thought of going to Fort McMurray, where I had been looking forward to the presence of other women, a few comforts, and a doctor in case the baby or I needed one. The three of us, Walter decided, would spend the winter trapping on those rich fur grounds.

We bought the scow and 34 single-spring traps. We also bought 400 pounds of flour, 50 pounds of white sugar, and four 50-pound sacks of potatoes. I remember that we paid $12 for each of those sacks. Coal oil[1] was $2 a gallon at Fitzgerald. We completed our grub list with beans, rice, salt pork, oatmeal,

---

scow (SKOU) barge; tub-like boat for carrying cargo
cuddling (KUD ling) holding and petting
muskrat (MUSK rat) brown animal that lives in and near water, about two feet long; also called
   marsh rat and *rat* in the selection
presence (PREZ uns) nearness; being there
[1]**coal oil:** kerosene, sometimes made from coal

baking powder, salt, and tea—and corn-meal for the dogs.

We loaded the scow and shoved off on August 23 for the trip down the Slave to our trapping grounds. We were in completely unfamiliar country. It was the first time either of us had been that far north. We were on our way into what Walter had been told was good fur country. He was completely happy. I'll confess that I wasn't quite so cheerful as he was about wintering with a child not yet a year old hundreds of miles from the nearest doctor.

Nels and Pete had told us to look for an old sawdust pile on the west shore of the river. We should settle down around there, they had said. We passed the saw-dust pile on our fourth day of floating. We tied up the scow, let our two dogs loose for a run, got the tent up, and carried our supplies up the bank. It was close to mid-night when we finished. We tied the dogs to trees and turned in.

After we had gotten to sleep, I was awakened by some animal gnawing on the salt pork[2] we had brought into the tent. At first I thought one of the dogs had gotten loose. But as my eyes grew accus-tomed to the dim light in the tent I made out a large skunk.

The tent was only 9 × 12 feet. That skunk was working on the pork within three feet of my face. I shook Walter awake. We tried to drive the skunk off, but it wouldn't budge.

"I'll have to shoot it or we won't have any pork," Walter finally said. We knew it wasn't a very good idea, but we had no choice.

Shooting a skunk inside a tent is a big mistake. Whoever invented tear gas[3] simply copied something that skunks have used for thousands of years. It wouldn't be truthful to say the air turned blue, but it certainly turned something. Our eyes started to water. We were almost blinded. We began to gag. I grabbed the baby and fumbled my way outside. After a minute or so, Walter stumbled out behind me, dragging the dead skunk. He threw it over the riverbank. We hauled our bedding outside and spent the rest of the night in the open. We were tired enough to sleep anywhere. The next morning I told Walter that his way of saving our salt pork was no good. The pork smelled almost as bad as the tent.

Next we started work on a cabin for our winter home. We planned to live in it only until November, when the lakes would freeze and we'd have to quit trapping. So we threw it up hurriedly. It was built of small green logs. It was soon finished, and about October 1 we put our traps out.

As it happened, we stayed on in that rough cabin until spring. For one thing, there was a lot of fur, mink as well as muskrat. There was also firewood handy. The cabin stood in a thick grove of spruces, where it was sheltered from the wind.

---

[2]**salt pork:** fat pork cured with salt to keep fresh
[3]**tear gas:** kind of gas that burns the eyes, sometimes use to control riots
gag (GAG) cough with a sick feeling

We had torn our scow apart to make doors and windows. I suggested to Walter that he build a boat. It was a clumsy boat, for we had no way to bend the heavy boards of the scow.

The trapping looked good, but now we faced another problem. Wild meat was so scarce that we got worried. There wasn't a moose or deer track anywhere. Before winter closed in on us, we had named that belt of timber and swampy lakes Starvation Wilderness. Snow came to stay on October 10. After that the whole country was white and lifeless.

Trapping was good. We were looking at our traps twice a day. We'd hike out to the lakes together. Then I'd take Olive and the dog team with a small toboggan and cover half the line. Walter would go over the other half. We'd meet at midday. On the way back to camp, he covered my end of the line and I took his.

We both trapped until the first of November. Then the lakes were frozen. The temperature had dropped too low for us to be out in the wind and cold. From December until the end of March, the temperature rarely climbed as high as 10° below zero. There were days when it went to 65° below. The wind cut like a knife. We huddled in our shack and tried to keep warm.

Spruce pitch dripped from the roof poles and matted my long curls that Walter liked so much. In desperation I finally took the scissors one day when he was out looking at fox traps and cut my hair as short as I could. He was so upset when he came home that his face turned gray.

We got through that bitter winter until February. By then we knew we'd run out of food long before June, when we had planned to catch the first steamboat coming up the Slave. We had known since October that I was pregnant. Our second baby would be born in July. We didn't dare to wait for the boat, knowing that before the end of winter we'd have nothing to eat.

We were in no shape for the 60-mile trip out to Fort Smith. Our two dogs were old and not strong enough to pull Olive and me on the sled. The baby could ride, but I'd have to walk. We didn't have suitable clothing for cold of 40° and 50° below zero. What we lacked were fur parkas and fur-lined moccasins. But as our food dwindled, we made ready for the trip. Walter would leave Olive and me at Fort Smith and come back in time to trap again as soon as the lakes opened.

We put hot water in the water bottle, and we heated stones. We wrapped the baby in our whole bedroll of four blankets with the stones and water bottle beside her, and struck out up the Slave. The empty toboggan with Olive aboard was all our dogs could pull.

It was bitterly cold, probably around

---

belt (BELT) area; region
toboggan (tuh BOG un) large, flat sled
parka (PAHR kuh) fur jacket with a hood
dwindle (DWIN dul) become less and less
bedroll (BED rohl) roll of blankets or other bedding

40° below. The going was hard. We made poor time. The dogs pulled willingly enough for a while. But the heavy going was too much for them. We had traveled about 15 miles when they began to give out. They stopped frequently. More than once they lay down in the snow. Walter urged them on and pushed all he could on the toboggan handles to help them. But we both knew we weren't going to go much farther.

The winter days are very short there in the North. By 3:30 in the afternoon, dusk was beginning to come down. Across the river there was a little cabin with smoke curling out of the chimney. I can't remember that I was ever gladder to see a human habitation.

Winter, George Gardner Symons. Scripps College, Claremont

---

habitation (hab ih TAY shun) a building to live in

The cabin belonged to two young trappers. We pulled in thinking we could stay the night. But there wasn't room to walk between the stove, beds, and table. It was plain that they couldn't put us up. They told us that four miles farther up the Slave another trapper, Bert Bennett, had a comfortable cabin. We rested a little while, and started for Bennett's place with the early dark thickening over the frozen snowy wilderness. I didn't feel as if I could go 500 feet, much less four miles.

That was one of the worst hikes I've ever had. Each mile of the four seemed like 10. The dogs stopped every few yards to lie down. Walter went ahead to break trail and pull them along with a short length of rope. I pushed on the toboggan handles for a change. It was too dark for Walter to see where he was putting his snowshoes, and he must have fallen 100 times. I had pain in every inch of the legs, my back, and all through my body. I finally realized I was leaning on the toboggan handles more than I was pushing, It seemed to me that the easiest thing to do would be to walk off into the snow and lie down and sleep forever.

But there was Olive to think of, I reminded myself. I could hear her whimper now and then and I wondered if she was freezing. There was nothing I could do about it if she was. I didn't dare open the bedroll she was wrapped in to look at her. I just kept putting one foot ahead of the other, stumbling and staggering along, terribly cold, until I lost all track of time and place.

A shout from Walter brought me out of my stupor. "Hello, there!" he yelled. I looked ahead and could see a square of light shining out of a window. Oh, what a welcome sight!

I don't remember Bennett opening the door, or Olive and me being carried into the warmth of the cabin. The first thing I recall was Walter pulling off my coat. Then somebody set a bowl of hot soup in front of me and shook me and told me to eat.

In a daze I watched Bennett take off Olive's rabbit-skin coat and start to feed her. They told me afterward that I cried out, "No, don't take her coat off. She'll freeze!" But I have no memory of that. I did not even realize that we were safe and warm inside four walls. The next thing I remember, Walter was telling me to get up for breakfast.

I was too stiff and sore to make it. But he pulled me out of bed and made me move my legs and body. It's surprising how much power of recovery you have at 21. I was four months pregnant, and I had run and walked 23 miles the day before in deep snow. When Bennett looked at his thermometer that morning it was 61° below. The wonder was that the three of us had not frozen to death on the trail.

We realized then that we could not make it to Fort Smith. It was dangerous and foolhardy to try. Luckily, Bennett had

---

stupor (STOO pur) dazed or dull state; loss of feeling
foolhardy (FOOL hahr dee) foolishly risky; much too bold

extra supplies that he could spare. He sold us flour and beans enough to see us through, and even lent Walter 24 good muskrat traps.

We stayed three days with Bennett. I regained my strength. At the end of the three days I was as good as new. The dogs were in better shape than when we'd begun our terrible trip up-river. We were ready to go back to our cabin and see the winter out. With muskrat at $1.50 each, there was more good money to be made as soon as the lakes started to open. When the first boat came up the Slave, we would be waiting for it.

We started out on a clear morning with the sun shining. Wind had drifted and packed the snow solidly enough that we seldom broke through. The dogs and Walter and I all had easy going. We pulled up in front of our lonely little cabin just as it was coming full dark.

We did not see or hear a living thing except each other, the dogs, and three foxes that Walter trapped, until the end of March. It seemed as if all the game, even rabbits, had died off or left the country. Neither of us had ever seen a winter wilderness so lifeless and still.

We fed the three fox carcasses to the dogs. They were starved enough to gulp them down. The beans and flour Bert Bennett had sold us were running low, and we were eating less than half of what we wanted.

Toward the first of April, we decided to start our mink and muskrat trapping, even though the lakes were still covered with three feet of ice. It wasn't so much that we wanted fur. We needed the muskrats as food for ourselves and the dogs. Things had reached a point where I hated to eat because we had almost nothing for the dogs. None of us would last much longer without meat.

We made a trip to the nearest lake where we had trapped before freeze-up. We found the shallow lake frozen solid. Not a muskrat was left. When we turned the dogs back toward camp that afternoon, Walter and I were about as worried as two people could get.

A few days after that we packed up the little food we had left. We took our tent, bedding, and traps, and went eight miles west to some bigger lakes that Walter had found earlier.

We put up the tent at the first lake. We found water under the ice, cut into muskrat houses, and caught a few muskrat. They eased the pinch of our hunger, but we were not taking enough for ourselves and the dogs.

At last Walter made the unhappy announcement that the dogs would have to be destroyed. I realized that was kinder than letting them starve. But the idea of it almost broke my heart. It had to be done, but I cried until I was sick.

Less than a week after that the weather broke in our favor. The sun came out warm and bright. The snow started to melt, and the lakes opened up around the shores. We began trapping muskrats by

carcass (KAHR kus) body of dead animal

Trapper in the Wilderness, Sydney Laurence. Shelburne Museum, Shelburne, VT

the dozens. If the night was cold and ice formed, our luck fell off. Some days we took only five or six pelts, but one day we took 70. We were living on muskrat meat, and for the first time that winter we had enough to eat. I boiled it and gave Olive the broth in her bottle. She thrived on it.

When spring comes to the North it comes with a rush. Suddenly it is sunny day after day. The days are long and warm. But the short dark hours of the spring nights are often cold. It was hard to keep warm in our tent, even with a fire in the tiny stove. That stove was to cause the worst disaster of all.

We continued trapping while the snow melted and the creeks rose and became little rivers. Walter and I agreed that we'd stay camped at the lake until May 10. Then we'd hike back to our cabin. We'd go up the Slave to Bert Bennett's place in our rowboat, and there

---

thrive (THRYV) grow healthy and strong

catch the first steamer of the season to Fort Smith. But things don't always go as people plan them.

On the morning of May 2, I was in the tent baking bannock in the little stovepipe oven. I stepped outside to look for Walter and saw him coming a quarter-mile up the lake. I took Olive by the hand and walked to meet him. She was toddling all over by then. When we met, I took part of his load of fresh pelts and the three of us started back.

All of a sudden we heard ammunition exploding at a terrible rate. Then smoke and flames rolled up around the tent. Walter dropped his sack of fur and ran. I grabbed Olive and hurried after him as fast as I could. When I got to the tent my husband was dragging out charred food and burning pieces of blankets. I grabbed the things as he pulled them out and doused them in the lake.

It was all over in 10 minutes. A tent burns fast.

What we had saved would have made a very small bundle. There were two or three half-burned pieces of blanket. There were the few matches in our pockets and in a waterproof container. Walter's .22 was safe. There were four shells in it, and Walter had a box in his pocket. The rest of our ammunition was gone. Most of the rat pelts had been hanging in a tree outside the tent and were safe.

Of our food, we had about four cups of flour, wet and mixed with cinders, and a pound or so of beans. For Olive, luckily, there were a few undamaged cans of milk.

With muskrat meat, that handful of supplies would have to see us through until we could reach Bennett's cabin. That meant a hard hike of 8 or 10 miles through difficult country, and then 23 miles by rowboat against the spring current of the mighty Slave. Worst of all, we knew we could not make the trip up-river until the Slave broke up. We had no idea when that would happen.

Things looked pretty grim. I was expecting a second baby in less than two months, and we knew we had a very rough time ahead. But there was no use sitting beside the ruins of our tent and worrying. The thing was to get started.

We hung our traps in trees where we would be able to find them the following fall. We ate our bannock and a good meal of muskrat we had roasted earlier, rolled Olive in the patches of bedding, and lay down under a tree to rest for a few hours. We did not dare to use a match for a fire. We had to hoard them for times of need.

When we awoke we made up our loads and were ready to start. I wrapped Olive in the blanket pieces. I'd carry her on my back. She was so thin she wasn't very heavy. I rolled one cooking pot, knives, forks, spoons, a cup, and the baby bottle in a scrap of blanket and tied it all on my back behind her. Walter's load consisted of the dry muskrat pelts,

---

bannock (BAN uk) kind of flat bread
charred (CHAHRD) partly burned
douse (DOUS) soak with water
hoard (HAWRD) store away; save

about 250 in all, our stove—it weighed only about 10 pounds—and three lengths of stovepipe.

We left the burned-out camp with me carrying all I could handle and Walter packing a load of about 110 pounds. Every creek was roaring full and was two or three times as wide as usual. Many times Walter had to make three trips through the swollen and icy creeks, one with his pack, one with Olive and my load, and a third to help me across.

It took two days of the hardest kind of travel to get back to our cabin. At the end of the first day we stopped and made a camp under a clump of spruces. We roasted a muskrat we had brought along. We went without breakfast and our noon meal the second day. But in the middle of the afternoon, I shot a small muskrat. It wasn't big enough to make a good meal for one hungry person, let alone three. But we stopped and cooked it on the spot and divided it up.

It was midnight when we trudged up to our cabin. We were tired, discouraged, and hungry. But at least we had a roof over our heads again and four walls to keep out the cold at night. We didn't mind too much going to bed without supper.

When daylight came, I got up and scraped each empty flour sack for the little flour that remained in it. One look at the Slave that morning confirmed our worst fears. Water was running between the ice and shore. We couldn't get out on the river. We wouldn't have dared. There was no hope of following the shore up to Bennett's place either, because of the many large creeks that flowed into the river. We had no choice but to wait for the ice to go out.

The 11 days between May 10 and the time when the ice finally went out of the Slave were a nightmare of hunger and worry—mostly hunger.

Because we were so short of matches, we kept plenty of wood on hand and fed the fire. We never let it go out.

I found a roll of wire and set snares for ducks, rabbits, muskrats—anything. In all, I snared two red squirrels and a blackbird. We pulled up dead grass along the edge of the water and ate the tender yellow shoots below. One day I saw a fool hen— a spruce grouse—perched on a low branch of a tree. I hurried to rig a snare on a pole. I reached up and dropped it over her head and jerked her to the ground. That was the best meat we had all that time. For once poor little Olive got all the broth she wanted.

Hunger cramps kept us awake at night, and when we slept we dreamed troubled dreams of food. In my own case, being seven months pregnant didn't make things any better. Right then I needed to eat for two. Each night we slept less. Each day we got weaker. The

---

confirm (kun FURM) prove true
snare (SNAIR) loop or noose for catching small animals or birds
shoot (SHOOT) first part of growing plant to appear
grouse (GROUS) kind of wild bird, a little smaller then a chicken

baby's whimpering for food tore us apart. Walter cursed himself over and over for bringing Olive and me down the Slave.

If we had brought a few traps back from our tent camp, we could have caught muskrats or ducks. But we'd left all the traps behind. For three days our only food was what we called spruce tea. I stripped green needles off and boiled them. We drank a few spoonfuls every couple of hours. It eased the hunger cramps and seemed to give us some strength.

Olive was no longer running around the cabin. She sat quiet and played with whatever was at hand. There was no color in her lips and cheeks. Her eyes looked hollow and dull. I can't put into words how worried and afraid Walter and I were.

We made crude hooks by bending safety pins and tried fishing in the open water along the shore of the river, using pieces of red yarn for bait. Our catch totaled one very small jackfish. I tapped a small birch tree (they were few and far between in that area) for sap. It tasted good, but we had only half a cup to divide among the three of us.

At last, at 10 o'clock on the morning of May 21, the ice in the Slave began to move. By midnight it was gone, and the water was rolling past our door. At 3:00 in the morning of the 22nd we shoved our little boat into the river and were on our way to Bennett's.

It was dangerous to try traveling so soon after the ice went out. Chunks of ice weighing many tons kept sliding off the banks and drifting down with the current, but we had no choice.

Walter rowed, and I sat in the stern and paddled and steered us away from floating ice. It was killing work. Our closest call came that first day. Rowing close to shore, we saw a huge block of ice come sliding off a pile 40 feet high. It crashed into the water almost alongside us. The force of it lifted our rowboat into the air and sent it flying. We wound up 150 feet out in the swiftest part of the current, right side up only because we had happened to be pointed in the right direction when the ice thundered down.

Walter and I drank spruce tea and gathered and ate grass roots. We also drank water often because it seemed to ease our hunger. We just kept rowing until we gave out. Then we'd rest, and then we'd row some more.

It took us six days to make the 23-mile trip up the Slave to Bert Bennett's cabin. They were as dreadful as any days I can remember. We pulled up to shore at his place at midnight on May 27—dirty, ragged, starving, and so burned by wind and sun that we hardly knew our own reflections when we looked in a mirror. In those six days we had eaten nothing but spruce tea, grass roots, and the inner bark of trees.

A Mr. and Mrs. King from Fort Smith were at Bennett's. They had come down on the ice in March. She gave us each half a biscuit and a couple of spoonfuls of stewed apricots, but the food was too much for our stomachs. We awakened three hours later with dreadful cramps and were miserably sick for the next 12 hours.

It was four days before I was well enough to be out of bed. Mrs. King fed me a few spoonfuls of canned soup and cream every hour, and at the end of that time I felt fine. By then Walter and Olive had bounced back too.

Bennett and the Kings fixed us up with some clothing. We waited out a comfortable and happy month until the *Miss Mackenzie* came up the Slave on her first trip of the year. We boarded her near the end of June, and the trip to Fort Smith was lovely.

We sold our furs in Fort Smith. We had 560 muskrat pelts, 27 mink, three red foxes, four skunks, and a few weasels. The fox pelts brought $25 each, the mink $10.

We paid off our debts and had $1,060 left in cash. We had never had money that came harder.

Our second daughter, Vala, was born on July 18. Vala was a scrawny, blue-gray baby, weighing only 3½ pounds. For three weeks my doctor did not think either she or her mother would live. But we made it, and Vala grew to be a healthy, pretty girl.

Walter went back to his trapline in the fall, but I'd had enough of the North. It's a place of great beauty, and the winter stillness is spellbinding, but it can also be terribly cruel. I knew I would never winter in a trapper's shack with my two little girls if I could help it. I stayed behind.

---

scrawny (SKRAW nee) thin and wiry
spellbinding (SPEL bynd ing) fascinating; very interesting

Review the Selection

UNDERSTAND THE SELECTION

Recall

1. Where does this story take place?

2. During what time of year does this story take place?

3. What is the occupation of the author's husband?

Infer

4. What hint is given fairly early in the story that this adventure may not turn out as well as planned?

5. What was the greatest problem that the author and her husband faced in the wilderness?

6. Why did the author and her husband never let their fire go out after their tent was destroyed?

7. What is the first thing to go wrong?

Apply

8. Why do you think the author's baby was so tiny when it was born?

9. Why did the couple kill their dogs?

10. Why do you think the couple left their traps behind when they returned to their cabin in May?

Respond to Literature

What did the author learn from her discoveries in "Starvation Wilderness"?

WRITE ABOUT THE SELECTION

One of the problems faced by the author and her husband in "Starvation Wilderness" was that they were inexperienced in dealing with such rugged country and climate. Suppose that you are planning a camping trip in the wilderness. What can you learn from the events of this story? Write a paragraph in which you discuss several things that you would do or not do on your trip, based on Olive A. Fredrickson's experiences.

Prewriting   Reread the story and make notes as you think of ideas for your paragraph. Be especially aware of things that go wrong during the couple's adventure—you will want to learn from their mistakes.

Writing   Use your notes to write a paragraph about the way you would undertake a trip in the wilderness. Be sure to give reasons for your actions, based on the story.

Revising   Sometimes a paragraph reads more smoothly when ideas are expressed in a different order. Try changing the order in which you discuss your ideas and decide if this makes a better paragraph. Consider adding or subtracting sentences. You may want to substitute sentences or phrases also.

Proofreading   Check your paragraph for mistakes in spelling, usage, and mechanics. Be sure to capitalize proper nouns you may have used.

THINK ABOUT CONFLICT

The conflict in a story provides a set of problems for the main character or characters to overcome. How successfully the characters meet these problems determines the outcome of the story. Very often the conflict in a story provides suspense— you find yourself asking questions such as "What will happen next?" or "Will this character survive?"

1. What is the conflict in "Starvation Wilderness"?

2. What was the outcome of the conflict?

3. What kinds of problems did the young couple have to overcome?

4. Do you think that some of these problems could have been avoided?

5. At what points in the story were you uncertain about the young couple's ability to survive?

READING FOCUS

Summarize Write a short paragraph about Olive A. Fredrickson's experiences living as a trapper in far northern Canada. In the first sentence, summarize the main conflict that she and her husband face. Then write two to four sentences that highlight their worst hardships.

DEVELOP YOUR VOCABULARY

You are probably used to looking in a dictionary to find the meanings of unfamiliar words. From the dictionary you can also learn the correct spelling and pronunciation of a word. You can learn the part of speech and origin of the word too. Some dictionaries include a phrase to show you how a word is used correctly in a sentence. Studying all the information in a dictionary entry will help you master a word, and make it a part of your working vocabulary.

Review the meanings of these words from "Starvation Wilderness" in your dictionary. Be sure to read all parts of the dictionary entry. Then use each word in an original sentence.

1. scow
2. presence
3. dwindle
4. douse
5. habitation
6. stupor
7. carcass
8. thrive
9. hoard
10. confirm

Two words rhyme when they have a similar sound. For example, *wait* and *date* rhyme, as do *sell* and *bell*. Many poems include words that rhyme, especially at the ends of lines.

As you read a poem, you can often recognize a **rhyme scheme**, or pattern of similar sounds. You can describe the rhyme scheme with letters. For example:

> Jack and Jill
> Went up the hill
> To fetch a pail of water.
> Jack fell down
> And broke his crown
> And Jill came tumbling after.

In this nursery rhyme, the rhyme scheme is aa b cc d. Lines 1 and 2 rhyme; lines 4 and 5 rhyme with a different sound. Lines 3 and 6 do not rhyme with any other lines.

Rhyme can make a poem enjoyable to read. As you read the poems in this selection, ask yourself:

1. What is the rhyme scheme of each poem?
2. Which sounds are rhymed in each poem?

READING FOCUS

Analyze Figurative Language Figurative language refers to the imaginative use of words, especially in comparisons. For example, a poet might write, "My love is a rose." This kind of figurative language, which makes a direct comparison between two things, is called a metaphor. In another kind of figurative language, personification, the poet describes a thing, animal, or idea as if it were a person. A poet might write, for example, "The roses hung their heads." As you read the poems, identify the kind of figurative language that is used in each.

WRITING CONNECTION

Write a simple poem that has the rhyme scheme aa b cc d.

Harriet Tubman, Series No. 10, Jacob Lawrence.
Hampton University Museum

DREAMS

by Langston Hughes

Hold fast to dreams
For if dreams die
Life is a broken-winged bird
That cannot fly.

Hold fast to dreams
For when dreams go
Life is a barren field
Frozen with snow.

---

barren (BAR un) bare, sterile

UNTITLED

Anonymous

There were three girls walked down the road,
As down the road walked she:
    The girl she was,
    The girl they saw,
    The girl she wanted to be.

SYMPATHY

by Paul Laurence Dunbar

I know why the caged bird sings, ah me,
    When his wing is bruised and his bosom sore—
When he beats his bars and he would be free;
It is not a carol of joy or glee,
    But a prayer that he sends from his heart's deep core,
But a plea, that upward to Heaven, he flings—
I know why the caged bird sings!

---

plea (PLEE) appeal; request

Paul Laurence Dunbar (1872–1906)

After Paul Laurence Dunbar graduated from high school, the best job that he could find was that of an elevator operator in a local hotel. His life took a decided turn for the better when his poetry was discovered by William Dean Howells, an outstanding American literary critic. Dunbar soon became well-known in literary circles around the country.

Paul Laurence Dunbar was the son of former slaves. He grew up in Dayton, Ohio, where he was the only African American in his high school class. Dunbar's literary ability was obvious during high school, where he wrote poetry and served as editor of the high school newspaper and yearbook. Dunbar also published an African American newsletter, which was printed by his high school classmate Orville Wright, one of the famous Wright brothers.

Dunbar's poetry often captured the humor and gentleness of the lives of African American people in the rural South. He became most famous for his poems written in dialect, although he also wrote poems in standard English.

Many of Dunbar's poems seem old-fashioned today, partly because of their style, and partly because they reflect racial attitudes that have become outdated in late-20th-century America. Yet many of his writings, such as the selection in this unit, have stood the test of time.

In addition to books of poetry, Paul Laurence Dunbar also wrote short stories and novels. He died when he was only 33 years old, having produced nearly all of his work in just ten years.

Review the Selection

UNDERSTAND THE SELECTION

Recall

1. What is the meaning of the word "dreams" in the first poem?

2. What is the subject of "Untitled"?

3. In the poem "Sympathy," what is the poet observing?

Infer

4. Why does the author of "Dreams" feel that dreams are important?

5. What is the meaning of "Life is a barren field/Frozen with snow"?

6. In the untitled poem are there really three girls walking down the road? Explain your answer.

7. What might the caged bird symbolize in "Sympathy"?

Apply

8. In "Sympathy," what might the caged bird rather be doing than singing?

9. Dunbar was an African American whose parents were slaves. How does this fact fit in with the meaning of his poem?

10. Can you apply the meaning of the untitled poem to any of the stories or plays you have read in this unit?

Respond to Literature

What discoveries about life are reflected in these three poems?

WRITE ABOUT THE SELECTION

Each of the three poems in this selection expresses something that the poet has learned about life. Which poem do you agree with most or feel most strongly about? Which poem expresses something that you have also discovered? Write a paragraph in which you relate the theme of one of the poems to your own life experience.

Cluster all the details and feeling you have that relate to the poem that you chose. Write down everything that comes to mind. You can decide what to use later.

Prewriting Read each of the poems several times. As you read, ask yourself, "Have I ever felt this way? When?" Jot down your ideas on a piece of paper. Decide which poem you will use as the subject of your paragraph.

Writing Use the ideas from your notes to write your response to one of the poems. Try to include specific events or examples from your life that relate to the poem you have chosen.

Revising Add vivid words to make your ideas come alive. Substitute specific verbs for ordinary ones. For example, "My mind raced" is more exciting than "I thought."

Proofreading Make sure that all the words you have used are spelled correctly. Look up in the dictionary any words that you are unsure of and correct the spelling if necessary.

THINK ABOUT RHYME

The **rhyme scheme** is the pattern of similar sounds in a poem. Usually words rhyme at the ends of lines, although sometimes words rhyme within lines. Rhyme makes a poem pleasing to read.

Another technique that adds to the enjoyment and meaning of a poem is **repetition**. A poet will often repeat certain words or sounds in order to create an effect.

1. What is the rhyme scheme in "Dreams"?

2. What phrase is repeated in the poem? Why do you think it is repeated?

3. What is the rhyme scheme in the untitled poem?

4. What word is repeated in the untitled poem? What effect does this repetition create?

5. What is the rhyme scheme in "Sympathy"?

READING FOCUS

Analyze Figurative Language Which poem that you read used personification? Which used metaphors? Which poem did you like best? Explain how the poet's use of figurative language influenced your choice.

DEVELOP YOUR VOCABULARY

Many words in English have more than one meaning. For example, the word *bore* can mean to make a hole in something, or it can mean something or someone who is boring. When you read a word such as *bore*, you can often tell from the context what the word means. If you are uncertain of the meaning of a word with multiple meanings, you should look up the word in the dictionary.

Study these words from this selection. Tell which meaning of each word is used in the poems. Then write an original sentence to show how to use each meaning of each word.

1. dreams
2. fast
3. fly
4. field
5. core
6. saw
7. beats
8. free
9. wing
10. flings

UNIT 4 Review

Write About Theme

All of the characters in this unit have made discoveries. They have made discoveries about themselves, others, the world around them, and life. As you have read their stories, you have made discoveries also. Perhaps you discovered something about a real person, place, or event. Perhaps you discovered a new way of looking at an issue based on the message of a selection. Choose four selections from this unit and tell what you have discovered as a result of reading them.

Prewriting Before you begin to write, decide which four of the selections had the greatest impact on you. Think for a few moments about each one and ask yourself, "What did I discover as a result of reading this selection? What new ideas, thoughts, and feelings do I have now that I did not have before?"

Writing Use the notes from your prewriting to write about the discoveries you have made. Include how you think these discoveries will make a difference in your life.

Revising Read your paper to make sure that it is well-organized. Does each paragraph contain one main idea? Does each paragraph have a clear topic sentence? Add or remove details to make the paragraph better organized.

Proofreading Correct any mistakes in spelling, usage, and mechanics.

Write About Genre

In this unit you have studied the elements of nonfiction in two of the selections. Now you can use these elements to analyze those selections.

First, decide which selection you feel most strongly about, either in a positive or negative way. Then compare and contrast it with the other two selections in terms of plot and story development, point of view, tone, and theme.

Prewriting Review briefly the work that you did for the "Think About . . ." for the nonfiction sections. Then make a chart in which you write the names of the two selections across the top. List the four literary elements down the side of the chart. Fill in your chart with details about each element from the selections.

Writing Use your chart to write a comparison of the two selections. If you feel that one selection used a particular element more effectively than the other, say so—but be sure to back up your opinion with evidence from the selection.

Revising Add to your paper any transitional phrases that will make your ideas flow more smoothly. The following are examples of transitional phrases: *first, most important, finally, next.*

Proofreading Correct any mistakes in spelling, usage, and mechanics. Use quotation marks around titles of short selections.

Vocabulary

A helpful way to find the meaning of a word you do not know is to use context clues. Context clues help you figure out what a word means by the way it is used in a sentence.

Example: "I'm not an Example!" grumbled Amanda *rebelliously*. "I'm me!"

If you did not know the meaning of the word *rebelliously*, you could guess the meaning by the context clues. You know that Amanda is unhappy, and that she disagrees with her mother. You also can see that *rebelliously* must go with the word *grumbled*. Therefore, you could recognize that *rebelliously* means resisting authority or control.

Use context clues to determine the meaning of each italicized word, and then write out its meaning.

1. A rabbit hopped out from under the berry bush. He *nuzzled* the berry I'd spat out and ate it.

2. Why did they have to see me like this? Why did I have to look at Mom's eyes when she faced the most terrible *ordeal* of her life?

3. Across the river there was a little cabin with smoke curling out of the chimney. I can't remember that I was ever gladder to see a human *habitation*.

4. Mrs. Jones stopped, jerked him around in front of her, put a *half nelson* about his neck, and continued to drag him up the street.

Grammar, Usage, and Mechanics

When you write a sentence, it is important that the subject and the verb agree. The basic rule for subject-verb agreement is:

A **singular subject** must use a **singular verb**.

Chee *guesses* that his in-laws have become poor.

A **plural subject** must use a **plural verb**.

Chee's in-laws *guess* that Chee wants his daughter back.

The subject of a sentence is usually a noun or a pronoun. Pronouns can cause problems when they function as subjects of sentences. The pronouns *he*, *she*, and *it* always use a singular verb. *We* and *they* always use a plural verb. The pronoun *I* usually uses a plural verb:

I go to school.
    not
I goes to school.

The pronoun *you* always uses a plural verb.

Correct any errors in subject-verb agreement in the following sentences. (Not all of the sentences have errors.)

1. You takes the food I brought.

2. The old man gives Amanda the gold medal.

3. The old man and Amanda talks to each other.

4. "This is private property—I has my rights!"

5. My grandfather look at me strangely.

SPEAKING AND LISTENING

When you make a speech about literature in your English class, you usually have some kind of script to follow. You decide what topic or selection you are going to discuss, and then you follow certain guidelines to help in the discussion. Sometimes it's fun to build a lesson around a more spontaneous activity. Speaking extemporaneously doesn't mean speaking without preparation. It does mean, however, that you don't have to write anything out and you don't have to memorize. It is an example of impromptu speaking.

Although this type of speaking may be new to you, you will have a bit of fun in this lesson. Read the following strategy so you'll be a well-informed participant.

1. Think about all the various selections in this unit. Focus on the characters or people to whom you've been introduced. Along with others in your class, name as many as you can. If necessary, glance back at the selections.

2. Now, choose two people or characters you have read about. Go back to the selections where they can be found.

Read sections of the selection that describe or give information about the character. Become familiar with things the characters say, do, feel, and how they look and act. Think of adjectives to describe the characters.

3. Finally, imagine each character as an animal. What animal would he or she be? To help you decide, go back to the ideas you came up with in step two. Compare the character's traits to those of an animal. Decide what animal, in your opinion, is most like that character.

That's basically it! The next part is the most fun and really the easiest. As a class, or in small groups, take turns speaking about "Characters or People as Animals." Limit your speaking time to a minute or less so that everyone has a chance to speak. In your talk tell about the character's traits, the animal you've compared him to, and why you feel it is an appropriate comparison. Other students may talk about the same person or character; if so, don't worry. It will be fun to hear another classmate's interpretation.

CRITICAL THINKING

Fact and Opinion When reading nonfiction, it is important to be able to tell the difference between fact and opinion. A **fact** is something that can be proven or verified. For example, it is a fact that Kaw Indians go through the Ta-Na-E-Ka ritual at age 11.

An **opinion**, on the other hand, cannot be proven. An opinion is what a person thinks or believes about something. Opinions are usually based on a combination of emotions and facts. An example of an opinion is that the Ta-Na-E-Ka ritual is not very important.

In a true story, facts include such information as time, place, details of events, general data about characters, and so on. Opinions tend to be expressed by the characters in the story or by the author's comments about the events and characters. Opinions may also be suggested by the theme or message of the story. Choose one nonfiction selection from the unit and answer the following questions.

1. What seems to be the author's opinion about the events of the story and the outcome of the story? How can you tell? Do any characters in the story voice opinions that differ from the author's opinion?

2. If you were writing a newspaper report of the events of this story, what facts would you include? How would the story in a newspaper differ from the same story written as a piece of literature?

EFFECTIVE STUDYING

Note Taking An important skill that will help you do better in school is note taking. Note taking in class is important because you need to remember the information and explanations that the teacher gives. To take notes in class, use a spiral or loose-leaf notebook with enough blank pages to ensure that you will not run out of paper in the middle of class. Use the same notebook every day, so that your notes for that subject will be all together and in the right order.

As you take notes in class, try to write an outline of the lesson. Some teachers write an outline on the board, which is very helpful. Even if there is no written outline, you can tell how a teacher has organized the lesson if you listen carefully.

Sometimes as you are taking notes, the teacher will say something that you do not understand or cannot hear clearly. Write down what you hear as best you can. Then circle what you wrote. After class or during a time when you can ask questions, ask the teacher to explain it to you.

Many students find it helpful to copy over the notes that they take in class. You can do this each night or before a test.

Test Preparation

When you take a test, rewrite the directions in your own words. This way, you will understand exactly what you have been asked to do.

Heroes

The Hero can be Poet, Prophet, King, Priest or what you will, according to the kind of world he finds himself born into.

—Thomas Carlyle

Aspects of Negro Life. An Idyll of the Deep South, Aaron Douglas.
The Schomburg Center/New York Public Library

Heroes

Who are your heroes? Do you look up to famous athletes such as Jackie Joyner-Kersee and Michael Jordan? Is your idea of a hero an astronaut or a rock star? Perhaps you most admire a courageous person in your own school or neighborhood.

The dictionary defines a hero as someone known for great strength, courage, and daring. A hero can also be a person honored for special achievements and attributes. As Thomas Carlyle points out, heroes are shaped, in part, by the times and the circumstances in which they find themselves. For example, Martin Luther King, Jr., became a hero in a world that was ready to hear his message about civil rights. However, in the end, could it have been personal courage in the face of hostility that actually shaped the circumstances—and the times? The true nature of heroism has always aroused great interest, even debate, among people everywhere.

The selections in this unit focus on heroes. You will meet likely heroes and unlikely heroes, real heroes and imaginary heroes.

■ LIKELY HEROES

Sometimes literature presents a situation in which a person has to choose between being a public hero and a private hero. This is the kind of situation in which two Puerto Rican boys find themselves in the short story "Amigo Brothers." In order to win a championship boxing match, each boy must beat his best friend. What would you do in a situation like this? Although the story ends with only one champion, both boys become heroes.

■ UNLIKELY HEROES

There are certain actions that make a person a hero in any time and any place. One is risking one's life for another. In the short story

"Terror in the North," a high school girl finds the strength to rescue a baby boy during an earthquake. In the story "On the Ledge," a police officer risks his life to prevent a suicide. This story has a surprise ending as the police officer finds himself in need of a rescue—and a very unlikely hero emerges.

Have you ever thought about being a hero? Have you ever day-dreamed about doing something daring or courageous? In his short story "The Secret Life of Walter Mitty," James Thurber paints a humorous and somewhat sad picture of a man whose heroism exists only in his own fantasies.

■ REAL HEROES

"I Have a Dream" is a famous speech by Martin Luther King, Jr. King was a special kind of hero who was assassinated because of his passionate devotion to the cause of racial equality. Is there a cause that you believe in so deeply that you would rather die than give it up?

■ MYTHICAL HEROES

In literature, as in life, many people become heroes during war. One of the most famous heroes in literature is a mythological figure named Ulysses, whom the poet Homer created as a great warrior in ancient Greece. You will read about two of the hero's adventures in "Ulysses and the Trojan Horse" and "Ulysses Meets the Cyclops." You may discover similarities between Ulysses and your own personal heroes.

Who your heroes are tells a lot about you—the person you are and the person you hope to become. Perhaps you will find a hero of your own in these pages. As you read each selection, you might ask yourself, What is a hero? What do my heroes have in common with the hero in this selection?

Early in a story, an important plot problem is introduced. This is the first of a series of problems the character must solve. In a good story each problem is more interesting than the one before it. This is called **rising action**. The rising action in a story eventually leads to a climax. The **climax** is the most exciting part of the story. It is the part where the conflict comes to a head.

Some short stories end with the climax, but most do not. These stories continue beyond the climax with an element called the **resolution**. The resolution answers any remaining questions that the reader might have and gives the story a sense of completion.

As you read "Amigo Brothers," ask yourself:

1. What is the climax of the story?
2. What plot question remains unanswered?

READING FOCUS

Recognize Changes in Relationships
The relationship between two story characters often involves conflict, or the meeting of two opposing forces. How the conflict is resolved often involves changes in the relationship of the characters. Try to recognize such changes as you pay attention to the characters' actions and words in this story.

WRITING CONNECTION

Think of a recent situation in your own life that could be the basis of a short story. List the events of the plot, then indicate which of these events would be the climax of the story. Write a few sentences to describe what you might add to the story as a resolution.

AMIGO BROTHERS

ADAPTED

by Piri Thomas

Antonio Cruz and Felix Vargas were both seventeen years old. They were so together in friendship that they felt themselves to be brothers. They had known each other since childhood, growing up on the lower east side of Manhattan in the same tenement building on Fifth Street between Avenue A and Avenue B.

Antonio was fair, lean, and lanky, while Felix was dark, short, and husky. Antonio's hair was always falling over his eyes, while Felix wore his black hair in a natural Afro style.

Each youngster had a dream of someday becoming lightweight champion of the world. Every chance they had the boys worked out, sometimes at the Boys Club on 10th Street and Avenue A and sometimes at the pro's gym on 14th Street. Early morning sunrises would find them running along the East River Drive, wrapped in sweat shirts, short towels around their necks, and handkerchiefs Apache style around their foreheads.

While some youngsters were into street negatives, Antonio and Felix slept, ate, rapped, and dreamt positive. Between them, they had a collection of *Fight* magazines second to none, plus a scrapbook filled with torn tickets to every boxing match they had ever attended, and some clippings of their own. If asked a question about any given fighter, they would immediately zip out from their memory banks divisions, weights, records of fights, knockouts, technical knockouts, and draws or losses.

Each had fought many bouts representing their community and had won two gold-plated medals plus a silver and bronze medallion. The difference was in their style: Antonio's lean form and long reach made him the better boxer, while

---

amigo (uh MEE goh) A Spanish word meaning *friend*. Other Spanish words in the story add flavor to the text but will not be defined.
tenement (TEN uh munt) low-grade housing
Apache (uh PACH ee) Native American group of the southwest
negative (NEG uh tiv) bad habit or behavior
bout (BOUT) fight
medallion (muh DAL yun) large medal

Felix's short and muscular frame made him the better slugger. Whenever they had met in the ring for sparring sessions, it had always been hot and heavy.

Now, after a series of elimination bouts, they had been informed that they were to meet each other in the division finals that were scheduled for the seventh of August, two weeks away—the winner to represent the Boys Club in the Golden Gloves Championship Tournament.

The two boys continued to run together along the East River Drive. But even when joking with each other, they both sensed a wall rising between them.

One morning less than a week before their bout, they met as usual for their daily workout. They fooled around with a few jabs at the air, slapped skin, and then took off, running lightly along the dirty East River's edge.

Antonio glanced at Felix who kept his eyes purposely straight ahead, pausing from time to time to do some fancy leg work while throwing one-twos followed by upper cuts to an imaginary jaw. Antonio then beat the air with a barrage of body blows and short devastating lefts with an overhand jaw-breaking right.

After a mile or so, Felix puffed and said, "Let's stop a while, bro. I think we both got something to say to each other."

Antonio nodded. It was not natural to be acting as though nothing unusual was happening when two ace-boon buddies were going to be blasting each other within a few short days.

They rested their elbows on the railing separating them from the river. Antonio wiped his face with his short towel. The sunrise was now creating day.

Felix leaned heavily on the river's railing and stared across to the shores of Brooklyn. Finally, he broke the silence.

"Gee, man. I don't know how to come out with it."

Antonio helped. "It's about our fight, right?"

"Yeah, right." Felix's eyes squinted at the rising orange sun.

"I've been thinking about it too, *panin*. In fact, since we found out it was going to be me and you, I've been awake at night, pulling punches on you, trying not to hurt you."

"Same here. It ain't natural not to think about the fight. I mean, we both are *cheverote* fighters and we both want to win. But only one of us can win. There ain't no draws in the eliminations."

Felix tapped Antonio gently on the shoulder. "I don't mean to sound like I'm bragging, bro. But I wanna win, fair and square."

Antonio nodded quietly. "Yeah. We both know that in the ring the better man wins. Friend or no friend, brother or no . . ."

Felix finished it for him. "Brother. Tony, let's promise something right here. Okay?"

---

sparring (SPAHR ing) practice boxing with another
elimination (ih lim uh NAY shun) in a tournament, dropped after one loss
barrage (buh RAHJ) huge number, as of bombs or blows
devastating (DEV uh stayt ing) carrying destruction

"If it's fair, *hermano*, I'm for it." Antonio admired the courage of a tug boat pulling a barge five times its welterweight size.

"It's fair, Tony. When we get into the ring, it's gotta be like we never met. We gotta be like two heavy strangers that want the same thing and only one can have it. You understand, don'tcha?"

"*Si*, I know." Tony smiled. "No pulling punches. We go all the way."

"Yeah, that's right. Listen, Tony. Don't you think it's a good idea if we don't see each other until the day of the fight? I'm going to stay with my Aunt Lucy in the Bronx. I can use Gleason's Gym for working out. My manager says he got some sparring partners with more or less your style."

Tony scratched his nose pensively. "Yeah, it would be better for our heads." He held out his hand, palm upward. "Deal?"

"Deal." Felix lightly slapped open skin.

"Ready for some more running?" Tony asked lamely.

"Naw, bro. Let's cut it here. You go on. I kinda like to get things together in my head."

"You ain't worried, are you?" Tony asked.

"No way, man." Felix laughed out loud. "I got too much smarts for that. I just think it's cooler if we split right here. After the fight, we can get it together again like nothing ever happened."

The *amigo* brothers were not ashamed to hug each other tightly.

"Guess you're right. Watch yourself, Felix. I hear there's some pretty heavy dudes up in the Bronx. *Sauvecito*, okay?"

"Okay. You watch yourself too, *sabes*."

Tony jogged away. Felix watched his friend disappear from view, throwing rights and lefts. Both fighters had a lot of psyching up to do before the big fight.

The days in training passed much too slowly. Although they kept out of each other's way, they were aware of each other's progress via the ghetto grapevine.

The evening before the big fight, Tony made his way to the roof of his tenement. In the quiet early dark, he peered over the ledge. Six stories below the lights of the city blinked and the sounds of cars mingled with the curses and the laughter of children in the street. He tried not to think of Felix, feeling he had succeeded in psyching his mind. But only in the ring would he really know. To spare Felix hurt, he would have to knock him out, early and quick.

Up in the South Bronx, Felix decided to take in a movie in an effort to keep Antonio's face away from his fists. The flick was *The Champion* with Kirk Douglas, the third time Felix was seeing it.

---

welterweight (WEL tur wayt) boxer in a weight division between lightweight and middleweight
pensively (PEN siv lee) thoughtfully
psyching (SYK ing) getting into shape mentally (slang)
mingle (MING gul) mix

The champion was getting beat, his face being pounded into raw wet hamburger. His eyes were cut, jagged, bleeding, one eye swollen, the other almost shut. He was saved only by the sound of the bell.

Felix became the champ and Tony the challenger.

The movie audience was going out of its head, roaring in blood lust at the butchery going on. The champ hunched his shoulders grunting and sniffing red blood back into his broken nose. The challenger, confident that he had the championship in the bag, threw a left. The champ countered with a dynamite right that exploded into the challenger's brains.

Felix's right arm felt the shock. Antonio's face, superimposed on the screen, was shattered and split apart by the awesome force of the killer blow. Felix saw himself in the ring, blasting Antonio against the ropes. The champ had to be forcibly restrained. The challenger was allowed to crumble slowly to the canvas, a broken bloody mess.

When Felix finally left the theater, he had figured out how to psyche himself for tomorrow's fight. It was Felix the Champion vs. Antonio the Challenger.

He walked up some dark streets, deserted except for small pockets of wary-looking kids wearing gang colors. Despite the fact that he was Puerto Rican like them, they eyed him as a stranger to their turf. Felix did a fast shuffle, bobbing and weaving, while letting loose a torrent of blows that would demolish whatever got in its way. It seemed to impress the brothers, who went about their own business.

Finding no takers, Felix decided to split to his aunt's. Walking the streets had not relaxed him, neither had the fight flick. All it had done was to stir him up. He let himself quietly into his Aunt Lucy's apartment and went straight to bed, falling into a fitful sleep with sounds of the gong for Round One.

Antonio was passing some heavy time on his rooftop. How would the fight tomorrow affect his relationship with Felix? After all, fighting was like any other profession. Friendship had nothing to do with it. A gnawing doubt crept in. He cut negative thinking real quick by doing some speedy fancy dance steps, bobbing and weaving like mercury. The night air was blurred with perpetual motions of left hooks and right crosses. Felix, his *amigo* brother, was not going to be Felix at all in the ring. Just an opponent with another face. Antonio went to sleep,

---

lust (LUST) powerful desire
superimposed (soo pur im POHZD) placed on top of
awesome (AW sum) causing fear and wonder
restrained (rih STRAYND) held back
wary (WAIR ee) on guard; watchful
torrent (TAWR unt) rushing stream or downpour
demolish (dih MOL ish) reduce to ruins
fitful (FIT ful) uneasy; very restless
perpetual (pur PECH oo ul) never stopping; without pause

hearing the opening bell for the first round. Like his friend in the South Bronx, he prayed for victory, via a quick clean knockout in the first round.

Large posters plastered all over the walls of local shops announced the fight between Antonio Cruz and Felix Vargas as the main bout.

The fight had created great interest in the neighborhood. Antonio and Felix were well liked and respected. Each had his own loyal following. Betting fever was high and ranged from a bottle of soda to cold hard cash on the line.

Antonio's fans bet with unbridled faith in his boxing skills. On the other side, Felix's admirers bet on his dynamite-packed fists.

Felix had returned to his apartment early in the morning of August 7th and stayed there, hoping to avoid seeing Antonio. He turned the radio on to *salsa* music sounds and then tried to read while waiting for word from his manager.

The fight was scheduled to take place in Tompkins Square Park. It had been decided that the gymnasium of the Boys Club was not large enough to hold all the people who were sure to attend. In Tompkins Square Park, everyone who wanted could view the fight, whether from ringside or window fire escapes or tenement rooftops.

The morning of the fight Tompkins Square was a beehive of activity with numerous workers setting up the ring, the seats, and the guest speakers' stand. The scheduled bouts began shortly after noon and the park had begun filling up even earlier.

The local junior high school across from Tompkins Square Park served as the dressing room for all the fighters. Each was given a separate classroom with desk tops, covered with mats, serving as resting tables. Antonio thought he caught a glimpse of Felix waving to him from a room at the far end of the corridor. He waved back just in case it had been him.

The fighters changed from their street clothes into fighting gear. Antonio wore white trunks, black socks, and black shoes. Felix wore green trunks, white socks, and white boxing shoes. Each had dressing gowns to match their fighting trunks with their names neatly stitched on the back.

The loudspeakers blared into the open windows of the school. There were speeches by dignitaries, community leaders, and great boxers of yesteryear. Some were well prepared, some improvised on the spot. They all carried the same message of great pleasure and honor at being part of such a historic event. This great day was in the tradition of champions emerging from the streets of the lower east side.

Interwoven with the speeches were the

---

unbridled (un BRYD uld) uncontrolled
blare (BLAIR) make a loud noise
dignitary (DIG nuh ter ee) important person
improvised (IM pruh vyzd) made up quickly, without planning
emerging (ih MURJ ing) coming out of
interwoven (in tur WOH vun) mixed with

sounds of the other boxing events. After the sixth bout, Felix was much relieved when his trainer Charlie said, "Time change. Quick knockout. This is it. We're on."

Waiting time was over. Felix was escorted from the classroom by a dozen fans in white T-shirts with the word FELIX across their fronts.

Antonio was escorted down a different stairwell and guided through a roped-off path.

As the two climbed into the ring, the crowd exploded with a roar. Antonio and Felix both bowed gracefully and then raised their arms in acknowledgment.

Antonio tried to be cool, but even as the roar was in its first birth, he turned slowly to meet Felix's eyes looking directly into his. Felix nodded his head and Antonio responded. And both as one, just as quickly, turned away to face his own corner.

Bong—bong—bong. The roar turned to stillness.

"Ladies and Gentlemen, *Señores y Señoras.*"

The announcer spoke slowly, pleased at his bilingual efforts.

"Now the moment we have all been waiting for—the main event between two fine young Puerto Rican fighters, products of our lower east side."

"Loisaida," called out a member of the audience.

"In this corner, weighing 134 pounds, Felix Vargas. And in this corner, weighing 133 pounds, Antonio Cruz. The winner will represent the Boys Club in the Tournament of Champions, the Golden Gloves. There will be no draw. May the best man win."

The cheering of the crowd shook the window panes of the old buildings surrounding Tompkins Square Park. At the center of the ring, the referee was giving instructions to the youngsters.

"Keep your punches up. No low blows. No punching on the back of the head. Keep your heads up. Understand? Let's have a clean fight. Now shake hands and come out fighting."

Both youngsters touched gloves and nodded. They turned and danced quickly to their corners. Their head towels and dressing gowns were lifted neatly from their shoulders by their trainers' nimble fingers. Antonio crossed himself. Felix did the same.

BONG! BONG! ROUND ONE. Felix and Antonio turned and faced each other squarely in a fighting pose. Felix wasted no time. He came in fast, head low, half hunched toward his right shoulder, and lashed out with a straight left. He missed a right cross as Antonio slipped the punch and countered with one-two-three lefts that snapped Felix's head back, sending a mild shock coursing through him. If Felix had any small doubt about

---

acknowledgment (ak NOL IJ munt) recognition; thanks
bilingual (by LING gwul) able to use two languages
nimble (NIM bul) quick and accurate
pose (POHZ) position; way of standing
countered (KOUNT urd) returned a blow with another blow
coursing (KAWR sing) running or flowing

Amigo Brothers ■ 415

their friendship affecting their fight, it was being neatly dispelled.

Antonio danced, a joy to behold. His left hand was like a piston, pumping jabs one right after another with seeming ease. Felix bobbed and weaved and never stopped boring in. He knew that at long range he was at a disadvantage. Antonio had too much reach on him. Only by coming in close could Felix hope to achieve the dreamed-of knockout.

Antonio knew the dynamite that was stored in his *amigo* brother's fist. He ducked a short right and missed a left hook. Felix trapped him against the ropes just long enough to pour some punishing rights and lefts to Antonio's hard midsection. Antonio slipped away from Felix, crashing two lefts to his head, which set Felix's right ear to ringing.

Bong! Both *amigos* froze a punch well on its way, sending up a roar of approval for good sportsmanship.

Felix walked briskly back to his corner. His right ear had not stopped ringing. Antonio gracefully danced his way toward his stool none the worse, except for glowing glove burns, showing angry red against the whiteness of his midribs.

"Watch that right, Tony." His trainer talked into his ear. "Remember Felix always goes to the body. He'll want you to drop your hands for his overhand left or right. Got it?"

Antonio nodded, sprayed water out between his teeth. He felt better as his sore midsection was being firmly rubbed.

Felix's corner was also busy.

"You gotta get in there, fella." Felix's trainer poured water over his curly Afro locks. "Get in there or he's gonna chop you up from way back."

Bong! Bong! Round two. Felix was off his stool and rushed Antonio like a bull, sending a hard right to his head. Beads of water exploded from Antonio's long hair.

Antonio, hurt, sent back a blurring barrage of lefts and rights that only meant pain to Felix, who returned with a short left to the head followed by a looping right to the body. Antonio countered with his own flurry, forcing Felix to give ground. But not for long.

Felix bobbed and weaved, bobbed and weaved, occasionally punching his two gloves together.

Antonio waited for the rush that was sure to come. Felix closed in and feinted with his left shoulder and threw his right instead. Lights suddenly exploded inside Felix's head as Antonio slipped the blow and hit him with a pistonlike left, catching him flush on the point of his chin.

Bedlam broke loose as Felix's legs momentarily buckled. He fought off a series of rights and lefts and came back with a strong right that taught Antonio respect.

Antonio danced in carefully. He knew

---

dispelled (dih SPELD) driven away; ended
feinted (FAYNT id) pretended to attack one place while really attacking another
flush (FLUSH) straight; even with
bedlam (BED lum) confusion
momentarily (moh mun TER uh lee) for an instant

Felix had the habit of playing possum when hurt, to sucker an opponent within reach of the powerful bombs he carried in each fist.

A right to the head slowed Antonio's pretty dancing. He answered with his own left at Felix's right eye which began puffing up within three seconds.

Antonio, a bit too eager, moved in too close and Felix had him entangled into a rip-roaring, punching toe-to-toe slugfest that brought the whole Tompkins Square Park screaming to its feet.

Rights to the body. Lefts to the head. Neither fighter was giving an inch. Suddenly a short right caught Antonio squarely on the chin. His long legs turned to jelly and his arms flailed out desperately. Felix, grunting like a bull, threw wild punches from every direction. Antonio, groggy, bobbed and weaved, evading most of the blows. Suddenly his head cleared. His left flashed out hard and straight catching Felix on the bridge of his nose.

Felix lashed back with a haymaker, right off the ghetto streets. At the same instant, his eye caught another left hook from Antonio. Felix swung out trying to clear the pain. Only the frenzied scream-ing of those along ringside let him know that he had dropped Antonio. Fighting off the growing haze, Antonio struggled to his feet, got up, ducked, and threw a smashing right that dropped Felix flat on his back.

Felix got up as fast as he could in his

---

flailed (FLAYLD) waved or beat aimlessly
evading (ih VAYD ing) avoiding
frenzied (FREN zeed) very excited; raving

own corner, groggy but still game. He didn't even hear the count. In a fog, he heard the roaring of the crowd, who seemed to have gone insane. His head cleared to hear the bell sound at the end of the round. He was glad. His trainer sat him down on the stool.

In his corner, Antonio was doing what all fighters do when they are hurt. They sit and smile at everyone.

The referee signaled the ring doctor to check the fighters out. He did so and then gave his okay. The cold water sponges brought clarity to both *amigo* brothers. They were rubbed until their circulation ran free.

Bong! Round three—the final round. Up to now it had been tic-tac-toe, pretty much even. But everyone knew there could be no draw and that this round would decide the winner.

This time, to Felix's surprise, it was Antonio who came out fast, charging across the ring. Felix braced himself but couldn't ward off the barrage of punches. Antonio drove Felix hard against the ropes.

The crowd ate it up. Thus far the two had fought with *mucho corazón.* Felix tapped his gloves and commenced his attack anew. Antonio, throwing boxer's caution to the winds, jumped in to meet him.

Both pounded away. Neither gave an inch and neither fell to the canvas. Felix's left eye was tightly closed. Claret red blood poured from Antonio's nose. They fought toe-to-toe.

The sounds of their blows were loud in contrast to the silence of a crowd gone completely mute. The referee was stunned by their savagery.

Bong! Bong! Bong! The bell sounded over and over again. Felix and Antonio were past hearing. Their blows continued to pound on each other like hailstones.

Finally the referee and the two trainers pried Felix and Antonio apart. Cold water was poured over them to bring them back to their senses.

They looked around and then rushed toward each other. A cry of alarm surged through Tompkins Square Park. Was this a fight to the death instead of a boxing match?

The fear soon gave way to wave upon wave of cheering as the two *amigos* embraced.

No matter what the decision, they knew they would always be champions to each other.

BONG! BONG! BONG! "Ladies and Gentlemen. *Señores* and *Señoras.* The winner and representative to the Golden Gloves Tournament of Champions is . . ."

The announcer turned to point to the winner and found himself alone. Arm in arm the champions had already left the ring.

---

game (GAYM) ready and willing
clarity (KLAR uh tee) clearness
claret red (KLAR it RED) deep purplish red
mute (MYOOT) unable to talk; quiet

Review the Selection

UNDERSTAND THE SELECTION

Recall

1. Where did Antonio and Felix live?

2. What did each boy hope to become?

3. What big decision do the boys make before the fight?

Infer

4. Why did the boys feel a wall rising between them?

5. When the boys first learned that they were going to fight against each other, what were they tempted to do?

6. Why does Felix see the movie?

7. What does the author mean when he says that Felix "had a habit of playing possum when hurt"?

Apply

8. Why do you think that the author does not tell who is the winner of the fight?

9. What is the message, or theme, of this story?

10. Imagine yourself in Felix's or Antonio's place. Would you have been able to fight your best friend? Why or why not?

Respond to Literature

Were Felix and Antonio heroes? Explain why you do or do not think so.

WRITE ABOUT THE SELECTION

At the end of "Amigo Brothers," the announcer is about to point to the winner of the fight. Who do you think the winner is? How do you think each boy reacts when notified who the winner is? Do you think they care who won? Write an episode to add to "Amigo Brothers" that tells what happened after the fight.

Prewriting Make an informal outline of what you think happened after the fighters left the ring. You might want to include details about the reaction of the crowd and any further statements by the announcer. You might want to limit your ending to the reactions of the two boys on learning the identity of the winner.

Writing Use your informal outline as a guide to help you to write the last episode to the story. You might also want to reread a few paragraphs of the original story to make a smooth connection between the author's and your writing style.

Revising When you revise your paragraph, consider adding dialogue where appropriate.

Proofreading Before you correct your final handwritten paragraph, decide whether you will use any Spanish words. All Spanish words should be written in *italics*. You can indicate italics by underlining the word on your paper. Also correct any errors in spelling, punctuation and mechanics.

420 ■ Unit 5

THINK ABOUT PLOT ELEMENTS

The plot of any story has certain elements. The action of a story that leads to the climax is called **rising action**. In rising action, you learn about the main characters and everything that is going to be important in the story. The rising action leads to the climax or most exciting part of the story. Then the story moves to its conclusion. The set of actions bringing the story to an end after the climax is called the **falling action**. With falling action, the story winds down to the resolution.

1. What is the climax of "Amigo Brothers"?

2. Does the story have a resolution? Explain.

3. In what way is this story similar to "The Lady or the Tiger?" which you read in Unit 3?

4. What plot questions are introduced in "Amigo Brothers"?

5. Which plot question remains un-answered?

READING FOCUS

Recognize Changes in Relationships
As you read, you discovered the conflict between the two characters and how that conflict affected their relationship. How did their relationship change? Give three specific examples from the story.

DEVELOP YOUR VOCABULARY

Many words in the English language are derived from Spanish. For example, the Spanish word *pueblo* means "village." In English, the word refers to only one type of dwelling in a Native American village in the southwestern United States. Another Spanish word that has found its way into English is *amigo*, which means "friend." If you like Mexican food, you are probably familiar with a flatbread called *tortilla*. Tortilla is a variation of the word *torta*, which means "cake."

In the short story, "Amigo Brothers," a number of Spanish words appear in the text. The author uses these words to add flavor to the story. Use a Spanish-English dictionary to find the meanings of the following words from "Amigo Brothers." Then write a definition for each word.

1. panin
2. cheverote
3. hermano
4. sabe
5. salsa

Focus ON FICTION

You can increase your enjoyment and understanding of fiction by remembering its four major elements. To review, they are setting, characters, plot, and theme. Now you can add to your understanding by learning about four additional elements: **point of view**, **tone**, **symbolism**, and **writing technique**.

Point of View   Every story must be written from a certain point of view. Someone, a character or speaker, must tell the story.

Most stories are written from either a first-person or third-person point of view. When **first-person** point of view is used, the narrator is a participant in the story. He or she may be either a major or minor character. Throughout the story, this character refers to himself or herself as "I" and "me." Since everything in the story is told from this character's point of view, the action and narration are limited to what only this character can see, hear, think, know, or feel.

In a **third-person** narrative, the narrator is not a participant in the story. The narrator must refer to each character in the story as "he" or "she." In some third-person stories, the narrator is **omniscient**, or all-knowing. The narrator stands outside the story and knows what goes on in the minds of all the characters. In other stories, the narrator takes a **limited** point of view and knows the thoughts and feelings of only a single character. A third-person narrative is less personal than a story told from first-person point of view.

Tone   The author's attitude toward his or her subject as well as toward his or her reader is called the tone. It may be funny, sad, light-hearted, or sarcastic. The choice of tone can even be ironic. You will recognize this tone in "The Secret Life of Walter Mitty."

Symbolism   In literature, a symbol is something that stands for something else. Usually a symbol stands for something that you cannot see or touch; it may be a feeling, quality, or idea. For example, in the short story "Amigo Brothers," the boys' scrapbook symbolizes the way they feel about boxing and each other.

Sometimes a symbol is an action rather than an object. In "Amigo Brothers," the two boys hug each other tightly after agreeing not to see each other until the championship fight. The hug can be seen as a symbolic gesture that tells the way the two boys feel about each other.

Writing Technique   Authors use many special techniques to enhance a short story. These include dialogue, flashback, foreshadowing, description, narration, and commentary.

Dialogue helps an author to create a character. You know from your own experience that you can tell many things about a person by the way he or she talks. In a story, dialogue tells the reader what a character says and how he or she says it.

Often, events in a story are told in chronological order. Sometimes, however, an author makes use of flashback. In **flashback**, a scene from an earlier time is inserted into the story.

As you read "On the Ledge," look to see what elements of the short story are present. Ask yourself these questions:

1. What is the point of view of the story? Is the narrator's point of view omniscient or limited?
2. What writing techniques does the author use? How do these techniques enhance the story?

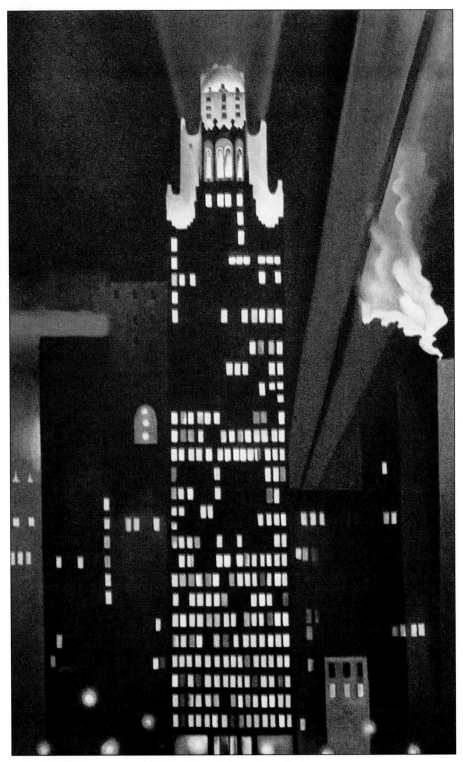

Radiator Building - Night, Georgia O'Keeffe, Alfred Stieglitz Collection

ON THE LEDGE

by Thompson Clayton

Sergeant Gray leaned out a sixth-floor window. Eight feet to his left, on a narrow ledge, stood a young man with frightened eyes. The young man's back was flat against the building. His arms were spread wide. His fingers gripped the edges of the rough bricks.

Gray looked down and swallowed hard. Six floors below, a crowd had gathered. Somewhere down on the street a siren screamed.

If I go out there, Gray thought, *I'll fall for sure.* High places had always scared Gray. He looked over at the young man. The youth's open shirt was wet with sweat. A strong wind blew his pants tight against his legs.

"Take it easy, fella," Gray said. The youth was about the size of his own 17-year-old son. "There's a lot of people down there you could hurt if you fall."

The young man looked down. His eyes seemed to be completely white. He said nothing.

"What's your name, pal?" asked Gray.

The boy swallowed and answered. "Walt," he said. "Walter Whitfield."

"Walt, you've got a lot of guts to go out there. More than I have. You must have a big problem. You want to talk about it?"

"You a cop?" asked Walter.

"I try to be," said Gray.

"Then I don't want to talk to you," said Walter.

FOCUS ON FICTION
STUDY HINTS

As the story opens, the boy's position on the ledge is symbolic of his position in life.

Notice that the point of view of the story is the third person. But the reader sees things primarily from Gray's point of view. This is called limited third person.

By now you can tell that the tone of the story is one of extreme urgency; time has all but run out for Walter Whitfield.

The writer now uses
Sergeant Gray's physical
condition as a symbolic
representation of his
state of mind.

Notice how the author
uses dialogue to develop
the characters of Gray
and Walter.

Gray took off his cap and mopped his forehead. His head was wet and sticky. His damp shirt stuck to his back.

"Would you talk to someone else, Walter?" Gray asked.

"Maybe."

"Who, Walter? Your mother?"

"My mother's dead," Walter said. His voice shook.

"I'm sorry, Walter. Would you talk to your girlfriend then?"

"No!" Walter said angrily.

"Your brother?"

Once again Walter swallowed hard. "I might," he answered.

"What's his name?" asked Gray.

"John—John Whitfield."

"Does he live in town?"

"He has an office on Belton Street."

"Know his phone number?" Gray asked.

"No, it's in the book."

"Get it," Gray said over his shoulder to a policeman named Morely.

Morely reached for a phone book. "I'll have it in a minute," he said.

"We're calling him, Walter," Gray said with a smile. He looked down at the street. A long silver-and-red fire truck was backing into a space cleared by the police.

"I'll jump," said the boy. His teeth showed white against his tanned face. "If they raise a ladder, I'll jump."

Gray leaned out and signaled the firefighters below. They stopped and looked up. Gray waved his arms to show the firefighters they were to stop.

"All right, Walter. They won't raise it," Gray said.

"I've got Walt's brother on the phone," said Morely. "He says he's on his way."

"Your brother's coming," said Gray. "Think you can hold on?"

"I can make it." The burning noonday sun was now full on the youth's face. He licked his lips.

"Can I get you a drink?" asked Gray.

"No!"

"Anything else?"

"Only my brother," Walter replied.

Gray watched the boy's face. In the last minute the color had drained away. "You feeling OK, Walter?"

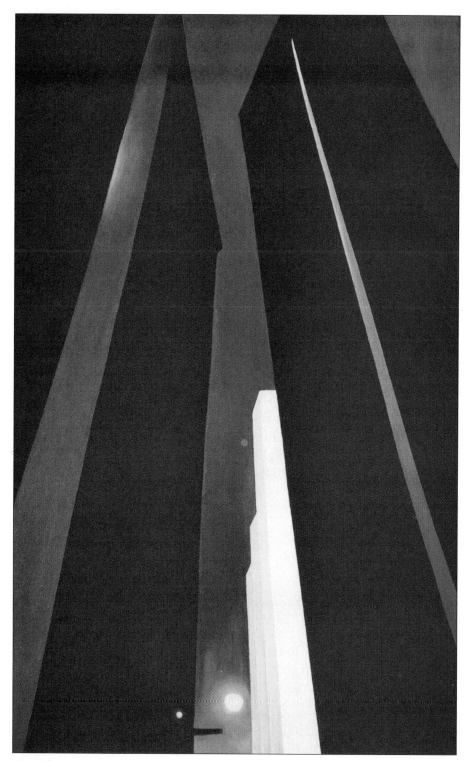

City Night, Georgia O'Keeffe. The Minneapolis Institute of Arts

"Dizzy," Walter answered.

Gray swung around to Morely. "You think you could go out there?"

"Just thinking about it scares me half to death," said Morely.

The author gives a hint of what Gray will have to do as no one comes forward to help.

Gray's eyes looked over the small group in the room. "Any of you done any high climbing? We need somebody to go out to help that kid. He might faint."

The men looked away. Two or three young office girls looked at him with wide eyes. There were no takers. Gray turned to the window again.

Looking at the youth, Gray was surprised at the sudden change. Walter's face now looked gray. His knees were shaking.

"Hang in there, Walter," Gray said. He tried to keep his voice calm. He wished now that they had put up the ladder. Maybe Walter wouldn't have jumped.

Down in the street the crowd had grown. Besides the fire truck, there were three police cars and an ambulance.

Gray looked over at Walter again. The boy started to lean outward—away from the building. For a moment he seemed about to fall. But then he caught himself, grabbing at the brick wall. His fingers showed white under the strain.

Gray could see that Walter was about to give up. "Morely," he called, "that boy's not going to make it!"

"What are we going to do?" Morely asked, fear in his voice.

"If you'll hold on to me, I'll try to reach him," Gray answered.

Slowly, carefully, he climbed over the windowsill and out onto the ledge.

"Walter, I'm coming to help you," he said softly. Walter's mouth opened, but no sound came out.

Morely reached out the window and grabbed Gray's left leg. Gray knelt on a ledge just six inches wide. He did not look down. He began inching his way toward Walter.

Gray could see that Walter was shaking with fear. Gray had to calm him somehow.

The author uses both dialogue and tone to reveal more about the kind of person Gray is.

"Walter, can you move a little closer . . . so I can reach your hand?" Gray said softly. "Take it easy . . . a little at a time."

Walter said nothing. But he was slowly trying to slide his foot toward Gray. He stretched out his hand, trying to touch Gray's. They were still two feet apart.

"I can't," Walter said, his voice shaking.

"Hold on," said Gray. His mouth felt dry. "I'm coming." He moved closer to Walter. Morely could no longer hold him.

Making a quick move, Gray reached for Walter's shaking hand. Then suddenly Gray's knee slipped. Six floors below the watching crowd gasped. Gray tried to regain his balance. He wavered back and forth. He was going over—

Suddenly he felt a hard hand. Somehow, in that terrible moment, Walter had found the strength and courage to save him.

Slowly the two made their way back to the window. Inside, they lay on the floor, drained of all strength.

"Sergeant," Walter said softly.

"Yeah, kid," Gray answered.

"I'm sorry," Walter said. Gray smiled.

It was then that he knew Walter Whitfield was going to make it.

Notice that Gray and Walter say few words to each other here, but they have reached a mutual understanding and respect.

---

waver (WAY vur) move in an unsteady way

Review the Selection

UNDERSTAND THE SELECTION

Recall

1. Where does the story take place?

2. What is Walter's predicament?

3. What does Sergeant Gray try to do?

Infer

4. What do you think Walter is planning to do?

5. What can you infer about Walter's relationship with his brother?

6. What clue makes you suspect that Walter may have been in trouble with the law in his past?

7. How would you describe Sergeant Gray's attitude toward Walter?

Apply

8. Do you feel that Sergeant Gray said and did the right things in this situation? Why or why not?

9. Predict what might have happened if Sergeant Gray had not gone out after Walter.

10. How do Walter's actions at the end of the story indicate a change in him?

Respond to Literature

Do you think that this story has one or two heroes? Explain your answer.

WRITE ABOUT THE SELECTION

As you read "On the Ledge," you learned a little about Walter from his conversations with Sergeant Gray. Do you think that knowing more of Walter's background might help to explain why he is on the ledge? Try to flesh out Walter's character by writing a paragraph in which you give some additional information about him, such as what he is thinking and feeling as he awaits his brother's arrival.

Prewriting Begin by making a list of questions about Walter, such as, why is he angry when Sergeant Gray mentions his girlfriend? After each question, jot down what you think might be a possible answer.

Writing Use your list of questions and answers to develop a character sketch of Walter Whitfield. Let the paragraph reflect your idea of the kind of person you think Walter is. You must base your sketch on information from the story, but keep in mind that the purpose of your paragraph is to provide information about Walter that goes beyond the story.

Revising Make sure that all of the details in your paragraph are consistent with the story. Eliminate or change any details that are not consistent.

Proofreading Whenever a story uses dialogue, be sure to insert quotation marks correctly. Reread your sketch again to ensure that you have made a paragraph indention each time a different character speaks.

THINK ABOUT STORY ELEMENTS

Four additional elements of the short story are point of view, tone, symbolism, and writing techniques. **Point of view** is the position from which the story is told. **Tone** is the author's attitude toward the subject matter and toward the reader. **Symbolism** is using a concrete object or action to stand for something. **Writing techniques** include dialogue and flashback. Dialogue, conversation between characters in a story, can reveal aspects of each speaker's personality, provide background information, or advance the plot. Flashbacks allow writers to give you important information that occurred before the events of the story.

1. Describe the point of view of "On the Ledge."

2. What is the symbolic meaning of Gray's mopping his forehead?

3. What is the tone of the story?

4. What do you learn about Gray through dialogue?

5. What do you learn about Walter through dialogue?

DEVELOP YOUR VOCABULARY

You can improve your understanding of a word and its meaning by knowing the part of speech it belongs to. For example, in the sentence "His damp shirt stuck to his back," the word *damp* is an adjective. By knowing that *damp* is an adjective and by knowing that it means wet or moist, you can use the word effectively in other sentences.

Each of the words in italics is a noun, verb, or adjective. Use the dictionary to identify the part of speech of each italicized word. Then use each word in an original sentence.

1. His fingers *gripped* the edges of the rough bricks.

2. Walter had found the *strength* to save him.

3. Somewhere down the street a *siren* screamed.

4. On a *narrow* ledge stood a young man.

5. He began *inching* his way toward Walter.

6. He *wavered* back and forth.

Learn About

READING FOCUS

Understand the Sequence of Events
To understand the plot of a story, you need to be able to tell the sequence of events. Writers do not always relate the events of a story in the order in which they occurred. For example, the author might describe certain present events at the beginning of a story. Then, he or she might describe a series of events from the past, as background. As you read, notice words and phrases that refer to time, such as "three days ago" or "when she was a child," to understand the sequence of events.

FORESHADOWING

Writers use **foreshadowing** to give the reader hints about what is going to happen in a story. You can think of fore-shadowing as a clue that encourages you to make predictions as you read. For example, in the story "On the Ledge," the author gives you several clues that Sergeant Gray may eventually go out on the ledge to help Walter. One clue is that Gray is thinking about how scared he is of high places and about what might happen *if* he went out.

The story you are about to read is filled with foreshadowing. As you read "Terror in the North," ask yourself:

1. How does the opening sentence by Stina's history teacher foreshadow the events of the story?
2. How do Stina's reactions to her teacher's speech foreshadow trouble ahead?

WRITING CONNECTION

Write an opening sentence for a story that has one or more details that could foreshadow the events of the plot. For example, you might write, "My sister, who is usually very talkative, is sitting silently by the window."

TERROR
IN THE NORTH

ADAPTED

by Eloise Engle

"*S*ometime during our lives," said the history teacher, "we all face our moment of truth."

Stina Olson sat up straight in her seat. How did he know that a problem like this had been troubling her? Could he tell just by looking at her that she was questioning what kind of person she really was?

"*As history shows," he continued, "few people really know how they will behave under extreme stress. Heroism often appears in wartime. Or sometimes we find heroic deeds in peacetime, when the enemy is fire, flood, hurricane, or earthquake."*

Stina Olson relaxed again. He's certainly not talking about me, she thought. I'm the world's greatest coward.

About four o'clock on the afternoon of March 27, 1964, Stina decided she would *not* go along with the others from school. They were going to help clean and paint their town, Seward, Alaska. Seward was scheduled to receive the All-American Cities Award in just one week. There were plenty of last-minute jobs to be done before tourists from all over flocked in. But this was not her concern. She was not an Alaskan in any sense of the word. She had, in fact, arrived only a few months before, to live with her aunt and uncle after her mother had died. Living in Seattle, she had always felt close to the 49th state. But now things were different. Being an Alaskan, she had learned, meant far more than just living here. Oh, it was all mixed-up. But it had something to do with a pioneer spirit, a love for the wilderness, and a little thing called "guts." No matter how hard she tried, she could not find these things within herself. So lately she had simply given up the idea of ever fitting in.

It wasn't that the people of Seward hadn't been friendly when she first arrived—the adults, that is. But the kids had a kind of "show me" attitude. At least it seemed that way to Stina. She had

---

extreme (ik STREEM) very great
stress (STRES) pressure; uncomfortable strain
Seattle (see AT ul) city in the state of Washington, the most northwestern of the "lower 48" states
  and the closest to Alaska

always been self-conscious about being shorter and more slender than other girls her age. This, along with her blonde hair, blue eyes, and fair skin, took at least two years off her 16. Not being very good at sports was another mark against her.

There was the time when Dan Darby had asked her to go along with the gang on a hiking trip. She had packed a lunch and climbed into her heaviest jeans and boots. Then she started out, only nearly to collapse from fright when they reached the top of a cliff that dropped straight down into Resurrection Bay. Dan, who was almost six feet tall and just about the best-looking boy in town, just shook his head in wonder. "Boy, they sure grow 'em frail in the 'Lower 48' these days."

She forced herself to sneak another look. The city below jutted out into the turquoise-blue water. Colorful fishing boats sailed in and out of the bay. The sun shone down on the sparkling water, and Stina had to agree to the country's beauty. But that didn't help that little cowardly streak running up her spine.

"I . . . I'm going to start back down," she murmured.

"Okay, okay." Dan took her arm and guided her along the dangerous mountainside. He was quiet for quite a while. Then he said, "You'll get used to it . . . eventually . . . I think."

But she didn't. She went fishing for silver salmon and wound up seasick.

Now, at five o'clock, she headed for the Stetson house. She was to baby-sit for their three-month-old infant. She thought that she was at least freeing two adults for the clean-up job. *I'm the one behind the gun,* she told herself grimly. *Even if I don't fit in here, I can do something calm and simple like babysitting.*

The Stetsons' house had been built only two years before. It was one of the nicest in town. Stina truly enjoyed being there because of the wide view of the harbor from the living-room window.

"The baby has been fed and he's just about ready to fall asleep," Mrs. Stetson told Stina. "There are sodas in the refrigerator, and . . . oh yes, some delicious roast moose. Help yourself."

After they left, Stina settled down in an easy chair by the window. She began looking through a magazine. For some strange reason she couldn't concentrate, not even on the pictures. Her whole body felt tense. She didn't know why. Was it because twilight was now creeping over the bay? Or was it simply because she was alone and mad at herself? No, there was something more.

She shuddered and tried to think of something pleasant. But it was no use. She pushed up her sweater sleeves and saw the goosebumps on her arms. *Now,*

---

self-conscious (SELF KON shus) very aware of oneself; embarrassed or shy
frail (FRAYL) weak
jutted (JUT id) stuck out
eventually (ih VEN choo uhl ee) in the end; at some time
grimly (GRIM lee) harshly; sternly
concentrate (KON sun trayt) pay close attention

why do I feel this way? She glanced at her watch. Five thirty. *Something is happening somewhere . . . I know it!*

Something *was* happening somewhere. About 150 miles southeast, and about 12 miles beneath the icy green waters of Prince William Sound, powerful forces were at work on the earth's crust. Twisting, straining layers of rock began to move. The raging forces beneath the thin, rocky crust would not be stilled. The tremendous power, held back for centuries, could no longer be kept in harness. The largest single catastrophe ever to hit any state in the union began a rampage that would affect one million square miles. . . .

"Who's there?" Stina called out in answer to a pounding at the door.

"It's me. Dan." He hurried into the room carrying a large paper sack. "I can only stay a minute. I brought you some of the gang's leftover hot dogs." He looked through the bag. "And here are some potato chips and cake."

Stina was more ashamed than ever. She forced herself to laugh. "You're great, Dan. Now I won't have to eat moose for supper."

He started toward the door. "I'll try to stop in later. That is . . . if you want me to."

"Oh, I do," she blurted out. "I . . . I really don't mean to seem unfriendly. I honestly like it here but . . ." *There was*

that strange feeling again! "Dan, don't go. Please stay and have a soda."

She hurriedly poured some soda over ice. Then she set the glasses on the coffee table. But they did not stay put. The ice tinkled as the fizzing soda danced over the rims of the glasses. Stina frowned. She looked in puzzlement at Dan. Then she looked past him at the china figurines on the bookcase. These, too, were bouncing up and down. Suddenly, there was a strange and terrible sound, a sort of "Vroooooo." It came from far away or under the earth. Stina's whole body stiffened. "What . . . what was that?" she gasped.

Dan shrugged his shoulders and laughed lightly. "Oh, probably just a little earthquake. We have 'em all the time. Alaskans get used to 'em. Sit tight, and don't be afraid."

The whole house began to shake violently. Furniture fell over and slid around the room. The chimney on the roof crumbled, and now Stina began to feel seasick. "Oh, no . . . no!" she screamed, as she almost fell to the floor.

Dan wasn't laughing anymore. "It's a good strong one, I'll say that for it," he said. He grabbed her arm and pushed her toward the doorway where there would be support from overhead. "Don't panic now."

Now the pictures on the wall began to crash to the floor. Lamps sailed across the room. The floor beneath them cracked

---

catastrophe (kuh TAS truh fee) a sudden, horrible disaster
rampage (RAM payj) wild outbreak
blurted (BLURT id) said suddenly
figurine (fig yuh REEN) small statue

Softly, Vivian Caldwell

and groaned. The kitchen cupboard doors swung open, emptying dishes, silverware, canned foods, pots, and pans onto the floor. Flour, sugar, milk, syrup all crashed into a huge heap. The shattering glass and splintering house joints roared in her ears as she jerked free from Dan.

"Let go of me!" she screamed. "I've got to get out of here." This must be a nightmare. It couldn't be real. But even as she tried to get to the front door, her feet flew from under her.

It was probably less than a minute since the horrible shaking began, but it seemed as if it would never end. "Please stop," she cried. "Please!" Looking out the window she could see trees crashing down. Huge cracks ripped open the earth and horrible black mud squirted up. The ground itself was rolling in waves. In the distance she could see the dock area. "Look, Dan!" she gasped.

They stared, horror-stricken. The entire waterfront north of Washington Street slid into the bay. With it went the dock, warehouse, and huge fuel-storage tanks of an oil company. And then the other waterfront buildings north to San Juan dock, the small boat harbor—everything in sight—slipped away in underwater slides. Almost immediately, the lid blew off in another oil-storage tank area. Orange flames leaped into the air as eight tanks exploded. And in back of the flames, speeding down the bay at hundreds of miles an hour, was a huge tidal wave of sea water.

Dan grabbed Stina's arm. "We've got to get out of here. That wave is coming inland!" Somehow Stina managed to follow Dan out of the house. They scrambled up on top of some oil barrels and from there onto a neighbor's garage. "This will never hold," Dan yelled. "Here, we'll have to jump over to the housetop."

He went first, then braced himself to catch Stina. "Hurry!" he called.

She bent down to leap—and then she remembered! Oh no! Oh no! "Dan, I forgot about the baby. I've got to go back for him!"

"You can't, Stina! There isn't time! You'll be killed!"

But she could hear nothing except the pounding of her own heart. It was as if suddenly tons of strength had been pumped into her trembling body. She did not look back to the safety of the rooftop. Nor did she glance outward to the Bay, with the wall of water racing nearer and nearer. She thought only of the helpless infant whose life would be gone if she could not reach him in time. As she struggled up the broken steps of the house, she remembered the words of the history teacher. . . . Something about a "moment of truth." Yes, this was her moment of truth. She was terrified. But she was not running from her responsibility in order to save her own skin. This discovery about herself seemed to pour into her even more strength. Stumbling past broken furniture, upturned chairs, and falling plaster, she reached the bedroom. Then she snatched up the baby, wrapped him in a blanket, and ran out of the house again.

"Over here, Stina. Hurry!" Dan yelled.

Stina's throat was hot and dry. But her legs could still move, and that was what counted. She handed Dan the baby and began to climb up onto the rooftop. She saw the towering wall of water bearing down on them. Two minutes later it struck the Stetsons' house, tearing it to pieces. The garage they had been on top of, only minutes before, went next.

Beneath her, she felt the porch of the house being torn away. The bedrooms, splintering and swirling, went next. The baby, now in Stina's arms, was crying. As long as he was crying, there was strength and life in his tiny form. Stina was grateful that he could not know of his nearness to death.

"Hang on tight," Dan ordered. Suddenly the rooftop raft sailed dizzily away in the swirling water. There was nothing left of the house but the living room beneath them. As they sped on through the muddy water, she saw a raging fire in the distance. She dimly wondered if its fiery fingers would reach as far inland as

---

tidal wave (TYD ul WAYV) huge, destructive, ocean wave
bearing (BAIR ing) pressing; advancing rapidly

their rooftop perch.

They bumped into trees, parts of houses, and buildings. It seemed certain their raft would split wide open. Unbelievable minutes, that seemed like an entire lifetime, went by. At last they found themselves caught between trees. Dan leaped into action. He tied the roof to the trees with the television wires. Now, at least, they were anchored to something. But the waves reached as high as the attic and lapped at the roof itself.

The sixth and last of the tidal waves finally fell back. Only then did Dan risk lowering himself into the house. Stina, holding the baby, sat tight. "Be careful, Dan," she yelled.

As she waited, darkness fell. She could still see familiar objects sailing by. The moonlight reflected on a car. As it floated by like a toy, it flipped over on its side. Minutes later, the bodies of two dogs came near. She almost cried out because she thought she recognized one of them as her family's pet.

It seemed as if Dan had been gone forever. What could he be doing? "Dan,

La Vague, Gustave Courbet. The Brooklyn Museum, Gift of Mrs. Horace Havemeyer

are you all right?" she called out.

"I'm coming," he answered, and swung himself onto the rooftop again. "We're in luck . . . two candles, a lighter, and a can of juice for Junior."

Stina was grateful for them. But as the heavy chill in the air grew sharper, she shivered more and more.

"Do you suppose there's some kind of insulation in the roof?" she asked. "If we could get at it, it might help to keep us warm."

"Good idea," Dan said. He began pulling up shingles and tearing out insulation with which they could wrap themselves for warmth. Then there was nothing to do except . . . wait.

"Somebody will rescue us," he comforted Stina. "Our best bet is to stay put."

"I know. I'm not afraid anymore."

"So I noticed," Dan said, smiling. "And I take back any kidding I ever did about you. Just wait till word gets around."

Down at the waterfront, the raging fires had been carried back to sea by the returning waves. Dock pilings that had been snapped off were floating upright. Coated with tar, their top sections were aflame. They looked like candles floating in the night all over the bay.

What seemed hours dragged by. Then Stina's heart leaped as she saw the beautiful gleam of approaching flashlights. There were sounds of human voices calling. "You up there. Are you all right?"

Dan cupped his hands to his mouth and shouted, "We're fine."

He peeked inside the blanket to look at the baby. Then he put his arm around Stina. "All three of us are okay," he said huskily, "thanks to you, Stina."

Stina managed a smile. Then she bent forward to yell as loudly as she could, "There are three wet, cold Alaskans up here. Come and get us!"

---

pilings (PYL ingz) wooden poles driven into the ground to form part of a wall or a foundation

Review the Selection

UNDERSTAND THE SELECTION

Recall

1. Where does this story take place?

2. How old is Stina?

3. What happens while Stina is baby-sitting for the Stetsons?

Infer

4. Why was Stina questioning the kind of person she was?

5. What can you infer about Dan's feelings toward Stina at the beginning of the story?

6. Why was Stina embarrassed when Dan brought her leftover food?

7. Why did Stina not look back when she went to rescue the baby?

Apply

8. What caused Stina to ask Dan to stay with her at the Stetsons' house?

9. What realization about herself gives Stina the greatest strength?

10. At the end of the story, what is the significance of the phrase "three wet, cold Alaskans"?

Respond to Literature

What action of Stina's illustrates the history teacher's opening statement? How realistic do you think this action is?

WRITE ABOUT THE SELECTION

Stina's rescue of the baby would make a wonderful human interest story for the news media. Suppose that you are a news reporter asked to cover the Alaskan earthquake. You interview Stina and Dan; then write a feature story for a newspaper or a TV news broadcast.

Prewriting   Begin by clustering the facts that must always be present in a news story: who, what, when, where, why. Use your cluster to write interview questions. Then write down what you think Stina and Dan might say in an interview.

Writing   Use your cluster and notes to write a feature story about Stina's rescue of the baby. Remember that a good news story must capture the reader's interest. Also keep in mind that when writing a news story, it is important *not* to include your own opinion, but to let the story speak for itself.

Revising   You can improve the effectiveness of your story by adding direct quotes from Stina and Dan. Make sure that you use proper punctuation when using direct quotations.

Proofreading   As you reread your story for errors in spelling, pay careful attention that recurring names are spelled the *same* way throughout the story. The name Olson, for instance, could be misspelled very easily as Olsen. Concern for small proofreading details will lend credibility to your story.

THINK ABOUT FORESHADOWING

Foreshadowing prepares the reader for a surprise by giving hints about what might happen later in the story.

Foreshadowing also involves the reader in a kind of predicting game. Part of the fun of reading the story is seeing if your predictions are correct. Answer these questions about foreshadowing.

1. How does the opening speech in "Terror in the North" clearly foreshadow Stina's immediate future?

2. What specific situations does the history teacher mention that relate to the events of the story?

3. How does Stina's reaction to the speech foreshadow what will happen to her?

4. What definite clues about the upcoming disaster are present while Stina is babysitting?

5. What change in Dan's behavior signals the severity of the earthquake?

READING FOCUS

Understand the Sequence of Events
Use your understanding of the sequence of events to answer this question: Which events took place *before* March 27, 1964?
An earthquake occurs.
Stina moves to Alaska.
Stina goes hiking with other kids and becomes scared.
Stina looks after the Stetsons' baby.
Stina rescues a baby.

DEVELOP YOUR VOCABULARY

Synonyms are words that have the same, or almost the same, meaning. For example, in the sentence "Stina's action was very courageous," the word *courageous* could be replaced by the word *brave*. *Brave* is a synonym for *courageous*. The basic purpose of a thesaurus is to provide lists of synonyms for the words you look up. Some dictionaries provide synonyms after the definitions.

Consult a thesaurus or a dictionary to find synonyms for the italicized words in the sentences below. Decide which word could replace the italicized word in each sentence. Try to choose words that are new to you. Then use each new word in an original sentence.

1. The rescue required *extreme* strength.

2. The police officer knew how to work under *stress*.

3. Stina felt *self-conscious* around the other young people.

4. The teacher spoke *grimly* to the students.

5. Compared to the others, Stina was considered *frail*.

Learn About

STORY TECHNIQUES

A writer may choose to use special techniques in order to tell a story. The main technique of a fiction writer is **narration**. This is reporting the events of the story in chronological order. The purpose is to make the story clear. **Description** is another technique that brings scenes and feelings alive for the reader. Another technique is **flashback**. In flashback, an episode from an earlier time is inserted into the story. Writers also use **dialogue**. Dialogue is two or more characters talking to each other. **Repetition** of an idea or phrase can be used to make a point clear to the reader.

As you read "The Secret Life of Walter Mitty," ask yourself these questions:

1. What special techniques does the writer use to enhance the story?
2. How do these techniques help make the story believable?

WRITING CONNECTION

Choose two of these techniques to tell about an important event in your life. Although you are writing about a real event, you can use another writer's tool—imagination—to create appropriate effects even if they did not really happen.

READING FOCUS

Identify Cause and Effect Many of the events in a story are linked by cause and effect. A cause is something that brings about a certain result. The result is called an effect. To determine the cause of an event in a story, ask yourself, Why did it happen? The cause might be some other event in the story. In other cases, the cause may be a certain feeling or attitude a character has.

THE SECRET LIFE OF WALTER MITTY

by James Thurber

"We're going through!" The Commander's voice was like thin ice breaking. He wore his full-dress uniform, with the heavily braided white cap pulled down rakishly over one cold gray eye. "We can't make it, sir. It's spoiling for a hurricane, if you ask me." "I'm not asking you, Lieutenant Berg," said the Commander. "Throw on the power lights! Rev her up to 8,500! We're going through!" The pounding of the cylinders increased: ta-pocketa-pocketa-pocketa-*pocketa-pocketa*. The Commander stared at the ice forming on the pilot window. He walked over and twisted a row of complicated dials. "Switch on No. 8 auxiliary!" he shouted. "Switch on No. 8 auxiliary!" repeated Lieutenant Berg.

"Full strength in No. 3 turret!" shouted the Commander. "Full strength in No. 3 turret!" The crew, bending to their various tasks in the huge, hurtling eight-engined Navy hydroplane looked at each other and grinned. "The Old Man'll get us through," they said to one another. "The Old Man ain't afraid of Hell!" . . .

"Not so fast! You're driving too fast!" said Mrs. Mitty. "What are you driving so fast for?"

"Hmm?" said Walter Mitty. He looked at his wife, in the seat beside him, with shocked astonishment. She seemed grossly unfamiliar, like a strange woman who had yelled at him in a crowd. "You were up to fifty-five," she said. "You know I don't like to go more than forty.

hydroplane (HY droh playn) a seaplane

You were up to fifty-five." Walter Mitty drove on toward Waterbury in silence, the roaring of the SN202 through the worst storm in twenty years of Navy flying fading in the remote, intimate airways of his mind. "You're tensed up again," said Mrs. Mitty. "It's one of your days. I wish you'd let Dr. Renshaw look you over."

Walter Mitty stopped the car in front of the building where his wife went to have her hair done. "Remember to get those overshoes while I'm having my hair done," she said. "I don't need overshoes," said Mitty. She put her mirror back into her bag. "We've been all through that," she said, getting out of the car. "You're not a young man any longer." He raced the engine a little. "Why don't you wear your gloves? Have you lost your gloves?" Walter Mitty reached in a pocket and brought out the gloves. He put them on, but after she had turned and gone into the building and he had driven on to a red light, he took them off again. "Pick it up, brother!" snapped a cop as the light changed, and Mitty hastily pulled on his gloves and lurched ahead. He drove around the streets aimlessly for a time, and then he drove past the hospital on his way to the parking lot.

. . ."It's the millionaire banker, Wellington McMillan," said the pretty nurse. "Yes?" said Walter Mitty, removing his gloves slowly. "Who has the case?"

"Dr. Renshaw and Dr. Benbow, but there are two specialists here. Dr. Remington from New York and Mr. Pritchard-Mitford from London. He flew over." A door opened down a long, cool corridor and Dr. Renshaw came out. He looked distraught and haggard. "Hello, Mitty," he said. "We're having the devil's own time with McMillan, the millionaire banker and close personal friend of Roosevelt. Obstreosis of the ductal tract.[1] Tertiary. Wish you'd take a look at him." "Glad to," said Mitty.

In the operating room there were whispered introductions: "Dr. Remington, Dr. Mitty. Mr. Pritchard-Mitford, Dr. Mitty." "I've read your book on streptothricosis," said Pritchard-Mitford, shaking hands. "A brilliant performance, sir." "Thank you," said Walter Mitty. "Didn't know you were in the States, Mitty," grumbled Remington. "Coals to Newcastle,[2] bringing Mitford and me up here for tertiary." "You are very kind," said Mitty. A huge, complicated machine, connected to the operating table, with many tubes and wires, began at this moment to go pocketa-pocketa-pocketa. "The new anesthetizer is giving way!" shouted an intern. "There is no one in the East who knows how to fix it!" "Quiet, man!" said Mitty, in a low, cool voice. He sprang to the machine, which was now going pocketa-pocketa-queep-pocketa-queep. He began fingering delicately a row of

---

[1]**obstreosis of the ductal tract:** Thurber has invented this and other medical terms

[2]**coals to Newcastle:** The proverb, "bringing coals to Newcastle," means bringing things to a place unnecessarily—Newcastle, England, was a coal center and so did not need coal brought to it.

glistening dials. "Give me a fountain pen!" he snapped. Someone handed him a fountain pen. He pulled a faulty piston out of the machine and inserted the pen in its place. "That will hold for ten minutes," he said. "Get on with the operation." A nurse hurried over and whispered to Renshaw, and Mitty saw the man turn pale. "Coreopsis has set in," said Renshaw nervously. "If you would take over, Mitty?" Mitty looked at him and at the craven figure of Benbow, who drank, and at the grave, uncertain faces of the two great specialists. "If you wish," he said. They slipped a white gown on him; he adjusted a mask and drew on thin gloves; nurses handed him shining . . .

"Back it up, Mac! Look out for that Buick!" Walter Mitty jammed on the brakes. "Wrong lane, Mac," said the parking-lot attendant, looking at Mitty closely. "Gee. Yeh," muttered Mitty. He began cautiously to back out of the lane marked "Exit Only." "Leave her sit there," said the attendant. "I'll put her away." Mitty got out of the car. "Hey, better leave the key." "Oh," said Mitty, handing the man the ignition key. The attendant vaulted into the car, backed it up with insolent skill, and put it where it belonged.

They're so cocky, thought Walter Mitty, walking along Main Street; they think they know everything. Once he had tried to take his chains off, outside New Milford, and he had got them wound around the axles. A man had had to come out in a wrecking car and unwind them, a young, grinning garage-man. Since then Mrs. Mitty always made him drive to a garage to have the chains taken off. The next time, he thought, I'll wear my right arm in a sling; they won't grin at me then. I'll have my right arm in a sling and they'll see I couldn't possibly take the chains off myself. He kicked at the slush on the sidewalk. "Overshoes," he said to himself, and he began looking for a shoe store.

When he came out into the street again, with the overshoes in a box under his arm, Walter Mitty began to wonder what the other thing was his wife had told him to get. She had told him twice, before they set out from their house for Waterbury. In a way he hated these weekly trips to town—he was always getting something wrong. Kleenex, he thought. Squibb's, razor blades? No. Toothpaste, toothbrush, bicarbonate, carborundum, initiative and referendum?[3] He gave it up. But she would remember it. "Where's the what's-its-name?" she would ask. "Don't tell me you forgot the what's-its-name." A newsboy went by shouting something about the Waterbury trial.

---

[3]**carborundum** (kahr buh RUN dum), **initiative** (ih NISH uh tiv) and **referendum** (ref uh REN dum): Thurber is purposely making a nonsense list: carborundum is a hard substance used for scraping, initiative is the right of citizens to introduce ideas for laws, and referendum is the right of citizens to vote on laws.

. . ."Perhaps this will refresh your memory." The District Attorney suddenly thrust a heavy automatic at the quiet figure on the witness stand. "Have you ever seen this before?" Walter Mitty took the gun and examined it expertly. "This is my Webley-Vickers 50.80," he said calmly. An excited buzz ran around the courtroom. The judge rapped for order. "You are a crack shot with any sort of firearms, I believe?" said the District Attorney, insinuatingly. "Objection!" shouted Mitty's attorney. "We have shown that the defendant could not have fired the shot. We have shown that he wore his right arm in a sling on the night of the fourteenth of July." Walter Mitty raised his hand briefly and the bickering attorneys were stilled. "With any known make of gun," he said evenly, "I could have killed Gregory Fitzhurst at three hundred feet *with my left hand*." Pandemonium broke loose in the courtroom. A woman's scream rose above the bedlam and suddenly a lovely, dark-haired girl was in Walter Mitty's arms. The District Attorney struck at her savagely. Without rising from his chair, Mitty let the man have it on the point of the chin. "You miserable cur!"

"Puppy biscuit," said Walter Mitty. He stopped walking and the buildings of Waterbury rose up out of the misty courtroom and surrounded him again. A woman who was passing laughed. "He said 'Puppy biscuit,'" she said to her companion. "That man said 'Puppy biscuit' to himself." Walter Mitty hurried on. He went into an A&P, not the first one he came to but a smaller one farther up the street.

"I want some biscuit for small, young dogs," he said to the clerk. "Any special brand, sir?" The greatest pistol shot in the world thought a moment. "It says 'Puppies Bark for It' on the box," said Walter Mitty.

His wife would be through at the hairdresser's in fifteen minutes, Mitty saw in looking at his watch, unless they had trouble drying it; sometimes they had trouble drying it. She didn't like to get to the hotel first; she would want him to be there waiting for her as usual. He found a big leather chair in the lobby, facing a window, and he put the over-shoes and the puppy biscuit on the floor beside it. He picked up an old copy of *Liberty* and sank down into the chair. "Can Germany Conquer the World Through the Air?" Walter Mitty looked at the pictures of bombing planes and of ruined streets.

. . . "The cannonading has got the wind up in young Raleigh,[4] sir," said the sergeant. Captain Mitty looked up at him through tousled hair. "Get him to bed," he said wearily. "With the others. I'll fly alone." "But you can't, sir," said the sergeant anxiously. "It takes two men to handle that bomber and the Archies[5] are pounding hell out of the air. Von Richtman's circus[6] is between here and Saulier." "Somebody's got to get that ammunition dump," said Mitty. "I'm going over. Spot of brandy?" He poured a drink for the sergeant and one for himself. War thundered and whined around the dugout and battered at the door. There was a rending of wood and splinters flew through the room. "A bit of a near thing," said Captain Mitty carelessly. "The box barrage is closing in," said the sergeant. "We only live once, Sergeant," said Mitty, with his faint, fleeting smile. "Or do we?" He poured another brandy and tossed it off. "I never see a man could hold his brandy like you, sir," said the sergeant. "Begging your pardon, sir." Captain Mitty stood up and strapped on his huge Webley-Vickers automatic. "It's forty kilometers through hell, sir," said the sergeant. Mitty finished one last brandy. "After all," he said softly, "what isn't?" The pounding of the cannon increased; there was the rat-tat-tatting of machine guns, and from somewhere came the menacing pocketa-pocketa-pocketa of the new flame-throwers. Walter Mitty walked to the door of the dugout humming "Auprès de Ma Blonde."[7] He turned and waved to the sergeant. "Cheerio!" he said. . . .

Something struck his shoulder. "I've been looking all over this hotel for you," said Mrs. Mitty. "Why do you have to hide in this old chair? How did you expect me to find you?" "Things close in," said

---

[4]**has got the wind up in young Raleigh:** Has made young Raleigh nervous.
[5]**Archies:** a slang term for anti-aircraft guns
[6]**Von Richtman's circus:** a German airplane squadron
[7]**"Auprès de Ma Blonde"** (oh preh duh mah BLON duh): "Next to My Blonde," a popular French song.

Walter Mitty vaguely. "What?" Mrs. Mitty said. "Did you get the what's-its-name? The puppy biscuit? What's in that box?" "Overshoes," said Mitty. "Couldn't you have put them on in the store?" "I was thinking," said Walter Mitty. "Does it ever occur to you that I am sometimes thinking?" She looked at him. "I'm going to take your temperature when I get you home," she said.

They went out through the revolving doors that made a faintly derisive whistling sound when you pushed them. It was two blocks to the parking lot. At the drugstore on the corner she said,

"Wait here for me. I forgot something, I won't be a minute." She was more than a minute. Walter Mitty lighted a cigarette. It began to rain, rain with sleet in it. He stood up against the wall of the drugstore, smoking. . . . He put his shoulders back and his heels together. "To hell with the handkerchief," said Walter Mitty scornfully. He took one last drag on his cigarette and snapped it away. Then, with that faint, fleeting smile playing about his lips, he faced the firing squad; erect and motionless, proud and disdainful, Walter Mitty the Undefeated, inscrutable to the last.

Review the Selection

UNDERSTAND THE SELECTION

Recall

1. What is Walter Mitty's secret life? Where does he live it?

2. What characters does Mitty imagine himself as?

3. How do these characters behave under pressure?

Infer

4. What is Walter Mitty's life really like?

5. What kind of a person is Mrs. Mitty? How do you know?

6. How does she treat her husband? Give some examples.

7. How do other people treat Walter Mitty?

Apply

8. What do all of Mitty's imagined characters have in common?

9. Do you think that Mitty is a risk-taker? Explain your answer.

10. Why do you think the author ends the story with Mitty facing a firing squad? Is it an appropriate way to end the story?

Respond to Literature

Walter Mitty is certainly not a heroic figure. Why does "The Secret Life of Walter Mitty" appear in a unit about heroes?

WRITE ABOUT THE SELECTION

Do you have a secret life the way Walter Mitty does? Do you sometimes think of yourself as a hero? Your assignment is to write a fantasy episode about yourself in the style of Walter Mitty.

Prewriting Take a few minutes to brainstorm about some of your favorite fantasies. What kind of person do you dream about being? Do you see yourself as a famous athlete or movie star? Do you picture yourself as President of the United States? Do you see yourself as the most popular person in school? Perhaps you see yourself doing something brave, like rescuing a baby from a burning building. Decide which of your fantasies fits you best. Then brainstorm the details you want to include in your fantasy.

Writing Use your prewriting outline to create a fantasy in the style of Walter Mitty. Begin your paragraph with the incident that touches off the fantasy. Then end your paragraph with the incident that brings you back to reality; invent a character like Mrs. Mitty if you need to.

Revising Walter Mitty's fantasies are written in the third person with a fair amount of dialogue. They read like miniature short stories. Revise your paragraph so that your fantasy fits this same style.

Proofreading Be sure that your reader knows when you shift from reality to fantasy and back again by clearly marking new paragraphs.

THINK ABOUT STORY TECHNIQUES

Authors use special techniques to make fiction come alive. **Flashbacks** tell about episodes that happened before the story takes place. **Narration** moves the story forward in chronological order. **Description** adds details that appeal to your senses. **Dialogue**, conversation between characters, gives you, the reader information about characters, setting, and plot. **Repetition** emphasizes ideas and important points. James Thurber uses some of these special techniques in "The Secret Life of Walter Mitty. "

1. What special techniques does Thurber use in this story?

2. How do these techniques enhance the story?

3. What type of dialogue is used in the story?

4. How does this technique make the story more enjoyable?

5. How do these special techniques enable the author to develop the character of Walter Mitty?

READING FOCUS

Identify Cause and Effect As you read this story, you found the cause that brought about each event. Describe one example of cause and effect in "The Secret Life of Walter Mitty."

DEVELOP YOUR VOCABULARY

A **figurative expression** is a group of words with a meaning that goes beyond its literal meaning. Figurative expressions are part of everyday speech as well as literature. You probably hear or use several figurative expressions every day. An example is "falling head over heels in love." Of course this expression does not mean that the person really does a somersault; it means the person is deeply and uncontrollably in love.

Identify the figurative expression in each sentence from the story. Then write the meaning of each expression.

1. "Pick it up, brother!" snapped a cop as the light changed.

2. An excited buzz ran through the courtroom.

3. War thundered and whined around the dugout.

PERSUASIVE SPEECH

When was the last time that somebody talked you into something? Did that person take a stand on an issue and defend it in a logical way? Did the individual urge you to take action? If so, that person was using **persuasive speech**. The purpose of persuasive speech is to convince the listener to believe in a certain idea or take a certain action. Strong evidence—examples, reasons, and facts—is an important part of a persuasive speech. A good persuader doesn't offend by name calling but is calm, objective, and reasonable.

Writers use certain words and techniques when they want to be persuasive. Look for repetition, parallel structure, and quotes. As you read "I Have a Dream," ask yourself these questions:

1. What techniques does Martin Luther King, Jr., use to persuade his audience to believe in his ideas?
2. How does the first line of his speech capture the listeners' attention and make them want to hear more?

WRITING CONNECTION

Suppose that you are running for an elected office, either in your school or in your community. Write a short speech in which you persuade people to vote for you.

READING FOCUS

Identify Main Idea and Supporting Details A piece of writing contains a main idea, which is the central point the author wishes to make. The main idea is developed by related sentences referred to as supporting details. The main idea may be expressed directly or may have to be inferred. As you read, try to locate the main idea of this selection and the details that support the main idea.

from

I HAVE A DREAM

by Martin Luther King, Jr.

I say to you today, my friends, that in spite of the difficulties
and frustrations of the moment, I still have a dream. It is a dream
deeply rooted in the American dream.

I have a dream that one day this nation will rise up and live out
the true meaning of its creed:

---

frustrations (frus TRAY shuns) unhappy feelings that come from not being
   able to reach one's goals
creed (KREED) formal statement of belief

"We hold these truths to be self-evident: that all men are created equal." . . .

I have a dream today. . . .

This is our hope. . . . With this faith we will be able to work together, pray together, struggle together, go to jail together, stand up for freedom together, knowing that we will be free one day.

This will be the day when all of God's children will be able to sing with a new meaning "My country, 'tis of thee, sweet land of liberty, of thee I sing. Land where my fathers died, land of the pilgrims' pride, from every mountainside, let freedom ring." And if America is to be a great nation this must become true. So let freedom ring from the prodigious hilltops of New Hampshire. Let freedom ring from the mighty mountains of New York. . . .

But not only that; let freedom ring from Stone Mountain of Georgia.

Let freedom ring from Lookout Mountain of Tennessee! . . . From every mountainside, let freedom ring.

When we let freedom ring, when we let it ring from every village and every hamlet, from every state and every city, we will be able to speed up that day when all of God's children, black men and white men, Jews and Gentiles, Protestants and Catholics, will be able to join hands and sing in the words of the old Negro spiritual, "Free at last! Free at last! Thank God almighty, we are free at last!"

---

self-evident (SELF EV ih dunt) needing no proof; obviously true
prodigious (pruh DIJ us) great; huge
hamlet (HAM lit) very small village
Gentiles (JEN tylz) originally, people who are not Jewish

Martin Luther King, Jr. (1929–1968)

"You are living a faith that most men preach about but never experience. . . . Your name has become a symbol of courage and hope for oppressed people everywhere." These were the words that the President of Morehouse College used to describe one of the school's most famous students, Dr. Martin Luther King, Jr.

Born in Atlanta, Georgia, as Michael Luther King, Dr. King adopted the name of the great Protestant reformer Martin Luther. After attending the local high school, King received his B.A. degree from Morehouse College, then trained for the ministry at Crozer Theological Seminary. Later he earned a Ph.D. from Boston University.

Martin Luther King's public career began in 1955, when a small group of civil-rights advocates in Montgomery, Alabama, protested racial segregation on the city's bus system. An African American woman named Rosa Parks refused to give up her seat on a bus to a white male and was quickly arrested. In response to the incident, local African Americans founded the Montgomery Improvement Association (MIA) and chose Martin Luther King, Jr., as their leader.

King went on to head the Southern Christian Leadership Conference (SCLC), which fought against racism in both the North and South. As he continued the fight against racial injustice, Dr. King went to jail more than 30 times, was attacked at his home with bombs and shotguns, and was slugged, stabbed, and stoned. Although King was a continual victim of violence, he refused to use or advocate violence himself.

Martin Luther King, Jr., died when he was only 39 years old. He was killed by an assassin's bullet one evening in Memphis, Tennessee. He had gone to Memphis to support a strike by the city's sanitation workers.

Review the Selection

UNDERSTAND THE SELECTION

Recall

1. What is the subject of King's speech?

2. What is King's dream?

3. To what audience is King speaking?

Infer

4. What can you infer about the circumstances surrounding the cause that King believes in?

5. What is the meaning of the phrase "a dream deeply rooted in the American dream"?

6. What does King imply must happen if America is to be a great nation?

7. How does King make it clear that his dream is not just for one geographic location?

Apply

8. To what feelings of his listeners was King appealing?

9. Predict what type of action people might take after hearing this speech.

10. Would you say King expects his dream to come true? Explain your answer.

Respond to Literature

In what way was King a hero to the people who heard this speech?

WRITE ABOUT THE SELECTION

Martin Luther King, Jr., expressed his hope for the United States in his famous "I Have a Dream" speech. Suppose that you were asked to give a speech with the same title. Do you have a dream for the United States? Is it similar to or very different from Dr. King's dream? Write a paragraph beginning with the words, "I have a dream. . . ." Let your paragraph reflect something that you would like to see happen in the United States.

Prewriting   Take a few minutes to brainstorm about some of the causes about which you feel strongly. Perhaps you dream of the day when illegal drugs are no longer a problem. Perhaps you dream of crime-free cities. Maybe you dream of a day when no one in America is homeless. Make a list of your ideas. Then choose the one that you feel is most important to you.

Writing   Use your prewriting idea to compose a paragraph about your dream for America. Remember that your goal is to persuade your readers to agree with you and to fight for the cause you believe in.

Revising   Read your paragraph aloud as if you were giving a speech. Rewrite any parts of your paragraph that sound awkward or wordy. Then reread the paragraph aloud.

Proofreading   Be on the alert to insert a word or words that have been omitted, or delete a word that is written twice. You want your final speech to be letter perfect for ease of delivery.

THINK ABOUT PERSUASIVE SPEECH

A persuasive writer knows how to capture the reader's attention and appeal to the reader's feelings. Effective persuasive writing includes examples, reasons, and facts as evidence to convince the reader to accept an opinion or to take action. A persuasive writer also knows how to use techniques such as repetition and quotations to enhance his or her persuasive piece.

1. How does the first line of King's speech capture your attention and make you want to read more?

2. What words or phrases does King repeat throughout his speech?

3. What quotations does King use?

4. Why are these quotations effective?

5. How persuasive is King's speech? Explain why you think so.

READING FOCUS

Identify Main Idea and Supporting Details As you read "I Have a Dream," you were able to identify the main idea of the speech and the supporting details. How would you summarize the main idea of the selection? What is one detail that supports this main idea?

DEVELOP YOUR VOCABULARY

Many English words have more than one meaning. For example, the word *meet* can mean "to meet someone" or it can mean "a contest, such as a track meet." You can tell which meaning of a word is being used by noting the meaning of the entire sentence in which the word appears.

Write the correct meaning of each italicized word. Then write an original sentence in which you use another meaning of the same word. Use the dictionary if you need help.

1. We let the bell *ring* for five minutes.

2. John is from the *state* of Alabama.

3. He allowed the bird to go *free*.

4. It is my *dream* to become a professional baseball player.

5. Juan is the *head* of his family since his father died.

Return to Minute Man, National Park Service

READING FOCUS

Recognize Similarities in Poetry Making comparisons between poems is one way to increase your enjoyment and understanding of poetry. Poems can be similar in their outward form, such as length and use of rhyme. They can also be similar in tone, point of view, or theme. As you read the four poems here, look for similarities between two or more of the poems.

Learn About

OPEN AND CLOSED FORM

The **form** of a poem is the outward arrangement of the poem, as opposed to the content or subject matter. Form includes such things as rhythm, rhyme, and arrangement of stanzas. In other words, form is how a poem looks as well as the techniques the poet uses to write.

The form of a poem can be closed or open. **Closed form** refers to poetry that has a recognizable pattern. Probably when you think of poetry, you think of a poem written in closed form. Most major types of poetry are closed, including sonnets, ballads, blank verse, and couplets. **Open form** poetry has no recognizable pattern. An example of open form is free verse, which is poetry written with an obviously irregular rhythm.

As you read the four Native American poems, ask yourself these questions:

1. Which poems have a closed form? What patterns are present?
2. Which poems have an open form?

WRITING CONNECTION

Write a simple four-line poem about a subject that interests you. First, write the poem in a regular rhythm and pattern of rhyme. Then try writing about the same subject using four lines of free verse.

Young Omaha, *War Eagle*, *Little Missouri*, and *Pawnees*, Charles Bird King. The Granger Collection

Warrior Song I

by the Omaha

No one has found a way to avoid death,
To pass around it;
Those old men who have met it,
Who have reached the place where death stands waiting,
Have not pointed out a way to circumvent it.
Death is difficult to face.

Warrior Song II

by the Omaha

I shall vanish and be no more,
But the land over which I now roam
Shall remain
And change not.

Buffalo Hunter, Unknown American. Gift of Harriett Cowles Hammett Grahm in Memory of Buell Hammett

Song of Failure

by the Teton Sioux

A wolf
I considered myself,
But the owls are hooting
And the night
I fear.

War Song

by the Teton Sioux

Soldiers,
You fled.
Even the eagle dies.

Review the Selection

UNDERSTAND THE SELECTION

Recall

1. What is the subject of "Song of Failure"?

2. What is the subject of "War Song"?

3. What is the subject of "Warrior Song I" and "Warrior Song II"?

Infer

4. What has happened on the battlefield in "War Song"?

5. How did the speaker in "Song of Failure" see himself at first?

6. How did his view of himself change?

7. What universal truth is expressed in "Warrior Song I"?

Apply

8. How does the speaker in "War Song" make defeat seem less painful?

9. Does "Warrior Song I" or "Warrior Song II" give a more personal view of the subject matter? Why?

10. Explain which poem expresses your own thoughts most closely.

Respond to Literature

What aspects of heroism are described in these four poems?

WRITE ABOUT THE SELECTION

The four Native American poems deal with four aspects of human experience—fear, failure, defeat, and death. In one way or another, these experiences are common to everyone. You have probably experienced some if not all of them at some time in your life. Which of the poems is most meaningful to you? Choose one of the poems, and write about how it relates to a feeling or experience that you have had.

Prewriting Take a few minutes to think about times when you have failed, have been afraid, or have been defeated in some way. Also, think about times when you have thought about death or perhaps have been touched by the death of someone you know. Then read the poems over several times, and make notes of the experiences that come to mind as you read each one.

Writing Choose the poem that most strongly appeals to you. Use your prewriting notes to write a paragraph in which you relate the poem to an experience or feeling that you have had. Be sure you connect your experience to the poem. You might compare and/or contrast your feelings with those of the Native American poets.

Revising If you are recounting an incident in the past tense, make sure that you use correct verb forms. Change any verb forms that are incorrect.

Proofreading See that there are no errors in spelling, usage, or mechanics.

THINK ABOUT FORM

A poem with closed form has a recognizable rhythm, rhyme and stanza pattern; an open form poem does not. If you are uncertain about the form of a poem, it may help to read the poem out loud. If there is a regular pattern of rhythm or rhyme, you should be able to hear it. If you still have trouble, try beating or clapping the long and short sounds of each line as you say it.

1. Would you describe the form of the four Native American poems as open or closed?

2. What features of these poems is your conclusion based on?

3. Do any of the poems have lines that rhyme?

4. How does the form of "War Song" enhance the meaning of the poem?

5. Describe the form of "Warrior Song I."

READING FOCUS

Recognize Similarities in Poetry Choose two of the poems you just read. Explain how they are similar in form, tone, point of view, and theme.

DEVELOP YOUR VOCABULARY

Homophones are words that sound alike but have different spellings and different meanings. For example, *weak* and *week* are homophones.

Choose the correct homophone to complete each sentence. Then use the other homophone in an original sentence.

1. You are (*so, sew*) lucky to have an older brother.

2. I don't know (*weather, whether*) I should go to the store or not.

3. A vegetarian is someone who does not eat (*meet, meat*).

4. I'd like a piece of apple pie, (*to, too*).

5. Do you (*need, knead*) a job?

Learn About

EPIC POETRY

An **epic** is a long narrative poem that tells about the adventures of heroes and gods. The style of an epic is usually formal and dramatic. Ancient epics were often orally passed down from one generation to the next. The central character of an epic is called an **epic hero**. This hero may be a character from history or from legend. The epic hero is often a great, larger-than-life figure.

The basis for the two selections you are about to read is the *Odyssey*, the great epic by Greek poet Homer. In the *Odyssey*, the epic hero is named Odysseus. However, in many versions of the epic adventures, he is often referred to as Ulysses.

As you read "Ulysses and the Trojan Horse" and "Ulysses Meets the Cyclops," ask yourself these questions:

1. How do the selections fit the definition of an epic?
2. What qualities does Ulysses have that make him an epic hero?

READING FOCUS

Understand Character Relationships
The relationships between characters are an important part of a story. To understand the relationship between any two characters, examine their actions as well as what they say to and about each other. Pay attention to how the relationships between the characters affect the plot.

WRITING CONNECTION

Think of a recent event in your life or in the news. Write a brief account of the event as if it were an epic adventure. Be sure to include an epic hero.

ULYSSES
AND THE
TROJAN HORSE

ADAPTED

by Homer

Across the sea from Greece, in what is now Turkey, there was once a fair, rich city, the most famous in the world. This city was called Ilium by its own people. In story and song, it is known as Troy. It stood on a sloping plain some distance back from the shore. Around the city were high, strong walls that no enemy could climb or batter down.

Inside the gates were the homes of the people. There was also a fine stone palace for the king and his sons, and a beautiful temple of Athena. Athena was the goddess who watched over the city. Outside the walls were gardens and farms and woodlands. Far in the distance rose the rocky heights of Mount Ida.

Troy was a very old city. For hundreds of years it had been growing in power and pride. "Ilium will last forever," the Trojans used to say as they looked at its solid walls and noble buildings. They were wrong. Sad changes began to take place, and cruel war cut down the pride of Troy.

The Greek armies came across the sea. They came to conquer the city. The reason was this: one of the princes of Troy, Paris by name, had done a grave wrong to Greece. He had stolen and carried away the most beautiful of all Greek women, Helen, the wife of Menelaus of Sparta. The Greeks cried for revenge. Heroes and warriors from every Greek city and town joined hands against Troy.

Of all the Greek heroes, the wisest and shrewdest was Ulysses, the young king of Ithaca. Yet he did not go willingly to war. No, he would rather have remained at home with his good wife, Penelope, and his son, Telemachus. He was far happier pruning his grapevines and plowing his fields than he could ever be in the turmoil of battle. But the princes of Greece demanded his help. Rather than be thought a coward, he agreed.

Trojan (TROH jun) of Troy; also a person of Troy
shrewdest (SHROOD ist) cleverest, often in a tricky way
turmoil (TUR moil) disorder; unrest

The Warrior Vase from Mycenae, Greece, Scala/Art Resource

"Go, Ulysses," said Penelope. "I'll keep your home and kingdom safe until you return."

And so he sailed away. Forgetting the quiet delights of home, he turned all his thoughts to war.

Ulysses and his Greek warriors came to Troy in a thousand little ships with sails and oars. They landed on the beach at the foot of the plain. They built huts and tents along the shore. They kindled fires.

Around their camp, they threw up a wall of earth and stones. Then they dared the warriors of Troy to come out and meet them in battle.

So the siege began. For more than nine years, the city was surrounded by determined foes. But the walls were strong, and the Trojans were brave. Fierce battles were fought outside the gates. Some were won by the Greeks, some by the Trojans. But neither side could gain a final victory.

---

siege (SEEJ) continued military attack; blockade

The Trojans could not drive the invaders from their shores. And the Greeks could not force their way into the city.

"Athena protects us," said the hopeful people of Troy. "While the Palladium is with us, our city can't be taken."

The Palladium was a beautiful statue that stood in the temple of Athena. The Trojans believed that it had a strange power to protect its friends.

"It's useless for us to fight longer," said some of the Greeks. "We can never win while the Palladium is in Troy."

"We've already stayed too long," said others. "Let's abandon this hopeless siege and go home."

But Ulysses wouldn't give up. On a dark and stormy night, he stole into the city. He got past the guards unseen. He crept into the temple of Athena while all the watchers were asleep. There he seized the Palladium and carried it in triumph to the Greek camp.

"Now we'll surely win," said the Greeks.

But still the Trojans persevered. Their gates were well guarded, and the siege went on.

One morning in the early summer, all Troy was awakened at daybreak. The guards on the walls were shouting: "They're gone! The Greeks are gone!"

Soon a hundred eager men, women, and children were standing on the wall. They strained their eyes in the gray light of dawn, trying to make out the hated tents by the beach and the dark ships along the shore.

"They're not there," said a guard. "There's no sign of the Greeks. Thanks to Athena, they've left us at last." Suddenly the guard pointed toward the shore and cried, "Look! There's a strange, dark object among the reeds. It's by the inlet where the boys used to go swimming. What is it?"

Everyone looked. Sure enough, there was something among the reeds. It was smaller than a ship and larger than a man. In the dim light of morning, it looked like a sea monster lately emerged from the waves.

Just then the sun rose above Mount Ida, casting a rosy golden light on sea and shore. It made every object on the beach plainly visible. There was no longer any doubt about the strange thing in the reeds.

"It's a horse!" shouted one and all.

"But not a real horse," said the guard. "It's much too large. It's a huge, ill-made image that the Greeks have left behind—perhaps to frighten us. And now I remember! For several days, there was something unusual going on behind the reeds and bushes there—workmen hurrying back and forth, and much noise of hammering. They were building this thing."

Just then Laocoön, a prince of Troy, joined them. He was an old man, wrinkled and gray—a priest of Apollo, wiser

---

persevered (pur suh VIRD) kept going by not giving up
reeds (REEDZ) tall grass that grows in a marsh
emerged (ih MURJD) came out
image (IM ij) copy; likeness

than most of his fellows. After looking long and carefully at the strange image, he turned to the crowd. "It's a trick," he said. "My children, beware of the cunning Greeks. They've made this image to fool you. I warn you to have nothing to do with it."

About the middle of the morning, Priam, the old king of Troy, issued an order. It was announced in all the streets. "Our enemies have gone," it said. "Peace and safety are ours once again. At noon the gates of the city shall be opened. At that time, our people may return to their peaceful occupations."

Then there was great joy in every corner of the city. It was as though day had dawned after a long and fearful night. How sweet it was to feel free from dread! How good to go about one's business in peace!

The women talked and sang as they began to clean their houses. The shop-keepers brought out their goods and offered fine bargains to the first buyers. The blacksmiths lighted fires in their forges, and began to hammer old spears into peacetime tools. The fishermen mended their nets. The farmers counted their rakes and hoes and plows. Everyone talked about the fine crops they would have on lands that had been idle so long.

But not all the people were so busy. Long before noon, a great crowd had gathered before the gate on the seaward side of town. They were anxious to get out of the long-surrounded city. No sooner was the gate opened than there was a wild rush across the plain toward the shore. Men as well as boys were eager to see whether the Greeks had left anything valuable behind.

They wandered along the beach, looking in every corner of the old camp. But all they found were a few bits of pottery, a broken sword or two, and a few cheap trinkets.

They kept well away from the inlet where the reeds grew. Even the boldest wouldn't go near the huge wooden horse. For Laocoön, the priest, had warned them again to beware of it. So they just stood at a distance and gazed at the strange, unshapely thing. What evil trick, they wondered, were the Greeks plotting?

Suddenly on the other side of the camp a great shouting was heard. Some Trojans who had been hunting in the marshes were seen approaching with a prisoner.

"A Greek! A Greek!" was the shout. Men and boys ran forward to see the captive and join in cursing him. The poor fellow was led by a leather thong twisted around his neck. As he stumbled along over the sand, the crowd jeered. They hit him with sticks and sand and anything they could lay hold of. The blood was trickling down his face. His eyes were

---

cunning (KUN ing) clever in a tricky way; sly
forges (FAWRJ iz) furnaces used to heat metal
idle (YD ul) unused; not busy
thong (THAWNG) strip of leather
jeered (JIRD) made fun of in a nasty way

swollen. But his persecutors, as they saw his wounds, only shouted louder. "A Greek! A Greek! Get rid of him!"

Then all at once the uproar stopped. Silence fell upon the crowd. For standing in his chariot nearby was one of the officers of the king.

"What prisoner is this? Why are you abusing him?" he asked.

"We think he's a Greek," answered the hunters. "We found him in the tall grass by the marshes. He was already wounded and half-blind. So it was easy for us to take him."

"Already wounded!" said the officer.

"That's strange." Then turning to the prisoner, he asked, "How is this? Tell me whether you're a Greek or a friend of Troy. What's your name, and your country?"

"My name," said the prisoner, "is Sinon. By birth I'm a Greek, yet I have no country. Until ten days ago, I called myself a friend of Greece. I fought bravely alongside her heroes. But see these wounds. Can I remain friendly to those who maimed me and would have taken my life, too?"

"Tell us about it," said the officer. "And tell us truly. Have the Greeks

Wooden Horse of Troy on 7th century B.C. vase found on Mykonos, Greece, Archaeological Museum, Mykonos, Greece/Erich Lessing/Art Resource

maimed (MAYMD) injured badly; crippled

sailed home for good?" He told the hunters to loosen the thong about the prisoner's neck.

"Yes, I'll tell you," answered Sinon. "And I'll be brief. When Ulysses stole the Palladium from your temple, the Greeks felt sure the city was about to fall. Then day after day passed, and they didn't win a single fight. So they began to despair. A council was held. It was decided to give up the siege and sail for home. But great storms arose on the sea. The south wind never let up. No ship could put to sea."

"But what about the horse?" cried the Trojans. "The horse!"

"The horse," said Sinon, "was built on the advice of the soothsayer, Calchas. He told the Greeks, 'Athena is angry because her statue, the Palladium, was stolen from her temple. That's why the storms rage so fiercely. And they'll go on raging until you make a statue of a horse and leave it on this shore as a sign of your shame and repentance. Never can your ships return to Greece until that is done.'

"So the statue was built. The soothsayer said it would carry prosperity and peace wherever it went. But the Greeks didn't want it to be a benefit to Troy. That's why they built it so wide and high that it can't be taken through your gates. They placed it among the reeds by the shore. They hoped the waves might carry it out to sea."

"Ah, so that's their plan, is it?" cried the excited Trojans. "Well, we'll see

about that!" And, forgetting about Sinon, the whole company and the king's officer rushed madly to the great horse.

"Beware, my countrymen, beware!" cried the voice of old Laocoön. He struggled through the crowd. "This is a trick of the Greeks. The horse won't bring you happiness and prosperity, but misery and ruin. Throw it into the sea, or burn it to ashes. But don't receive it into the city."

With these words, he hurled his spear at the huge image. The weapon struck it full in the chest. Those who stood nearest swore that they heard deep, hollow groans and a sound like the rattle of shields coming from the monster's throat.

"To the sea with it! The sea!" cried a few who believed in the old priest.

But most shouted, "To the city with it! The city! We'll outwit the Greeks yet!"

Some ran to the city for ropes and wheels. Others hurried to make a breach in the wall large enough for the monster to pass through. Ropes were tied to its neck and forelegs. Wooden rollers were put under the platform on which it stood.

Men with axes and hoes ran forward to clear a path across the plain. Then the strongest and most willing seized hold of the long ropes and began to pull. Others pushed from behind. Still others prayed to Athena.

So they tugged and sweated, and finally the huge image began to move.

---

soothsayer (SOOTH say ur) one who foretells the future
repentance (rih PEN tuns) feeling of sorrow about one's bad deeds; regret
prosperity (pro SPER ih tee) wealth; success

The Burning of Troy, Della Borla. The Uffizi, Scala/Art Resource

The wheels creaked and groaned. The shouts of the Trojans were so loud that the sound was heard far out to sea.

Slowly but steadily, the crowd advanced, dragging the wonderful horse that they believed would bless the city. The sun had set before they passed through the breach in the wall. Darkness was beginning to fall when the groaning wheels stopped. The great horse came to a standstill in a quiet corner close by the temple of Athena.

"My friends," said the king's officer, "we've done a fine day's work. Athena's horse rests near the place where it will stay. Now the happiness of Troy is certain. Go home. Tonight, for the first time in ten years, we can sleep secure."

With joyful shouts and friendly good nights, the crowd broke up. Every man went quietly to his own house. Soon the city was dark. The streets were silent and empty. And Athena's horse stood huge and wooden beside the temple wall.

About midnight, a man started to sneak out of the temple. He crept to the breach in the wall. In one hand he carried a basket of tar. In the other was a small torch that he had lighted at the temple fire. Carefully, he climbed to the top of the wall. Then he sat still and waited. Soon the sky began to grow lighter and the shadows in the city less dark. The moon rose, bright and round. The rooftops, the city wall, the plains, and the sea—all were silvered over with soft moonbeams.

---

breach (BREECH) broken place; gap

The man on the wall looked eagerly toward the sea. What were those dark objects moving swiftly over the water toward the shore? A thousand ships. The cunning Greeks had not started for home, as the Trojans had thought. They had gone only to the island of Tenedos. There they had lain all day, hidden in coves and inlets. Soon their vessels would again be beached in their old places by the empty camp.

The man on the wall was ready. He lifted his torch and dropped it carefully into the basket of tar. A bright flame rose up. It lit up the plain and the wall and the man's face. His eyes were red, his face wounded and swollen. It was Sinon.

Lights were soon seen on the ships. Then Sinon hurried down to the spot where the great horse was standing. With the flat edge of his sword, he struck its foreleg three times. There was a noise like the rattling of armor. Then a panel in the horse's chest slid aside. A man's head, in a gleaming helmet, appeared.

"Is all well, Sinon?" asked a deep voice.

"All's well, Ulysses. Our ships have landed, and our friends are marching across the plain. The foolish Trojans lie sleeping in their homes, little dreaming of what awaits them."

A rope ladder was let down, and Ulysses descended to the ground. Then fifty other heroes followed him, glad to be in the open air again. All was going the way Ulysses had imagined it would when he had planned the Trojan Horse.

"Sinon," said Ulysses, "what are those scars on your face? Did the Trojans abuse you?"

"They abused me, but they didn't make these wounds," answered Sinon. "I made them myself, so I could persuade the Trojans to fall into our trap."

"I understand, Sinon," said Ulysses. "People call me the man of wiles! But now that title must be yours. And now, for the ending of the whole business! Follow me, my men. Let fire and sword do their worst!"

The Trojans awoke from their dreams of peace to see their homes in flames. They heard the shouts of the triumphant Greeks. They knew that nothing was left for them but captivity or death. So the long siege came to an end, and the fair rich city beyond the sea was overthrown.

Ten years had passed since the siege began. When the city lay in ashes, the Greeks set out in their ships. All sought to return to their native lands. Fondly, then, the thoughts of Ulysses turned to his beloved wife, Penelope, and his child, and the rugged hills and shores of Ithaca.

"Spread the sails, my men, and row hard," he said. "For Penelope waits at home for my return, and keeps my kingdom for me."

But scarcely were his little ships well out to sea when fearful storms arose. The vessels were tossed now this way, now that. They were at the mercy of winds and waves that drove them far, far off course. Soon they were sailing by savage shores and strange lands where wild men lived.

---

coves (KOHVS) small inlets or bays
wiles (WYLS) tricks meant to trap or deceive

AUTHOR BIOGRAPHY
Homer (8ᵗʰ Century B.C.)

The person who is believed to be the author of these two selections is called Homer. Most scholars believe that Homer lived nearly 3,000 years ago in Greece. We know very little about Homer's life. Legends say that he was a blind poet. His friends are supposed to have led him from city to city.

In those days, stories were listened to, not read. Long stories were often put into rhyme, or poetry form, to make them easier to remember. Traveling poets like Homer told tales that had been handed down for generations. Homer learned many of the familiar rhymes and plots for his poems from those who came before him. He changed and improved the old tales and made up new ones, too. At some point in history, someone, maybe one of Homer's listeners, wrote down two long poems as Homer had told them.

These works are called the *Iliad* and the *Odyssey*. They are considered to be the basis for much Western literature. The *Odyssey* tells of the adventures of the Greek hero Odysseus (also called Ulysses) in the Trojan War, around the 12ᵗʰ or 13ᵗʰ century, and his long journey home after the war. These two selections, in story form rather than poetry, are based on a translation of the *Odyssey*.

Homer probably kept his audiences spellbound for hours. Sit back and suppose that a traveling poet is telling you of amazing deeds that were done long, long ago.

ULYSSES MEETS THE CYCLOPS

ADAPTED

by Homer

They were giants, oafs. Living on a large island of their own, they knew no law. They went by the name of Cyclops—it means "eye like a wheel." Each of the monsters had only one—a huge, round eye in the middle of its forehead.

The mouth of a cave gaped above the water. This was the home of one Cyclops. As we rowed nearer to land, we saw him, taking his sheep out to graze. He seemed no man at all. No, he looked like a hairy mountain, rising up all alone on a plain.

We beached our ship. "Stay here and be on the lookout," I told the crew. Taking my twelve best fighters, I went ahead. With me, I brought food and wine. This was no common wine. It was a ruby-red brandy given me by the gods.

---

oafs (OHFS) stupid, awkward persons
gaped (GAYPT) opened wide; yawned

I thought we might need a powerful drink like this. In fact, I knew it in my bones. We were setting foot in the lair of a beast—a wild man, all power and no law.

We scampered up to the cave. The Cyclops was still out with his sheep. So inside we went and feasted our eyes on his treasure—cheese, lambs and goats, bowls of milk.

My men crowded around me. They begged me, "Let's make off with the goats and the cheese. We ought to get back on the open seas while we can!"

Now I know they were right, but I didn't listen at that time. I wanted to see the caveman—and find out what gifts he might have for a guest like me. So we saw him. For some of my friends, it was an awful sight.

But we built a fire, ate some cheese, and waited. Towards evening, the Cyclops came back. A load of firewood was on his shoulder. He dumped it with a crash that echoed off the walls of the cave. In an instant, we all scurried to the far corner.

Next, he brought in the sheep he was going to milk. Then he picked up a huge rock and jammed it in the mouth of the cave. Two dozen wagons pulled by sweating horses could not have budged that rock.

He did his chores and fed the fire. As flames lit up the cave, his eye saw us. "Strangers," he said, "who are you? Are you good trading men? Or are you pirates?" His deep voice thundered against our hearts.

I answered, "We are soldiers on our way home. We ask your help. Our gods teach us to honor strangers. We beg you, great sir—do the same. Take care to please the gods, or Zeus will be angry."

From his savage chest came the answer. "You are a nitwit, trying to scare me with your gods," he said. "A Cyclops doesn't give a fig for any of them. We're more powerful. I'd never let you go for fear of Zeus—unless I felt like it. Tell me now, where did you leave your ship? Nearby?"

That was what he wanted to know! But I was too clever for him, and I lied boldly. "My ship?" I said. "It broke against the rocks of your shore. We are the only men left."

We got no pity from him. He grabbed at us. His hands caught two of my friends like squealing puppies. He beat their brains out and cut them up for his supper. He gobbled the meat like a hungry lion. We cried out to Zeus. But the Cyclops went on filling his giant belly.

Finally, having eaten enough, he lay down to sleep. Now I had the chance to act! Drawing my sword, I crept up close to him. I picked out the spot where I'd stab him. But I was stopped by a sudden thought. If I killed him, we'd all die. We could never push aside the huge rock that blocked the door. No, all we could do was moan and twiddle our thumbs till morning.

---

lair (LAIR) resting place of a wild animal; den
scurried (SKUR eed) moved quickly
Zeus (ZOOS) chief of the Greek gods

Soon after dawn, he did his chores. He snatched up another two men for breakfast. Then, gathering the sheep, he flicked aside the rock and went out. But in an instant, he had popped the rock back in again. He did it as easily as you'd stick the stopper in a bottle. We could hear him whistle as he climbed with his flock. Then there was silence.

What could we do? I looked around. Inside the cave lay the trunk of a fallen tree. The log was as long and thick as the mast of my ship. I chopped off a six-foot section and let my men scrape it smooth.

Next, I carved one end into a pointed spear. This my men and I plunged deep in the fire till it was as tough as iron. Finally, we dragged the weapon well back in the cave. Under one of the dung piles that lay everywhere, we hid it.

Just before evening, the Cyclops came back with his flock. Once inside, he wedged his stony door into place. He milked the sheep. He did his evening chores, caught two more men, and ate dinner.

Now was the time. I stepped forward, holding out a bowl. In it was the wine I'd brought with me.

"Here, Cyclops," I said, "have a little wine. You'll see what fine things we had in the hold of our ship."

He grabbed the bowl and drank. The drink pleased him so much that he had to have more.

"Give me another, please," he said. "And tell me your name. I'll give you a gift that will make you happy. Even a Cyclops knows grape juice from a heavenly drink like this!"

Three times I filled the bowl, and three times he emptied it. When he had gotten slow and silly, I called out to him. I spoke in friendly tones.

"Cyclops, you ask my name? My name is NOBODY. That's what my mother, my father, and all my friends call me."

"Then I'll eat NOBODY last—his friends come first. That's my gift to you."

Even as he spoke, he stumbled. He fell back and lay there with his giant head leaning to one side. Sleep captured him like any of us. Drunk, he lay there. He hiccupped. Wine dribbled from his lip, and bits of human meat stuck to his chin.

Now we drew out the rough-hewn spear. Again we thrust it in the fire. I whispered brave words to my men, urging them to get up their courage. As we pulled the spear out of the flames, it glowed red-hot. We dashed forward, raised the spear, and rammed it into the Cyclops's eye. Leaning on the spear, I twirled it till it was spinning like a drill. The eyeball sizzled. The veins popped. And the eye rolled down the giant's cheek.

Now the Cyclops roared so wildly that the cave walls shook. Full of fear, we scattered to the corners of the cave. The Cyclops yanked out the bloody spear and flung it to the ground. Then he began to roar, calling for the other Cyclops, who lived in caves nearby. Hearing him,

---

plunged (PLUNJD) pushed something quickly into something else
rough-hewn (RUF HYOON) roughly made; not polished
thrust (THRUST) shoved

they came and crowded round outside the cave door.

"What's wrong?" they called to him. "Why such a loud cry on this starry night? We can't get any sleep. Is someone stealing your flock? Has someone tricked you or hurt you?"

From inside the cave, the giant bellowed, "NOBODY! NOBODY'S tricked me! NOBODY'S hurt me!"

"Oh, well," they answered. "If nobody's hurt you, then we can't help." And they all went back to bed.

I was almost bursting with laughter. The name had fooled them! But now the Cyclops, groaning with pain, staggered to the door. He groped blindly and clawed away the boulder. Then he sat down in the doorway. His arms were spread wide to catch any fool who tried to escape. He was hoping I might try it. I wasn't going to. Instead, I plotted and planned. How could I outwit death?

Here's the plan I liked best: The giant's sheep were big and fat, with heavy wool. The Cyclops could see nothing. So I took some cords of willow from his bed. Standing the sheep three abreast, I tied them together. Under each three, I tied a man. Tucked up below the middle sheep, he was protected on both sides.

Last of all, I took the fattest ram, the finest of the whole flock. Myself I hid under his belly, snuggling up to his woolly curls. With the fleece wound around my fingers, I hung on. So we all breathed hard and waited for dawn.

When dawn rose, the sheep began to bustle and bleat. Their cries echoed round the cave. They moved toward the doorway, with us under them. The Cyclops, weak with pain, wouldn't let them pass. His fingers felt over the fleece of each ram. But he never found the men, hiding underneath. So he let each sheep out in turn.

Last of all came my ram, weighed down by his thick fleece—and me. The Cyclops felt him, then bent his face down. "Old thing," he said, "why are you the last to go? You never linger this way. Why now? Can you be sad about your master's eye? This NOBODY won't get out of here alive! I wish you had brain and voice to tell me where he is now. If only I knew where he hid from my anger! I'd smash him against the floor until his brains splashed all over the walls!"

Then, with a sigh, he stood aside and let us go. Once outdoors, I wriggled loose from the ram's belly. I dropped onto the soft grass. Then, going here and there, I set my men free. With many looks back, we herded the giant's fat sheep before us. We loaded them onto the ship and sailed away. But our sadness was as large as the ocean. Our sorrow was as endless as the future. We had our lives, but we'd lost our friends.

---

groped (GROHPT) felt about with the hands
ram (RAM) male sheep
bustle (BUS ul) move about busily
bleat (BLEET) make the natural cry of a sheep

Review the Selection

Recall

1. Why did the Greeks attack Troy?

2. How long did the war between the Greeks and the Trojans last?

3. Why did the Greeks land on the island of the Cyclops?

Infer

4. Why did the Trojans think the war was over?

5. Why did Ulysses steal the statue of Athena?

6. Why did Sinon wound himself?

7. Why did Ulysses tell the Cyclops that his name was "Nobody"?

Apply

8. What quality of Ulysses gave him victory over his enemies?

9. What mistakes did the Trojans make in their war with the Greeks?

10. What factors in the stories indicate that Ulysses is a warm and human person?

Respond to Literature

To the Greeks, Ulysses was the perfect hero because he was not only brave but also intelligent. Do you think that Ulysses would be a great hero today? Explain your answer.

WRITE ABOUT THE SELECTION

The Cyclops is one of the first monsters to appear in literature. Your challenge in this section is to write a paragraph in which you create a monster that would scare even the Cyclops.

Prewriting Think of all the monsters you have seen in movies or read about. Brainstorm some of the characteristics of these monsters. Then think about the specific attributes you want to describe: appearance; where the monster lives; what the monster eats; who the monster is most likely to scare. Now add a version or two about why your monster would frighten the Cyclops.

Writing Use your brainstorming to create a description of a very scary monster. You can write your description in the third person, or, like Ulysses, you can describe your monster from a first-person point of view.

Revising Look at the adjectives and adverbs that you have used in your paragraph. Are these the best words you can think of to describe your monster? Add any adjectives or adverbs that you feel will make your description more vivid.

Proofreading Because monsters naturally lend themselves to descriptive exaggeration, you may have been tempted to punctuate your writing with numerous exclamation marks. As you proofread, however, practice restraint in using exclamation marks. Your writing will be more effective.

THINK ABOUT EPIC POETRY

An **epic** is a long poem or prose piece that tells a heroic story. Ancient epics were often recited orally or sung. In some cultures, in Africa and in Ireland, as well as in other cultures, the oral tradition continues to this day.

Point of view is the position from which a story is told. In the first-person point of view, the storyteller is one of the characters in the story; action and commentary are limited to what that one character can see, hear, know, think, and feel. Although the impersonal third-person point of view is more common, both points of view are found in epic works.

1. How does the selection "Ulysses and the Trojan Horse" fit the definition of an epic?

2. From what point of view is this story told?

3. From what point of view is "Ulysses Meets the Cyclops" told?

4. How do the two different points of view affect the way you think about Ulysses, the epic hero?

DEVELOP YOUR VOCABULARY

A **noun** is a word that names a person, place, or thing. For example, in the sentence, "They hid inside a wooden horse," *horse* is a noun. A **verb** is a word that expresses action or a state of being. For example, in the sentence, "The Greeks attacked the Trojans," the word *attacked* is a verb.

Review the meanings of these words from "Ulysses and the Trojan Horse" and "Ulysses Meets the Cyclops." Decide whether each word is used as a noun or a verb in the stories. Then write an original sentence that uses each word in the same form, noun or verb, as in the story.

1. turmoil
2. siege
3. persevered
4. reeds
5. emerged
6. image
7. forges
8. thong
9. jeered
10. prosperity
11. breach
12. cove
13. wiles
14. oafs
15. gaped
16. lair
17. scurried
18. plunged

READING FOCUS

Understand Character Relationships As you read the selections, you were able to understand relationships between story characters. Choose one of the stories and describe what you feel is the most important relationship. Explain how this relationship affects the plot of the story.

UNIT 5 Review

Write About Theme

In this unit, you have read about many different kinds of heroes. You have thought about the qualities that make up a hero. Now is your chance to write about the heroes you liked best. Choose four characters from this unit for a "Heroes Hall of Fame." Write about the Heroes Hall of Fame in whatever way will describe your heroes best. For example, you may want to narrate a guided tour of the Hall of Fame, or you may want to have the heroes step from their places and tell their own stories.

Prewriting   Begin by choosing the four characters from this unit that you want included in the Heroes Hall of Fame. Then review each character's story. Cluster the details of each character's story that best illustrate why the character is a hero.

Writing   Use your prewriting cluster to develop a story entitled "The Heroes Hall of Fame." Be sure to describe the setting of the Hall of Fame.

Revising   As you revise your paper, keep in mind the point of view that you have chosen. For example, if you are writing a guided tour, then the entire story should be written in the third person. Eliminate or rewrite anything that is not consistent with the point of view that you have chosen.

Proofreading   If you have used dialogue or direct quotations, be sure you have used quotation marks and indented with each change of speaker.

Write About Genre

You have studied point of view, tone, symbolism, and techniques. These are all important elements of the short story. Choose two selections from this unit, one that you especially liked and one you disliked. Compare and contrast these works in terms of the literary elements that you have studied to explain why, in your opinion, one short story is better than the other.

Prewriting   Review the work that you did for the "Think About" sections in this unit. Then make a chart that has the name of the two selections you have chosen at the top and the four literary elements down the side. Fill in the spaces on the chart with details about each element from the stories. Include everything you can think of on your chart. You can decide later if you want to use all your facts and ideas.

Writing   Use your chart to prepare a paper in which you compare and contrast the two selections you have chosen. Be sure to organize your paper so that you move logically from one point to the next, and remember to prove your favorite is the superior story. You will need to do more than just point out the differences.

Revising   Transitional phrases can make your writing smoother. If you did not use such phrases as *first*, *next*, *most important*, and *finally*, add them when you revise.

Proofreading   Be sure to set off an introductory prepositional phrase that has more than three words with a comma.

Vocabulary

Since roots carry the basic meaning of the word, they are the foundation of developing your vocabulary. If you learn to figure out roots, you will improve your vocabulary and your reading comprehension. A **root** is a word or word part that is used to form other words. For example, the root in the word *excitement* is *excite*, which means to stir up strong feeling. Sometimes you can use the root word to find the meaning of a larger word.

Write the root in each of the following words. Use the root to find the meaning of the larger word. Check the meanings in a dictionary, then use each word in an original sentence.

1. dignitary	16. embattled
2. emerging	17. seaward
3. acknowledgment	18. prosperity
4. dispelled	19. repentance
5. momentarily	20. irresistible
6. frenzied	21. picturesque
7. evading	22. mythical
8. elimination	23. awesome
9. devastating	24. fitful
10. pensively	25. courageous
11. waver	26. monstrous
12. eventually	27. relationship
13. figurine	28. uncontrolled
14. frustration	29. historic
15. circumvent	30. gracefully

Grammar, Usage, and Mechanics

Using direct quotations can add to your writing. When you use a person's or a character's exact words, you must enclose the words in quotation marks. If there is an introductory expression, you must follow it with a comma. An interrupting expression must have commas before and after. A quotation that is followed by a concluding expression should end with a comma, question mark, or exclamation point.

Examples:

Introductory expression: Annie said, "The way I plan to do it is better."

Interrupting expression: "It angers me," he said, "that no one can do this right."

Concluding expression: "Get lost!" the young man bellowed.

Add quotation marks, commas, and end punctuation marks to these quotations.

1. Watch that right Tony said the trainer

2. Stina replied You're great, Dan

3. Let go of me she screamed

4. Hang on tight Dan ordered or we'll surely drown

5. The cop snapped Pick it up brother

SPEAKING AND LISTENING

One way to share vicariously in a character's adventures, trials, and triumphs is to do an imaginary interview with that character.

Part of the fun of an imaginary interview is the opportunity to identify with one of your favorite characters and to bring that character to life. Also, you have the opportunity to work with a partner.

In this unit you have met a variety of heroes. It's likely that one is someone you found to be interesting. To prepare yourself for this assignment, think about selections you've read in this unit, and recall the characters in them. Then, follow these guidelines to help you prepare your imaginary interview.

1. Pair up with another student. Glance over the selections in the unit and choose a character who would be a good candidate for an interview. Although the character doesn't have to be particularly likable, it should be someone you find memorable. The more diverse and complex the character is, the more interesting the interview.

2. Decide who will be the interviewer and who will be the character being interviewed. You could change roles midway if you like, or, if you choose, you could play both parts!

3. Talk about and decide with your partner whether you want to do a supportive kind of interview or if you prefer a more confrontational style.

4. Next, develop at least five questions that an interviewer might ask the character. The answers to the questions should reveal the character's opinions and his or her personality.

5. Make some notes on possible answers to the questions. Your job is to try to use words the character might use. Try to emulate the character in your answers.

6. As the interviewer, practice asking the questions. Use the appropriate tone and expressions in asking the questions. As the person being interviewed, practice the answers until they seem perfect. You want to sound spontaneous, so just consult your notes; don't read directly from them.

After you've practiced with your partner and feel confident, take your show to a larger audience. Try to keep your interview to three minutes. Following the steps above will help you to be adequately prepared.

CRITICAL THINKING

Inferences An **inference** is an understanding of something that has not been stated directly. It is based on a suggestion that the author makes indirectly. For example, in the story "On the Ledge," it can be inferred that Walter has a decent relationship with his brother.

When trying to infer an author's meaning, it is important not to jump to conclusions. For example, suppose that you are trying to infer something about the home life of the boys in "Amigo Brothers." It would be an invalid inference to say that Felix and Antonio are from broken homes, because there is no evidence to support this idea. It would be a valid inference, however, to say that the boys live in modest economic circumstances.

Good stories, poems, and plays always ask the reader to make inferences. Choose one selection from this unit that you feel contains important inferences, and answer the following questions.

1. Consider an inference that is central to the meaning of the story. What is it? What evidence can you find to back up the inference?

2. What invalid inferences might a reader be tempted to make when reading this story? How would these invalid inferences confuse the meaning of the story?

3. How does making inferences make a story more interesting?

EFFECTIVE STUDYING

Taking Tests In order to do well in school, it is important to know how to take objective tests. An **objective test** is one that requires you to recall factual information. It may consist of short answer questions, multiple choice questions, or true and false questions. An objective test may also include matching exercises.

These suggestions will provide a good strategy for taking an objective test.

1. Write your name on each page.

2. Skim through the test. Decide how much time to give each question. Notice if some questions are worth more points than others.

3. Jot down any information you want to remember in the margins of the test or on scrap paper, if this is allowed.

4. Answer the easy questions first. Circle the numbers of any questions you are not sure of.

5. Go with your first answer unless you have a very good reason to change it.

6. Go back over your test to make sure you have followed directions correctly and answered all of the questions.

Test Preparation

When taking an essay test, think before you write. Jot down your important points and work them into an outline. Do this on the back of your test paper or on scrap paper.

Generations

My grandmothers were strong.
They followed plows and bent to toil.
They moved through fields sowing seed.
They touched earth and grain grew.
They were full of sturdiness and singing.
My grandmothers were strong.

—Margaret Walker

The Family. Marisol, 1962. Painted wood and other materials, 6'10⅝" × 65½"
Collection, The Museum of Modern Art, New York

Generations

Can you picture yourself as a grandmother or grandfather? What kind of grandparent do you think you would be? Would you, as a grandparent, in any way resemble the grandmothers whom Margaret Walker describes in her poem "Generations"? In the poem that opens this unit, Margaret Walker talks about the qualities in her grandmothers that she admires. What qualities do you think your future grandchildren will admire in you?

Grandparents, parents, and children make up three generations in a family. The word *generation* comes from the Latin word *genus*, meaning "birth." The span of time that exists between the birth of parents and the birth of their children is equal to one generation.

The poems and stories in this unit are about generations—parents and children, grandchildren and grandparents. Some of the selections also touch on a larger meaning of the word *generation*—the idea of cultural heritage or tradition. Tradition is the handing down from one generation to the next of a body of customs, beliefs, proverbs, stories, and long established practices and teachings. The average period between the birth of one generation and the next is roughly 30 years. People are a product of their cultural heritage such as African American, Native American, European, or Asian. Reading these selections will help you become more aware of your own place in the generations of your family and within your cultural group.

■ PARENT AND CHILD

The generation outside of your own that you probably know best is your parents'. Have you ever wondered what life would be like if you could have chosen your parents? In the poem "Andre," the speaker realizes that, given that chance, he would choose his own parents from the many different parents in the world.

Sometimes being a parent can be painful, as two poems in this unit illustrate. In the poem "Bread," a man is sent to jail because he tries to steal food for his hungry child. In the poem "Otto," a father cannot give his children the gifts that they want for Christmas.

You may have heard the expression "generation gap." A generation gap exists when parents and children have trouble understanding one another's needs, feelings, and ideas because of the difference in their ages. One short story in this unit offers hope that the generation gap can, at least in part, be overcome. In the story "Somebody's Son," a boy runs away from home to find out more about life and himself. As you read the story, you will find out what happens when the boy decides that he is ready to go back home again. Perhaps the story will give you insight into what people of two different generations might feel about each other. How true do you find the relationship between generations in this story?

■ GRANDPARENTS AND GRANDCHILDREN

For many children and young adults, grandparents are special people. In the short story "The Medicine Bag," a teenaged boy and his family receive a surprise visit from the boy's 86-year-old Sioux great-grandfather. An important part of the story is the way the man passes on to his great-grandson a tradition of the Sioux Indians.

In the poem "Grandfather," Shirley Crawford writes about her grandfather's life and death and wonders who her own grand-children will be. In the poem "Medicine," Alice Walker considers the realities of illness and old age as she watches her grandparents.

■ IMPORTANT OTHERS

Perhaps you have had other people in your life who have been as important to you as family. In the humorous poem "Some People," Rachel Field explains why she prefers the company of some people and not others. The two short poems "Whale Hunting" and "Luther Leavitt" describe important people in the lives of two young poets.

With your family and with your cultural heritage, you are a link between the past and the future. How has your life been shaped by the generations that have come before you?

Learn About

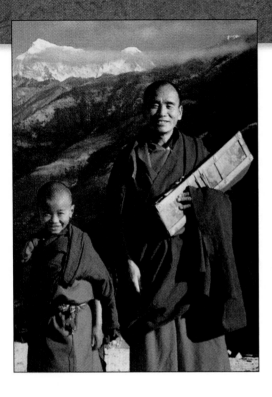

RHYTHM

Rhythm is a regular recurrence of units of sound. It is rhythm that makes you tap your feet when you are listening to music. It is also rhythm that makes you feel like dancing to music.

Poems, like music, often have distinct rhythmic patterns. You can discover the rhythm of a poem by reading the poem aloud and clapping the sound of each syllable in a word as you read. You will find that accents automatically fall on certain words, as well as on certain syllables within a word.

Some poetry does not have a recognizable and consistent rhythmic pattern. This type of poetry is called **free verse**. You can still clap out the rhythm of each line, but each line in the poem will have a different rhythm.

As you read the two poems, ask:

1. Do both poems have recognizable rhythmic patterns?
2. What are the rhythmic patterns?

WRITING CONNECTION

Choose a familiar nursery rhyme such as "Jack and Jill" or "Humpty Dumpty." Clap out the rhythm of the nursery rhyme as you say it aloud. Then see if you can fit words of your own to the rhythmic pattern of each nursery rhyme.

READING FOCUS

Compare and Contrast Poetry Elements
When you compare two things, you note similarities. When you contrast two things, you note differences. When you read poetry, there are several elements you can compare and contrast. These include topic, point of view, and style. For example, two poems might have the same point of view but different styles. As you read, pay attention to the elements of each poem that are similar and different.

ANDRE

by Gwendolyn Brooks

I had a dream last night. I dreamed
I had to pick a Mother out.
I had to choose a Father too.
At first, I wondered what to do,
There were so many there, it seemed,
Short and tall and thin and stout.

But just before I sprang awake,
I knew what parents I would take.

And *this* surprised and made me glad:
They were the ones I always had!

---

stout (STOWT) having a heavy-set body
sprang (SPRANG) past tense of the verb *spring*; arose suddenly

FAMILY ALBUM

by Diane Stevenson

1

A child with only the sun
in her eyes, my sister shields her face,
hand palm out, as if to say no.

2

Alone, the garden behind her fragments
of color, my mother seems to listen.
July, 1947: I am here, too, inside,
as yet invisible, though the sun
must filter through, like blood, to me.
I must be hearing her heart.

3

At two, I sit in the grass,
legs forward, facing the sun.
On the lawn in front of me,
a dark figure approaches,
almost touching my feet.
I look up, blink, and my father
records himself, a shadow,
just out of range.

4

Florida, 1960. My sister and I kneel,
behind us three generations of women.
No son's been born for a hundred years.
Even the palms are graceful women,
and hibiscus opens its wide, red mouth.

---

shields (SHEELDZ) defends; protects
fragments (FRAG muhnts) parts or pieces
range (RAYNJ) the area in which an object can be seen
hibiscus (hy BIS kus) a garden plant or shrub bearing large, showy flowers

Gwendolyn Brooks (1917–)

Gwendolyn Brooks is one of the leading poets of the United States and was the first African American poet to win a Pulitzer Prize. Her keen interest in people is expressed in her writing.

Born in Topeka, Kansas, Gwendolyn Brooks has spent most of her life in Chicago. The sights, sounds, and people of Chicago's South Side are the subject of many of her poems, which create a vibrant picture of African American urban life.

Numerous honors and awards have come to Brooks throughout her career. Her first published collection of poems, *A Street in Bronzeville* (1945), won her critical acclaim and *Mademoiselle* magazine's Merit Award as the outstanding woman of the year. Brooks has received two Guggenheim Foundation fellowships, the American Academy of Arts and Letters award, the Frost Medal, and a National Endowment for the Arts award. In 1968, she was named Poet Laureate of the State of Illinois. From 1985 to 1986, she was consultant in poetry to the Library of Congress.

Although Gwendolyn Brooks's formal education ended with junior college, she has through her own efforts continued her education. In addition to being a poet, she is an expert in modern literature, a writer of book reviews, and a frequent lecturer at colleges and universities. In 1990, she became a professor of English at Chicago State University.

Review the Selection

UNDERSTAND THE SELECTION

Recall

1. About what does the speaker of "Andre" dream?

2. What choice does he make?

3. About what family members is the author of "Family Album" writing?

Infer

4. Why do you think that Andre is glad about his choices?

5. Do you think Andre learned something about himself through this experience?

6. Where is the author of "Family Album" in July of 1947?

7. What can you infer about the importance of her father in the poet's life?

Apply

8. Suppose that you picked out your own parents. Why did you choose them?

9. If you were to write a poem called "Family Album," who would be the characters in your poem?

10. Who are the three generations of women that the poet refers to in Part 4 of "Family Album"?

Respond to Literature

Which of these poems more accurately reflects your feelings about members of other generations in your family? Explain.

WRITE ABOUT THE SELECTION

Each section of the poem "Family Album" is like the description of a photograph in a picture album. Based on what the poet has written, can you imagine what each member of the family is like? Write a paragraph in which you provide additional information about one or several of the characters described in the poem.

Prewriting   Across the top of a sheet of paper, write the names of the generations —grandmother, mother, etc.—that are represented in this poem. Under each name, write down your ideas of what that person might be like.

Writing   Use your prewriting list to decide which character or characters you wish to write about. You may find that your description will be more interesting if you include information about the character's relationships with other family members.

Revising   You may be able to improve your paragraph by adding a direct quote or reference from the poem. Feel free to place the quote where it will be the most effective—at the beginning, middle, or end of your paragraph.

Proofreading   If you have used a direct quotation or reference from the poem, be sure you have inserted quotation marks. The quote or reference may be so closely woven into your writing that you do not need to begin it with a capital letter. You decide. Be sure all your sentences end with periods, question marks, or exclamation marks.

THINK ABOUT RHYTHM

Rhythm refers to the regular rise and fall in the flow of sound in a poem. Rhythm can be thought of as a pattern of long and short sounds. In a poem, long sounds occur when a word or syllable is accented. Poets often select words for the sounds they create. Rhythm is the music of poetry.

1. Does the poem "Andre" have a regular rhythmic pattern?

2. If so, can you describe the pattern in terms of long and short syllables?

3. One line in "Andre" has a different pattern from all the rest. Which line is it? What is its rhythmic pattern?

4. Why do you think the author made one line different from the rest?

5. Does the poem "Family Album" have a regular rhythmic pattern? What does this tell about the type of poetry it is?

READING FOCUS
Compare and Contrast Poetry Elements
Compare and contrast the point of view in "Andre" and "Family Album." Who is the speaker? Is the speaker talking about the present or the past? Provide details from the poems as examples.

DEVELOP YOUR VOCABULARY

Synonyms are words that have the same or nearly the same meaning. The words *large* and *big* are synonyms; so are the words *small* and *little*.

In each of the following groups of words, all of the words are synonyms except one. On a separate sheet of paper, write the word in each group that does not belong with the others. Then choose one synonym in each group to use in an original sentence.

1. short, stout, heavy, bulky

2. covers, shields, opens, hides

3. fragments, pieces, colors, parts

4. invisible, hidden, unseen, alone

5. look, choose, pick, select

6. glad, uncertain, happy, joyful

7. thin, stout, frail, wiry

8. under, beneath, below, after

9. take, capture, approach, seize

10. remote, near, distant, far

Focus ON POETRY

As with many other skills, reading poetry takes practice. Your ability to understand and enjoy poetry will increase as you learn more about the various elements of poetry, including denotation and connotation, rhythm, sounds, form, and symbolism.

Denotation and Connotation   Good poets choose their words carefully, for they know that a word can often have more than one meaning. One kind of meaning is the dictionary definition of the word; that is called the word's **denotation**. Another meaning is what a certain word suggests or brings to mind; this is called the word's **connotation**.

A good example of denotation and connotation is the words *house* and *home*. Both words have nearly the same definition in the dictionary (denotation), but what the words suggest (connotation) is quite different. The word *house* suggests a building in which people live. The word *home* suggests not just a physical structure, but the emotional center of a family.

Rhythm   **Rhythm** is a regular pattern of strong and weak units of sound. Another word for strong is **accented**. In the normal flow of speech, certain syllables and words are accented. For example, in the sentence, "Father and Mother are home," the first syllables of *father* and *mother* are accented, and the word *home* is accented. The rhythmic pattern of the sentence is: strong-weak-weak/strong-weak-weak/strong.

Rhythm is part of what makes poetry enjoyable to read and to listen to. Many poems have distinct rhythmic patterns. For example, in the poem "Andre," most of the lines have a rhythmic pattern of weak-strong/weak-strong. You can discover the rhythm of a poem by reading the poem aloud and clapping each sound as you read. This will help you identify the accented and unaccented sounds.

Some poetry does not have a recognizable rhythmic pattern. This type of poetry is called **free verse**. You can still clap out

Answer the
questions
9-10
Page 488

the rhythm of each line, but each line in the poem may have a different rhythm.

Sounds   Some ways poets use pleasing sounds are assonance, onomatopoeia, and alliteration.

Assonance is a type of rhyme in which the vowels but not the consonants sound alike. For example, the vowel *e* has the same sound in the words *met* and *neck*.

Onomatopoeia is the use of words that sound like the thing to which they refer. Some words that can be used this way include *bubbly, hiss, pop, tick-tock*. In the poem "Family Album," the use of the word *blink* can be considered onomatopoeia.

Alliteration is the repetition of the same sound at the beginning of words that are next to or near each other. The tongue twister "Peter Piper picked a peck of pickled peppers" is an example of alliteration. In the poem "Family Album," the last line of the second section contains alliteration: "I must be hearing her heart."

Form   The **form** of a poem is the way the poem is constructed. Form can be closed or open. **Closed poetry** includes the couplet, ballad, and epigram. **Open poetry** has no recognizable pattern. One kind of open poetry is free verse.

Symbolism   A **symbol** is something that stands for something else. Symbols are very important in poetry since poets must often use compact language.

There are many different kinds of symbols that a poet can use. Some are called **universal** or **general symbols** because they tend to mean the same thing to most people. Some symbols, called **contextual symbols**, have meanings just within the context of a particular poem.

As you read "Bread," ask yourself these questions:
1. What is the form of the poem?
2. What universal and contextual symbols are present?

BREAD

by Amado V. Hernandez

He had been imprisoned
for so many years,
time was a chain around his neck
knotted up in the windings of his life.

5   A piece of bread
and a can of broth
are left at the door by the guard,
he grabs them with dirty hands.

When the wretched man
10   is about to swallow,
the tear-soaked bread drops,
rubbing against the bruise in his heart.

He remembers why
he was imprisoned:
15   he stole a box of crackers
because his sick child was groaning with hunger.

Trying to get away
from the fist of the law,
he killed his pursuer—
20   and never saw his little girl again!

Now life wears away
wearily, though now every day
he is given the bread that might have saved
his child, who died of hunger.

FOCUS ON POETRY
STUDY HINTS

Bread is a universal symbol. What is its meaning?

Note the rhythmic pattern of each line. What form of poetry is this?

Note the alliteration of *bread* and *broth* at the end of lines 5 and 6.

What is the connotation of the word *grabs*?

Bread and *bruise* are an example of alliteration within two lines.

The words *wears* and *wearily* are an example of alliteration. *Saved* and *day* are an example of assonance. How is bread an important contextual symbol in this poem?

---

windings (WYND ingz) course of events
broth (BRAWTH) clear soup
wretched (RETCH id) miserable
pursuer (pur SOO er) one who chases another

Review the Selection

UNDERSTAND THE SELECTION

Recall

1. What is the setting of the poem?

2. What did the guard leave outside the door each day?

3. What crime did the central character commit?

Infer

4. What is the meaning of the metaphor "time was a chain around his neck"?

5. Why do you think the prisoner grabs at the bread and broth?

6. Why do you think he cannot swallow the bread?

7. For how long do you assume the man will be in prison?

Apply

8. What do you think might have happened if the man had not killed his pursuer?

9. Do you think that the man in the poem acted wisely? Why do you think he acted as he did?

10. How else might he have handled his problem?

Respond to Literature

Do you feel sympathy for the man in prison? Explain your response.

WRITE ABOUT THE SELECTION

There is an unexpected twist to the poem "Bread," which is expressed in the last stanza. The prisoner stole bread to try and save his child's life. Now in prison, when it is too late, he receives bread every day. What is your reaction to this turn of events? Write a paragraph in which you express your opinion about the series of events described in the poem.

Prewriting Read the poem several times. As you read, make notes about your feelings and reactions. Do not hold back; your emotions may be very strong.

Writing Use your notes to write a paragraph in which you react to the plight of the prisoner. As you write, you may find it helpful to imagine first that you are the man stealing the crackers—how would you feel? Then imagine that you are the storekeeper whose crackers are stolen. Finally, imagine that you are the police or the prison guard. To add realism to your writing, you might want to include a few slang terms that you use every day.

Revising The final sentence of your paragraph should sum up your opinion. Try writing your final sentence several different ways, then choose the sentence that provides the strongest conclusion.

Proofreading Make sure that your paragraph is correct in subject/verb agreement. If you chose to use any slang terms, do not enclose them in quotation marks. It will only distract the reader.

THINK ABOUT THE ELEMENTS

Some important elements of poetry include denotation and connotation, symbolism, sounds, rhythm, and form. **Denotation** is the literal meaning of a word, while **connotation** is the meaning or feeling that a word evokes. When **symbolism** is used, a concrete thing stands for a more abstract idea. The symbolic meaning of a word may be **universal** or **contextual**. Sometimes, poets choose words according to their sounds, using such devices as **alliteration**, **assonance**, and **onomatopoeia**. **Rhythm** is the pattern of accented and unaccented sounds. **Form** is the way that a poem is constructed.

1. What is a universal symbol for food in the poem? What is a contextual symbol of the man's loss and regret?

2. What form is the poem written in?

3. Give two examples of alliteration.

4. Give an example of assonance.

5. What is the connotation of the word *grabs*?

DEVELOP YOUR VOCABULARY

Homophones are words that sound alike but have different spellings and meanings. The words *beet* and *beat* are examples of homophones. If you can recognize that homophones have different spellings for different meanings, you will make fewer errors in usage.

Give a homophone for each of the italicized words in the sentences below. Then use both words in one sentence.

1. He took a *piece* of apple pie.

2. He *ate* the pie quickly.

3. The *bread* was on the table.

4. He had been imprisoned *there* for many years.

5. It took *so* long to get home.

6. Can I get something *for* you?

7. The *time* passed slowly.

8. He tried *to* get away.

Learn About

TONE

The **tone** of a piece of literature is the author's attitude toward the subject of his or her writing. Tone can also include the author's attitude toward the reader.

The tone of a story or poem can be funny, serious, lighthearted, sarcastic, or sad. An author may write in a friendly, personal way, or in a formal, impersonal way. From the tone of a story or poem, you may think that the author has an emotional feeling for the subject, or you may get the opposite impression.

As you read "Somebody's Son," ask yourself:

1. What is the author's attitude toward David?
2. How does the author address the reader?

READING FOCUS

Understand Character Relationships
You can better understand the characters in a story by noticing their relationships with other people. A character might be friends with one person but have a less positive relationship with another person. Each relationship brings out a different side of the character. To note similarities and differences in relationships, look at how the characters behave toward each other and what they say to each other.

WRITING CONNECTION

Think of an incident that happened to you recently. Write two descriptions of that incident, using a different tone for each version. For example, suppose that you decide to write about a fight that you had with a brother or sister. You might try writing the first version of the incident with a humorous tone, then write the second version of the incident with a sad tone.

SOMEBODY'S SON

by Richard Pindell

He sat, washed up on the side of the highway, a slim, sun-beaten driftwood of a youth. He was hunched on his strapped-together suitcase, chin on hands, elbows on knees, staring down the road. Not a car was in sight. But for him, the dead, still Dakota plains were empty.

Now he was eager to write that letter he had kept putting off. Somehow, writing it would be almost like having company.

He unstrapped his suitcase and fished out of the pocket on the underside of the lid a small, unopened package of stationery. Sitting down in the gravel of the roadside, he closed the suitcase and used it as a desk.

Dear Mom,

If Dad will permit it, I would like to come home. I know there's little chance he will. I'm not going to kid myself. I remember he said once, if I ever ran off, I might as well keep on going.

All I can say is that I felt leaving home was something I had to do. Before even considering college, I wanted to find out more about life and about me and the best way for us (life and me) to live with each other. Please tell Dad—and I guess this'll make him sore all over again—I'm still not certain that college is the answer for me. I think I'd like to work for a time and think it over.

You won't be able to reach me by mail, because I'm not sure where I'll be next. But in a few days I hope to be passing by our place. If there's any chance Dad will have me back, please ask him to tie a white cloth to the apple tree in the south pasture—you know the one, the Grimes Golden beside the tracks. I'll be

---

hunched (HUNCHT) bent over

going by on the train. If there's no cloth on the tree I'll just quietly, and without any hard feelings toward Dad—I mean that—keep on going.

Love, David

The sunset that evening was a violent one. Jagged clouds, trapped in cross-currents, rammed each other like primitive men-of-war and burst into flames, burning one by one into deep purple ash.

It made the boy sad to see the sun go down. He had learned that always at the moment when darkness prevails, loneliness draws closer.

A series of headlights made a domino of the highway. High beams flickered over him curiously. He put out his thumb almost hesitantly, wishing he didn't have to emerge so suddenly, so menacingly. One by one, the cars passed him, their back draft slapping him softly, insultingly, on the cheek.

Much later, turning woodenly to gaze after a car, he saw the glow of taillights intensify. Brakes squealed. The car careened wildly to a stop, and he was running down the road to capture it, his breath rushing against his upturned collar and the taillights glowing nearer as in a dream.

A door was flung open like a friendly arm reaching out to a tired swimmer. "Hop in, boy."

It was a gruff, outdoors voice. "I pret' near missed you. You ain't easy to see out there."

"Thanks, mister."

"Forget it. Used the thumb a lot myself when I was a kid."

"How far are you going?" asked David.

The man named a small place in Iowa about two hundred miles away. David settled back in anticipation of a good ride.

"Where you headin'?" the man asked him.

David glanced at him. His nose was big and jutting; his mouth, wide and gentle. His was a face formed without beauty—and without hesitation. He had a tough-friendly way of accepting David as a man, something which David was still young enough to appreciate as a fine luxury.

---

prevails (prih VAYLZ) gains power over
careened (kuh REEND) turned on one side

The boy looked out on the highway with affection. It would be a good ride with a good companion. "Home," he said with a grin. "I'm heading home."

The man heard the smile in the boy's voice and chuckled. "That's a good feelin', ain't it? Where 'bouts?"

"Maryland. We have a farm about thirty miles outside of Baltimore."

"Where you been?"

"West Coast, Canada, a little of Mexico."

"And now you're hightailin' for home, huh?" There was a note in the man's voice as if this were a pattern he understood intimately.

"Yes, sir."

David smiled wryly to himself, remembering another day. It was in the San Joaquin Valley. He was picking grapes. As usual, the sun ruled mercilessly. Grape leaves drooped. Pickers were humped in varying attitudes of defense, some with bandannas covering the backs of their necks. Even the dirt had sagged beneath the blazing heat, crumbling into limp, heavy powder.

David looked down at his feet plowing through the grayish stuff. For four hours now it seemed he had not raised his eyes from his feet. He stopped abruptly and looked back down the row, measuring his progress. He had gone maybe fifty yards.

The faint clink of scissors landing in his half-filled basket came to him and then the foreman was bawling at him, "Hey! Where do you think you're going? It ain't lunchtime yet!" David stared at his feet and the dust; and his feet were stretching out as far as they could reach, his fist was tight around the handle of his suitcase, and the dust swirling madly behind him. He didn't even stop to pick up his money.

When he reached the highway and the cars kept passing him, it was all he could do to keep from jumping out in front of them to make them stop.

"Yeah," the driver was saying now, "I know how it is." The comers of his eyes crinkled as if he were going to smile, but he didn't. "I was out on that same old road when I was a kid. Bummin' around. Lettin' no grass grow under me. Sometimes wishin' it would."

---

wryly (RY lee) humorously; twisted to one side

"And then, afterward," David asked, "did you go back home?"

"Nope. I didn't have no home to go back to, like you do. The road was my only home. Lost my ma and pa when I was a little shaver. Killed in a car wreck."

"That's rough," David said with such feeling the man glanced at him sharply.

The boy was staring into the night. The man shifted his grip on the wheel, deftly straddling a dead jack rabbit. He spoke softly to the boy as if he were aware he was interrupting important thoughts. "Bet you could do with some sleep."

"You sure you won't be needing me later to help keep you awake?" David asked.

"Don't worry 'bout me none. I like drivin' at night. You just lean back there and help yourself."

"Well, okay," David said. "Thanks."

Sometime later, he was awakened by a sharp decrease in speed. They were entering a town. He sat up and jerked the letter out of his jacket pocket. He had almost forgotten.

"Excuse me, sir, but would you mind stopping at a mailbox so I can mail this? I want to make sure that it gets home before I do."

"Course not," the man said. "Here's one comin' up now." He pulled over to the curb and stopped.

When the boy got back in, the man smiled kindly. "Bet your folks'll be tickled to hear from you."

"I hope so, sir." David tilted his head back and closed his eyes.

The next day, rides were slow. They were what David called "farmer rides," a few miles here, a couple of miles there, with long waits in between.

Toward nightfall, he forsook the unfriendly asphalt and swung onto a panting, slow-moving freight aimed stolidly east. As the train trundled laboriously over the Mississippi, a few drops of rain slapped the metal floor of his gondola car, and then, suddenly, he was surrounded by water, the river beneath him, and everywhere else, walls of rain. He crawled into a corner and huddled under some scraps of heavy paper that had been used to wrap freight.

---

deftly (DEFT lee) cleverly
asphalt (AS fawlt) road pavement
stolidly (STOL id lee) dully; unemotionally
trundled (TRUN duld) rolled along; moved on wheels

For thirty miles, the rain pounded him, slashing his paper hut to tatters and turning his clothes into puddles of mush.

As, cold and wet, he swayed with the motion of the car, his last seven months haunted him. A spinning constellation of faces, flaring up and dying away, careened toward him. Faces of truck drivers, waitresses, salesmen, cops, employment agents, winos, tramps, cowboys, bartenders. Faces of people who had been kind to him; faces of people who had used him. They went on and on.

Well, he would never see them again. He had experienced them quickly, dazedly, as they had experienced him. He had no idea where they were now, and they did not know where he was.

Finally the rain stopped. He lunged erect, inviting the warm, night air to dry him. He looked out over the top of his racketing steel box. He faced east—toward home. They didn't have any idea where he was, either.

The train was hammering along beside a highway. He stared at the houses on the other side. How would it be at home? Would his house be like that one, the one with the porch light burning? Or would it be like that one, where the porch was dark and where over each of the lighted windows a yellow shade was pulled down firmly to the sill?

A couple of days later, in the middle of Maryland, maddeningly close to home, the flow of rides narrowed to a trickle and then ceased altogether. When cars weren't in sight, he walked. After a while, he didn't even bother to stop and hold out his thumb. Furiously, he walked.

Later, seated on the passenger train—the only freights around here ran at night—he wished with slow, frightened heartbeats that he were back on the road, headed the other way.

Three inches from his nose was the dust-stained window through which in a few minutes he would look out across his father's fields. Two different pictures tortured him—the tree with the white cloth and the tree without it. His throat closed and he could hardly breathe.

He tried to fortify himself with the idea that whether or not he still was welcome, at least he would see the place again.

The field was sliding closer, one familiar landmark at a time. He couldn't stop the train. The frenzied wheels were stamping out the end of the crescendo that had begun with the clink of the scissors in his half-filled basket of grapes. Nothing could postpone the denouement now. The tree was around the next bend.

He couldn't look. He was too afraid the cloth would not be there—too afraid he would find, staring back at him, just another tree, just another field, just another somebody else's strange place, the way it always is on the long, long road, the nameless staring back at the nameless. He jerked away from the window.

Desperately, he nudged the passenger beside him. "Mister, will you do me a favor? Around this bend on the right, you'll see an apple tree. I wonder if you'll tell me if you see a white cloth tied to one of its branches?"

As they passed the field, the boy stared straight ahead. "Is it there?" he asked with an uncontrollable quaver.

"Son," the man said in a voice slow with wonder, "I see a white cloth tied on almost every twig."

---

crescendo (krih SHEN doh) increasing in loudness
denouement (day noo MAHN) the final outcome
quaver (KWAY vur) shake, tremble

Review the Selection

UNDERSTAND THE SELECTION

Recall

1. What is the setting of the story?

2. To whom does David write a letter?

3. What is the purpose of the letter?

Infer

4. About how old is David? How do you know?

5. What can you infer about David's father's attitude toward college?

6. What can you infer about David's relationship with his mother?

7. What message was given to David at the end of the story?

Apply

8. Do you think that David's father might have changed during the time David was away? Explain your answer.

9. Why do you think that the man David rode with accepted David as a man?

10. Suppose that you are David. How would you feel as the train passed the apple tree?

Respond to Literature

How do the man on the highway and David's parents show different qualities of the same generation? How do they show similar qualities?

WRITE ABOUT THE SELECTION

At the end of "Somebody's Son," David realizes that he can go home again. What do you think happens when David finally gets home? What conversations might he have with his father? His mother? His friends? Add an episode to "Somebody's Son" that tells what happens after David returns home.

Prewriting   Create an informal outline of what might happen the day David arrives home. Include details of conversations David might have with his parents and others. Look for clues in the details of the story.

Writing   Use your prewriting outline to write a paragraph that adds an episode to "Somebody's Son." Be sure to tell about David's feelings as he walks into his house for the first time after his absence.

Revising   When you revise your paragraph, add dialogue that makes the feelings of David and his parents clear as well as specific details that make the setting clear.

Proofreading   Read over your paragraph to check for errors. Make sure that you have used correct punctuation when writing dialogue. Remember that periods, commas, question marks, and exclamation points all fall inside the quotation marks when they are part of a character's speech. Be sure that all your sentences end with periods, question marks, or exclamation marks.

THINK ABOUT TONE

The **tone** of a literary work communicates the author's attitude toward his or her subject. The tone may be humorous or serious, sarcastic or sad. Tone can also include the author's attitude toward the reader. Some literary works have a friendly, informal tone, while others have a more detached, formal tone.

1. What is the tone of "Somebody's Son"?

2. What does the tone tell you about the author's attitude toward his subject?

3. What do you feel is the author's attitude toward you, the reader?

4. In the story, David writes a letter. What is the tone of that letter?

5. What does the tone tell you about David's attitude toward his home and his parents?

READING FOCUS

Understand Character Relationships
As you read "Somebody's Son," you were able to understand the relationships between the characters. Describe the relationship between David and the driver. What did this relationship tell you about the driver's personality?

DEVELOP YOUR VOCABULARY

Some English words have silent letters. For example, in the word *knife*, the *k* is silent. Words with silent letters can be tricky to spell and pronounce. Another group of words that can be difficult to spell and pronounce are words with letter combinations that sound like other letters; for example, the *ph* in *pharmacy* sounds like *f*.

Identify the silent letters, or the letter combinations that sound like other letters, in each word below. Then use the word in an original sentence.

1. asphalt
2. denouement
3. knight
4. knowledge
5. wryly
6. gourmet
7. write
8. whisker
9. photograph
10. physics
11. thyme
12. wreck

Iowa Medicine Man, See-Non-ty, George Catlin.
Corbis Bettmann

READING FOCUS

Compare and Contrast Character Traits
When you compare and contrast the traits of characters, you note similarities and differences. Two characters in a story may have contrasting traits. For example, they might have different attitudes toward the same thing. Even a single character can have contrasting traits. He or she might change during the story or have mixed feelings about another character, for example. As you read, ask yourself questions such as: Do the characters feel the same way about what happens? Do the characters change by the end of the story?

PLOT

The plot is the plan or pattern of events that unfolds in a story. The five important elements of plot are exposition, complication, crisis, climax, and resolution.

The **exposition** is the introduction of the plot. In the exposition, you learn who the main character is and the kind of problems he or she will face in the story. Then comes the **complication**—a setback encountered by the main character in attempting to overcome the problem. The decisive moment is called the **crisis**. During the crisis, the main character either wins or loses the struggle to overcome the problem. The outcome of the crisis is called the **climax**, the most exciting part of the story, usually at or near the end. Many stories end with the climax, but some do not. These stories are followed by a **resolution**, a kind of wrap-up of the story in which further questions are answered.

As you read "The Medicine Bag," ask yourself:
1. What is the plot of the story?
2. What problem is presented for the main character to overcome?

WRITING CONNECTION

Choose a story in this book that you have read. Then make a list of the five plot elements as they appear in the story.

The Medicine Bag

by Virginia Driving Hawk Sneve

My kid sister Cheryl and I always bragged about our Sioux grandpa, Joe Iron Shell. Our friends, who had always lived in the city and only knew about Indians from movies and TV, were impressed by our stories. Maybe we exaggerated and made Grandpa and the reservation sound glamorous, but when we'd return home to Iowa after our yearly summer visit to Grandpa, we always had some exciting tale to tell.

We always had some authentic Sioux article to show our listeners. One year Cheryl had new moccasins that Grandpa had made. On another visit he gave me a small, round, flat, rawhide drum that was decorated with a painting of a warrior riding a horse. He taught me a real Sioux chant to sing while I beat the drum with a leather-covered stick that had a feather on the end. Man, that really made an impression.

We never showed our friends Grandpa's picture. Not that we were ashamed of him, but because we knew that the glamorous tales we told didn't go with the real thing. Our friends would have laughed at the picture because Grandpa wasn't tall and stately like TV Indians. His hair wasn't in braids but hung in stringy, gray strands on his neck, and he was old. He was our great-grandfather, and he didn't live in a tepee, but all by himself in a part log, part tar-paper shack on the Rosebud Reservation in South Dakota. So when Grandpa came to visit us, I was so ashamed and embarrassed I could've died.

There are a lot of yippy poodles and other fancy little dogs in our neighborhood,

---

Sioux (SOO) Native American tribes of the northern plains of the United States and nearby southern Canada

moccasins (MOK uh sunz) heelless slippers of soft flexible leather, originally worn by Native Americans

tepee (TEE pee) a cone-shaped tent of animal skins, used by the Plains Indians

Rosebud Reservation: a small Indian reservation in south-central South Dakota but they usually barked singly at the mailman from the safety of their own yards. Now it sounded as if a whole pack of mutts were barking together in one place.

I got up and walked to the curb to see what the commotion was. About a block away I saw a crowd of little kids yelling, with the dogs yipping and growling around someone who was walking down the middle of the street.

I watched the group as it slowly came closer and saw that in the center of the strange procession was a man wearing a tall black hat. He'd pause now and then to peer at something in his hand and then at the houses on either side of the street. I felt cold and hot at the same time as I recognized the man. "Oh, no!" I whispered. "It's Grandpa!"

I stood on the curb, unable to move even though I wanted to run and hide. Then I got mad when I saw how the yippy dogs were growling and nipping at the old man's baggy pant legs and how wearily he poked them away with his cane. "Stupid mutts," I said as I ran to rescue Grandpa.

When I kicked and hollered at the dogs to get away, they put their tails between their legs and scattered. The kids ran to the curb where they watched me and the old man.

"Grandpa," I said and felt pretty dumb when my voice cracked. I reached for his beat-up old tin suitcase, which was tied shut with a rope. But he set it down right in the street and shook my hand.

"*Hau. Takoza.* Grandchild," he greeted me formally in Sioux.

All I could do was stand there with the whole neighborhood watching and shake the hand of the leather-brown old man. I saw how his gray hair straggled from under his big black hat, which had a drooping feather in its crown. His rumpled black suit hung like a sack over his stooped frame. As he shook my hand, his coat fell open to expose a bright red satin shirt with a beaded bolo tie under the collar. His get-up wasn't out of place on the reservation, but it sure was here, and I wanted to sink right through the pavement.

"Hi," I muttered with my head down. I tried to pull my hand away when I felt his bony hand trembling, and looked up to see fatigue in his face. I felt like crying. I couldn't think of anything to say so I picked up Grandpa's suitcase, took his arm, and guided him up the driveway to our house.

Mom was standing on the steps. I don't know how long she'd been watching, but her hand was over her mouth and she looked as if she couldn't believe what she saw. Then she ran to us.

"Grandpa," she gasped. "How in the world did you get here?"

She checked her move to embrace Grandpa and I remembered that such a display of affection is unseemly to the Sioux and would embarrass him.

---

bolo tie (BOH loh TY) a man's string tie, held together with a decorated sliding device

"*Hau*, Marie," he said as he shook Mom's hand. She smiled and took his other arm.

As we supported him up the steps, the door banged open and Cheryl came bursting out of the house. She was all smiles and was so obviously glad to see Grandpa that I was ashamed of how I felt.

"Grandpa!" she yelled happily. "You came to see us!"

Grandpa smiled, and Mom and I let go of him as he stretched out his arms to my ten-year-old sister, who was still young enough to be hugged.

"*Wicincala*, little girl," he greeted her and then collapsed.

He had fainted. Mom and I carried him into her sewing room, where we had a spare bed.

After we had Grandpa on the bed, Mom stood there helplessly patting his shoulder.

"Shouldn't we call the doctor, Mom?" I suggested, since she didn't seem to know what to do.

"Yes," she agreed with a sigh. "You make Grandpa comfortable, Martin."

I reluctantly moved to the bed. I knew Grandpa wouldn't want to have Mom undress him, but I didn't want to, either. He was so skinny and frail that his coat slipped off easily. When I loosened his tie

Memories, Amado M. Peña, Jr. El Taller, Inc.

The Medicine Bag ■ 513

and opened his shirt collar, I felt a small leather pouch that hung from a thong around his neck. I left it alone and moved to remove his boots. The scuffed old cowboy boots were tight, and he moaned as I put pressure on his legs to jerk them off.

I put the boots on the floor and saw why they fit so tight. Each one was stuffed with money. I looked at the bills that lined the boots and started to ask about them, but Grandpa's eyes were closed again.

Mom came back with a basin of water. "The doctor thinks Grandpa is suffering from heat exhaustion," she explained as she bathed Grandpa's face. Mom gave a big sigh. "*Oh, hinh*, Martin. How do you suppose he got here?"

We found out after the doctor's visit. Grandpa was angrily sitting up in bed while Mom tried to feed him some soup.

"Tonight you let Marie feed you, Grandpa," spoke my dad, who had gotten home from work just as the doctor was leaving. "You're not really sick," he said as he gently pushed Grandpa back against the pillows. "The doctor said you just got too tired and hot after your long trip."

Grandpa relaxed, and between sips of soup, he told us of his journey. Soon after our visit to him, Grandpa decided that he would like to see where his only living descendants lived and what our home was like. Besides, he admitted sheepishly, he was lonesome after we left.

I knew that everybody felt as guilty as I did—especially Mom. Mom was all Grandpa had left. So even after she married my dad, who's a white man and teaches in the college in our city, and after Cheryl and I were born, Mom made sure that every summer we spent a week with Grandpa.

I never thought that Grandpa would be lonely after our visits, and none of us noticed how old and weak he had become. But Grandpa knew, and so he came to us. He had ridden on buses for two and a half days. When he arrived in the city, tired and stiff from sitting for so long, he set out, walking, to find us.

He had stopped to rest on the steps of some building downtown, and a policeman found him. The cop, according to Grandpa, was a good man who took him to the bus stop and waited until the bus came and told the driver to let Grandpa out at Bell View Drive. After Grandpa got off the bus, he started walking again. But he couldn't see the house numbers on the other side when he walked on the sidewalk, so he walked in the middle of the street. That's when all the little kids and dogs followed him.

I knew everybody felt as bad as I did. Yet I was so proud of this eighty-six-year-old man, who had never been away from the reservation, having the courage to travel so far alone.

"You found the money in my boots?" he asked Mom.

"Martin did," she answered, and roused herself to scold. "Grandpa, you shouldn't have carried so much money. What if someone had stolen it from you?"

---

thong (THAHNG) a narrow strip of leather

Grandpa laughed. "I would've known if anyone tried to take the boots off my feet. The money is what I've saved for a long time—a hundred dollars—for my funeral. But you take it now to buy groceries so that I won't be a burden to you while I am here."

"That won't be necessary, Grandpa," Dad said. "We are honored to have you with us, and you will never be a burden. I am only sorry that we never thought to bring you home with us this summer and spare you the discomfort of a long trip."

Grandpa was pleased. "Thank you," he answered. "But do not feel bad that you didn't bring me with you, for I would not have come then. It was not time." He said this in such a way that no one could argue with him. To Grandpa and the Sioux, he once told me, a thing would be done when it was the right time to do it, and that's the way it was.

"Also," Grandpa went on, looking at me, "I have come because it is soon time for Martin to have the medicine bag."

We all knew what that meant. Grandpa thought he was going to die, and he had to follow the tradition of his family to pass the medicine bag, along with its history, to the oldest male child.

"Even though the boy," he said still looking at me, "bears a white man's name, the medicine bag will be his."

I didn't know what to say. I had the same hot and cold feeling that I had when I first saw Grandpa in the street. The medicine bag was the dirty leather pouch I had found around his neck. "I could never wear such a thing," I almost said aloud. I thought of having my friends

see it in gym class or at the swimming pool and could imagine the smart things they would say. But I just swallowed hard and took a step toward the bed. I knew I would have to take it.

But Grandpa was tired. "Not now, Martin," he said, waving his hand in dismissal. "It is not time. Now I will sleep."

So that's how Grandpa came to be with us for two months. My friends kept asking to come see the old man, but I put them off. I told myself that I didn't want them laughing at Grandpa. But even as I made excuses, I knew it wasn't Grandpa that I was afraid they'd laugh at.

Nothing bothered Cheryl about bringing her friends to see Grandpa. Every day after school started, there'd be a crew of giggling little girls or round-eyed little boys crowded around the old man on the patio, where he'd gotten in the habit of sitting every afternoon.

Grandpa would smile in his gentle way and patiently answer their questions, or he'd tell them stories of brave warriors, ghosts, animals; and the kids listened in awed silence. Those little guys thought Grandpa was great.

Finally, one day after school, my friends came home with me because nothing I said stopped them. "We're going to see the great Indian of Bell View Drive," said Hank, who was supposed to be my best friend. "My brother has seen him three times so he oughta be well enough to see us."

When we got to my house, Grandpa was sitting on the patio. He had on his red shirt, but today he also wore a fringed

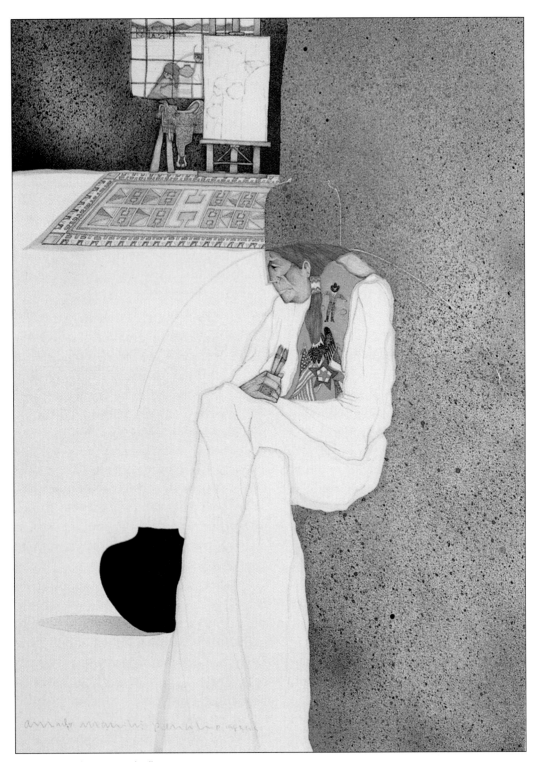

El Pintor, Amado Peña, Jr. El Taller, Inc.

leather vest that was decorated with beads. Instead of his usual cowboy boots, he had solidly beaded moccasins on his feet that stuck out of his black trousers. Of course, he had his old black hat on— he was seldom without it. But it had been brushed, and the feather in the beaded headband was proudly erect, its tip a brighter white. His hair lay in silver strands over the red shirt collar.

I stared just as my friends did, and I heard one of them murmur, "Wow!"

Grandpa looked up, and, when his eyes met mine, they twinkled as if he were laughing inside. He nodded to me, and my face got all hot. I could tell that he had known all along I was afraid he'd embarrass me in front of my friends.

"*Hau, hoksilas,* boys," he greeted and held out his hand.

My buddies passed in a single file and shook his hand as I introduced them. They were so polite I almost laughed. "How, there, Grandpa," and even a "How-do-you-do, sir."

"You look fine, Grandpa," I said as the guys sat on the lawn chairs or on the patio floor.

"*Hanh,* yes," he agreed. "When I woke up this morning, it seemed the right time to dress in the good clothes. I knew that my grandson would be bringing his friends."

"You guys want some lemonade or something?" I offered. No one answered. They were listening to Grandpa as he started telling how he'd killed the deer from which his vest was made.

Grandpa did most of the talking while my friends were there. I was so proud of him and amazed at how respectfully quiet my buddies were. Mom had to chase them home at supper time. As they left, they shook Grandpa's hand again and said to me,

"Martin, he's really great!"

"Yeah, man! Don't blame you for keeping him to yourself."

"Can we come back?"

But after they left, Mom said, "No more visitors for a while, Martin. Grandpa won't admit it, but his strength hasn't returned. He likes having company, but it tires him."

That evening Grandpa called me to his room before he went to sleep. "Tomorrow," he said, "when you come home, it will be time to give you the medicine bag."

I felt a hard squeeze from where my heart is supposed to be and was scared, but I answered, "OK, Grandpa."

All night I had weird dreams about thunder and lightning on a high hill. From a distance I heard the slow beat of a drum. When I woke up in the morning, I felt as if I hadn't slept at all. At school it seemed as if the day would never end and, when it finally did, I ran home.

Grandpa was in his room, sitting on the bed. The shades were down, and the place was dim and cool. I sat on the floor in front of Grandpa, but he didn't even look at me. After what seemed a long time he spoke.

"I sent your mother and sister away. What you will hear today is only for a man's ears. What you will receive is only for a man's hands." He fell silent, and I felt shivers down my back.

"My father in his early manhood," Grandpa began, "made a vision quest to find a spirit guide for his life. You cannot understand how it was in that time, when the great Teton Sioux were first made to stay on the reservation. There was a strong need for guidance from *Wakantanka*, the Great Spirit. But too many of the young men were filled with despair and hatred. They thought it was hopeless to search for a vision when the glorious life was gone and only the hated confines of a reservation lay ahead. But my father held to the old ways.

"He carefully prepared for his quest with a purifying sweat bath, and then he went alone to a high butte top to fast and pray. After three days he received his sacred dream—in which he found, after long searching, the white man's iron. He did not understand his vision of finding something belonging to the white people, for in that time they were the enemy. When he came down from the butte to cleanse himself at the stream below, he found the remains of a campfire and the broken shell of an iron kettle. This was a sign that reinforced his dream. He took a piece of the iron for his medicine bag, which he had made of elk skin years before, to prepare for his quest.

"He returned to his village, where he told his dream to the wise old men of the tribe. They gave him the name *Iron Shell*, but neither did they understand the meaning of the dream. The first Iron Shell kept the piece of iron with him at all times and believed it gave him protection from the evils of those unhappy days.

"Then a terrible thing happened to Iron Shell. He and several other young men were taken from their homes by the soldiers and sent far away to a white man's boarding school. He was angry and lonesome for his parents and the young girl he had wed before he was taken away. At first Iron Shell resisted the teacher's attempts to change him, and he did not try to learn. One day it was his turn to work in the school's blacksmith shop. As he walked into the place, he knew that his medicine had brought him there to learn and work with the white man's iron.

"Iron Shell became a blacksmith and worked at the trade when he returned to the reservation. All of his life he treasured the medicine bag. When he was old, and I was a man, he gave it to me, for no one made the vision quest any more."

Grandpa quit talking, and I stared in disbelief as he covered his face with his hands. His shoulders were shaking with quiet sobs, and I looked away until he began to speak again.

"I kept the bag until my son, your mother's father, was a man and had to leave us to fight in the war across the ocean. I gave him the bag, for I believed

---

vision quest (VIZH un KWEST) a search for a revelation that would aid understanding
Wakantanka (wah kahn TANGK uh) the Sioux religion's most important spirit—the creator of the world
butte (BYOOT) the top of a steep hill standing alone in a plain

Deer Rattle/Deer Dancer, Frank La Pend

it would protect him in battle, but he did not take it with him. He was afraid that he would lose it. He died in a far-away place."

Again Grandpa was still, and I felt his grief around me.

"My son," he went on after clearing his throat, "had only a daughter, and it is not proper for her to know of these things."

He unbuttoned his shirt, pulled out the leather pouch, and lifted it over his head. He held it in his hand, turning it over and over as if memorizing how it looked.

"In the bag," he said as he opened it and removed two objects, "is the broken shell of the iron kettle, a pebble from the butte, and a piece of the sacred sage." He held the pouch upside down and dust drifted down.

"After the bag is yours you must put a piece of prairie sage within and never open it again until you pass it on to your son." He replaced the pebble and the piece of iron, and tied the bag.

I stood up, somehow knowing I should. Grandpa slowly rose from the bed and stood upright in front of me holding the bag before my face. I closed my eyes and waited for him to slip it over my head. But he spoke.

"No, you need not wear it." He placed the soft leather bag in my right hand and closed my other hand over it. "It would not be right to wear it in this time and place where no one will understand. Put it safely away until you are again on the reservation. Wear it then, when you replace the sacred sage."

Grandpa turned and sat again on the bed. Wearily he leaned his head against the pillow. "Go," he said. "I will sleep now."

"Thank you, Grandpa," I said softly and left with the bag in my hands.

That night Mom and Dad took Grandpa to the hospital. Two weeks later I stood alone on the lonely prairie of the reservation and put the sacred sage in my medicine bag.

---

sage (SAYJ) plant belonging to the mint family

Virginia Driving Hawk Sneve (1933–   )

Writer and teacher Virginia Driving Hawk Sneve grew up on a Sioux reservation in South Dakota. Her knowledge of Sioux life and heritage has played an important role in her writings, which include novels, short stories, and nonfiction.

The Sioux history was an oral one, with stories handed down from one generation to another. As a result there are few written records of historical events among the Sioux. Time, the author explains, is less important to the Native Americans than to the white people; Native Americans are more concerned with the dramatic significance of an event and its impact on their lives than with when it occurred.

In addition to several novels and many short stories, Ms. Sneve has written a collection of biographies of Sioux leaders entitled *They Led a Nation*. In this book, she points out an interesting fact, that the word *chief* is not a Native American word. It was coined by non–Native Americans to refer to the leader of a Native American tribe. Yet Sneve often uses the word *chief* in her stories, because she feels that for her readers it evokes "a picture of stoic greatness, unflinching courage, and . . . manly beauty and strength. To use another word for these men would be to rob them of their glory."

Review the Selection

UNDERSTAND THE SELECTION

Recall

1. Who is the main character and narrator in this story?

2. Who comes to visit?

3. What problem does the visit present for the narrator?

Infer

4. Why did Grandpa travel to Iowa?

5. What different feelings did Martin have when he saw Grandpa walking down the street?

6. What can you infer about the relationship between men and women in the Sioux culture?

7. What indicates that Grandpa knew how Martin felt about wearing the medicine bag?

Apply

8. Compare Cheryl's initial reaction to Grandpa with Martin's reaction.

9. How do you account for the difference?

10. What qualities in Grandpa did Martin admire at the beginning of the story? At the end?

Respond to Literature

Why are Martin and his family especially important to Grandpa in terms of generations?

WRITE ABOUT THE SELECTION

The short story "The Medicine Bag" has several important themes. One of these themes is the importance of family traditions and cultural heritage. Another theme is Martin and Grandpa's successful bridging of a three-generation gap. Yet another theme is the blending of white and Native American cultures, both in terms of the iron shell in the medicine bag and in Martin's mother marrying a white man. Which theme is most meaningful to you? Write a paragraph in which you express your opinion about one of the themes in the story.

Prewriting Reread the story and list any theme you discover that was not mentioned above. Then choose from all the themes the one that has the most meaning for you. Cluster facts, details, and ideas about the theme you chose.

Writing Write a paragraph in which you express your opinion about the theme that you have chosen. Your opinion can be positive or negative; it can be based on your own experiences or the experiences of people you know.

Revising What point of view have you used for your paragraph? If you have written in the first person, try rewriting your paragraph in the third person, and vice versa. Decide which version is more effective.

Proofreading Make sure that all of your sentences have a subject and a verb. Correct any sentence fragments by rewriting them as complete sentences.

THINK ABOUT PLOT

Without a plot, there would be no story. The events that happen in a story make up the plot. The main elements of a plot are **exposition**, **complication**, **crisis**, **climax**, and **resolution**. In a well-written story, every event and action is important and related.

1. What is the exposition of the plot in "The Medicine Bag"? Where in the story does it occur?

2. What complication is introduced into the plot? How does this add to the problem of the main character?

3. What is the crisis of the story?

4. At what point does the climax occur? What is the outcome for the main character?

5. Does the story have a resolution? If so, what do you think it adds to the story?

READING FOCUS

Compare and Contrast Character Traits
What attitudes does Martin exhibit at the beginning of the story? How has he changed by the end?

DEVELOP YOUR VOCABULARY

Several words in the short story "The Medicine Bag" relate specifically to the Native American culture. Some of the words, such as *moccasins*, have found their way into the English language. Words from other cultures have also found their way into the English language. For example, you are probably familiar with the Eskimo word *igloo*, which is a house built of ice.

Find the meaning of each word. The cultural origin of the word is given in parentheses. Then use each word in an original sentence.

1. tepee (Native American); also teepee

2. siesta (Spanish)

3. amigo (Spanish)

4. cafe (French)

5. cabana (Spanish)

6. pueblo (Spanish)

7. marionette (French)

8. marina (Italian)

Learn About

READING FOCUS

Identify Theme As you read the next two poems, think about the theme, or message, of each one. How does the speaker's feeling toward the subject help you understand the theme?

FORM

The form of a poem is the way the poem is constructed. The two main types of poetic form are **closed** and **open**. Closed form includes most established forms of poetry, such as the couplet, the ballad, and the epigram. A **couplet** is a pair of lines that, together, form a complete unit —either because of their meaning or because of end rhyme. A **ballad** is a short narrative poem that is written in four-line stanzas that rhyme *abcb*. An **epigram** is a short, usually witty, poem, dealing with a single thought or event. Usually, it is composed of either one couplet or two couplets (also called a **quatrain**).

The main type of open poetry is free verse. **Free verse**, as you have already seen in several poems, is verse that has no regular rhythmic pattern.

As you read the poems in this selection, ask yourself:

1. In what form of poetry is "Medicine" written?
2. In what form is "Grandfather" written?

WRITING CONNECTION

Write a couplet that consists of two lines that rhyme. The couplet should express a complete thought; for example, "I'd like to go to bed and rest/But I must study for a test."

Medicine

by Alice Walker

Grandma sleeps with
my sick
    grand-
pa so she
5   can get him
during the night
medicine
to stop
  the pain

10   In
  the morning
    clumsily
    I
  wake
15   them

Her eyes
look at me
from under-
      neath
20 his withered
arm

    The
medicine
  is all
25   in
her long
  un-
    braided
      hair.

---

clumsily (KLUM zuh lee) ungracefully
withered (WITH urd) powerless; incapable of action

The Banjo Lesson, Henry Ossawa Tanner. Hampton University Museum

Grandfather

by Shirley Crawford

Grandfather sings, I dance.
Grandfather speaks, I listen.
Now I sing, who will dance?
I speak, who will listen?

5 Grandfather hunts, I learn.
Grandfather fishes, I clean.
Now I hunt, who will learn?
I fish, who will clean?

Grandfather dies, I weep.
10 Grandfather buried, I am left alone.
When I am dead, who will cry?
When I am buried, who will be alone?

Review the Selection

UNDERSTAND THE SELECTION

Recall

1. What situation is described in the poem "Medicine"?

2. What is the subject of the poem "Grandfather"?

3. In "Grandfather," what event has occurred?

Infer

4. Can you guess the approximate age of the speaker in the poem "Medicine"?

5. What can you infer about the grandparents in "Medicine"?

6. In "Grandfather," what question is the speaker asking?

7. In "Grandfather," what kind of relationship exists between the poet and her grandfather?

Apply

8. What relationship is most important in "Grandfather"? In "Medicine"?

9. How do you think the medicine got in the grandmother's hair?

10. Do you think that the speaker in "Grandfather" has children? Why?

Respond to Literature

How do these two poems give different views of grandparents and grandchildren?

WRITE ABOUT THE SELECTION

The poems "Grandfather" and "Medicine" are both written from the grandchild's point of view. How do you think the same stories might be told from one of the grandparents' point of view? Write a paragraph or poem in which you speak from the point of view of the grandfather in Shirley Crawford's poem or from the point of view of one of the grandparents in Alice Walker's poem.

Prewriting Decide which poem appeals to you more. Then begin to make notes about how the grandparent might tell the story. Ask yourself: What tone would the grandparent use? What aspect of the story would the grandparent emphasize? Take your cues from the details in the poem.

Writing Use your prewriting notes to write from the grandparent's point of view. Be sure to include in your poem or paragraph the grandparent's view of the grandchild.

Revising Try writing in the same form as the original poem. If you are writing based on Crawford's poem, use couplets. If you are writing based on Walker's poem, use free verse.

Proofreading Check your paper for errors in spelling. Then compare your form to the original. If you chose free verse like Alice Walker, for example, you may want to change where a line breaks.

THINK ABOUT FORM

The **form** of a poem is its outward structure. The two main types of poetic form are closed and open. **Closed** poetry includes such forms as the couplet, ballad, and epigram. **Open** form includes free verse and concrete poetry. In concrete poetry the arrangement of letters and words in the poem relates to the content—for example, a poem about Christmas written in the shape of a Christmas tree.

1. Is the form of "Medicine" closed or open?

2. How does the form the poet uses in "Medicine" reflect the speaker's age?

3. Is the form of "Grandfather" closed or open?

4. Does the poem "Grandfather" resemble a couplet, ballad, or epigram? If so, how?

5. In "Grandfather," what rhythmic relationship exists between various lines of the poem?

READING FOCUS

Identify Theme What is the subject of each poem? How did the speaker of each poem feel about the subject? What does this tell you about the theme of each poem?

DEVELOP YOUR VOCABULARY

An **adjective** is a word that describes a noun or pronoun. An adjective answers one or more of the following questions about the word it describes: What kind? Which one? How many? How much?

In a sentence, an adjective usually comes before the noun it describes. Sometimes, however, an adjective comes after the noun: for example, *Juan is sick.* The adjective *sick* describes Juan.

Review the meaning of each adjective listed below. Then use each adjective in an original sentence.

1. alone
2. sick
3. withered
4. long
5. unbraided
6. sparkling
7. interminable
8. personal
9. fancy
10. exciting
11. weary
12. patient
13. respectful
14. sacred

Learn About

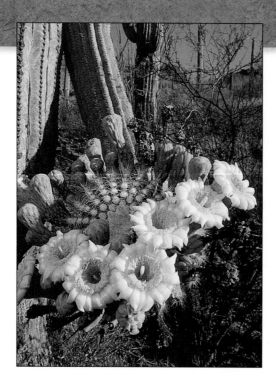

FIGURES OF SPEECH

Figures of speech are specific forms of figurative language. Most figures of speech compare two unlike things. Two important figures of speech are similes and metaphors.

In a **simile**, the word *like* or *as* is used to make a comparison. For example, you might say, "Riding in Grandpa's old car was like riding in a roller coaster."

In a **metaphor**, a comparison is made directly, without using *like* or *as*. For example, "My father is a tower of strength" is a metaphor. The phrase "tower of strength" describes a quality of the father.

Similes and metaphors add meaning by providing vivid images that describe a person, object, place, or idea.

As you read the poems in the next selection, ask yourself:

1. What similes or metaphors are used by the poets?
2. How do these figures of speech add meaning to the poem?

READING FOCUS

Make Inferences About the Speaker
When you make an inference, you use details in a poem or story to make a logical guess. The speaker in a poem is the person telling the story. If a line reads, "Matt's chin was on his chest after he heard the news," you might infer that the speaker thinks Matt was probably unhappy or depressed.

As you read the next two poems, look for details that help you make inferences about the speakers' thoughts and feelings.

WRITING CONNECTION

Look around you wherever you happen to be right now. Choose five objects or people that you can see clearly. Write a simile or metaphor to describe each.

Some People

by Rachel Field

Isn't it strange some people make
    You feel so tired inside,
Your thoughts begin to shrivel up
    Like leaves all brown and dried!

But when you're with some other ones,
    It's stranger still to find
Your thoughts as thick as fireflies
    All shiny in your mind!

My People

by Bernice George

    I am a Navajo, the Navajos are my people.
    They live in the hogans upon the dry desert,
    With a little shade house and a sheep corral.
    It is nice and peaceful there away
5   From the city street.
    There were the sad, dark years for my people,
    But my people didn't disappear.
    They started rebuilding, increasing
    In population.
10 I am proud that the desert floor,
    The lonely hogans,
    Have made me thoughtful and
    Respectful of my people.
    I am proud to be born in my people's land.
15 I shall never forget my home and people.

---

shrivel (SHRIV ul) wither, dry up, become wrinkled
hogans (HOH gunz) Navajo houses made of branches, clay, and sod
corral (kuh RAL) a fenced-in area for keeping livestock

Review the Selection

Recall

1. What is the subject of the poem "Some People"?

2. What is the subject of the poem "My People"?

3. Who is the speaker in "My People"?

Infer

4. What two groups of people does the poet describe in "Some People"?

5. What qualities of her people does the speaker admire in "My People"?

6. Can you infer whether the speaker in "My People" is with her people now?

7. What do you think the speaker means when she speaks of "sad, dark years for my people"?

Apply

8. What contrasts are made in "Some People"?

9. What personal experiences might have led the poet to write "Some People"?

10. Would you say that "My People" contains facts or opinions about the Navajo? Explain your answer.

Respond to Literature

In what way does the poem "My People" speak about generations?

WRITE ABOUT THE SELECTION

The poem "Some People" describes two different types of people. What do you think it would be like to meet each of these people at a party? How would they make you feel? Write one or two paragraphs in which you describe an encounter with each type of person described in the poem.

Prewriting   On a sheet of paper, make two columns. At the top of one column, write *Type 1*; at the top of the other, write *Type 2*. Under each heading list characteristics of the imaginary people you are going to describe; or you may, instead, want to base your descriptions on actual people you have met.

Writing   Use your prewriting notes to write one or two paragraphs in which you describe meeting at a party the two types of people described in the poem "Some People." Be sure to include details about the setting of the party. You may also wish to include dialogue.

Revising   Read over your paper and think about the tone you have used. Is your paper serious or humorous? Try adding specific verbs and vivid descriptions to make your paragraphs more interesting.

Proofreading   Make sure that each sentence in your paper begins with a capital letter and ends with a period, question mark, or exclamation point. If you have used dialogue, remember to insert quotation marks.

THINK ABOUT FIGURES OF SPEECH

Figures of speech add meaning to a poem by providing vivid images that help you see things in new ways. Two important figures of speech are similes and metaphors. A **simile** compares two different things by using the word *like* or *as*. A **metaphor** compares two different things directly, without using *like* or *as*.

1. Find two similes in "Some People."

2. What two images are conveyed by the use of these similes? Are the images similar, or are they opposite?

3. What other imagery does the author use in "Some People"?

4. What image is conveyed by this description? How does it add meaning to the poem?

5. Does the poem "My People" use similes or metaphors? Can you think of a reason for this?

READING FOCUS

Make Inferences About the Speaker
What can you infer about the speakers of these two poems? How do other people affect the speaker of "Some People"? How does the speaker of "My People" feel about her Navajo heritage? What clues in each poem helped you make these inferences?

DEVELOP YOUR VOCABULARY

A **figurative expression** is a group of words that has a meaning of its own—a meaning that will be different from the meanings of the individual words. For example, you might say, "The answer was on the tip of my tongue." The expression "tip of my tongue" means that you were just about to say the answer.

Identify the figurative expression in each of the sentences below. Then write a sentence explaining the meaning of each figurative expression.

1. He was running around like a chicken with its head cut off.

2. The story was about a woman with shattered hopes and broken dreams.

3. Keep a stiff upper lip.

4. I think it would be best to talk and get it off your chest.

5. Donna decided to go home and curl up with a good book.

THEME IN POETRY

You have learned about theme in short stories. Theme is also an important element of poetry.

Like storytellers, poets write because they have something to say. The **theme** of a poem may be what the poet values or feels deeply about. Two poems that you will read illustrate the poets' values in a few lines. In "Otto," the theme concerns a child's sensitivity to his father's difficulties. In "Christmas morning i," the theme concerns a child's relationship with a grandparent.

As with a short story, it is important not to confuse the theme of a poem with the subject. The **subject** of a poem is simply the topic. Keep in mind that two poems may have similar subjects but different themes.

As you read the poems "Otto" and "Christmas morning i," ask yourself:
1. What is the theme of each poem?
2. Are these themes similar or different?

WRITING CONNECTION

Review the poems that you have read in this unit and the preceding units. Choose the poem you liked best and discuss the theme.

READING FOCUS

Compare and Contrast Poems When you compare two things, you note the features that the two things share. When you contrast two things, you highlight differences between the two things. In poems, you can compare and contrast elements such as theme, style, and point of view. As you read the next two poems, look for ways they are different and ways they are the same.

OTTO

by Gwendolyn Brooks

It's Christmas Day. I did not get
The presents that I hoped for. Yet,
It is not nice to frown or fret.

To frown or fret would not be fair.
My Dad must never know I care
It's hard enough for him to bear.

Christmas morning i

by Carol Freeman

Christmas morning i
got up before the others and
ran
naked across the plank
floor into the front
room to see grandmama
sewing a new
button on my last year
ragdoll.

---

fret (FRET) become worried or upset
plank (PLANGK) a long, thick board

Review the Selection

UNDERSTAND THE SELECTION

Recall

1. When do both poems take place?

2. Who is the speaker in "Otto"?

3. Who is the speaker in "Christmas morning i"?

Infer

4. What does Otto understand about his father?

5. About whose feelings does Otto care most?

6. What does the speaker in the second poem infer when she sees her grandmother sewing?

7. How do you think the speaker will feel about her Christmas present?

Apply

8. In what way are both poems similar?

9. Do both poems express similar feelings? Why or why not?

10. Why do you think that the grandmother in the second poem was sewing a button on last year's ragdoll?

Respond to Literature

What do these poems have to say about the relationships between children and parents, and between children and grandparents?

WRITE ABOUT THE SELECTION

Each poem in this selection is spoken from the child's point of view. What do you think the speaker's father might say in the first poem? What do you think the grandmother would have to say in the second poem? Write a paragraph or poem in which you tell either story from the parent's or grandparent's point of view.

Prewriting Decide which poem you want to write about. Then read the poem several times and try to imagine that you are the father or the grandmother. Write down your ideas about how this person might feel. Also write down any additional details that you might want to add, such as the family's financial circumstances.

Writing Use your prewriting notes to write a poem or paragraph from the father's or grandmother's point of view. Be sure to include the older person's view of the child or grandchild. Take your cues from the details in the story.

Revising As you revise, consider using dialogue in your paragraph or poem. You can also present a character's thoughts in the form of dialogue.

Proofreading If you chose to write a poem, reread it now with careful attention to your punctuation at the end of each line. You may choose whatever you want —a comma, period, nothing at all—as long as you keep in mind that end-of-line punctuation plays an important part in *how* a poem is spoken.

THINK ABOUT THEME IN POETRY

The **theme** of a poem expresses what the poet values, feels, or thinks. Often a poem communicates an insight that the poet has gained about life, about others, or about self. Like the author of a short story, a poet may state the theme clearly or leave it for you to figure out for yourself. Since poetry usually involves far fewer words than a short story, it is more likely that the theme will be suggested rather than spelled out.

1. What is the theme of "Otto"?

2. What is the theme of "Christmas morning i"?

3. What is the subject of each poem?

4. Are the subjects similar or different?

5. Are the themes similar or different?

READING FOCUS

Compare and Contrast Poems Describe two ways the two poems you have read are alike. Describe two ways they are different. Consider style and point of view.

DEVELOP YOUR VOCABULARY

A **noun** is a word that names a person, place, or thing. A **verb** is a word that describes action or a state of being. Some words can be used as both nouns and verbs. For example, the word *dare* can be a noun: "He took the *dare* and dove into the water." The word *dare* can also be used as a verb: "I *dare* you to tell Father what you told me." The meaning of words that can be used as either nouns or verbs depends on their use in a particular sentence.

Each of the following words can be used as a noun or as a verb. Write original sentences that illustrate both uses of each word.

1. call
2. frown
3. bill
4. care
5. pass
6. throw
7. turn
8. button

Learn About

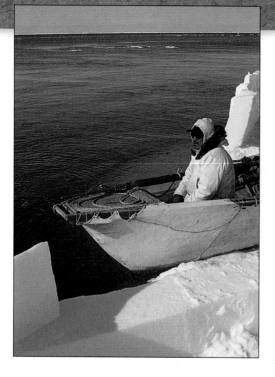

TONE

The attitude of a poem is called the **tone**. The tone indicates the speaker's feelings toward the subject and sometimes toward the reader.

You can better understand the importance of tone if you think of the way tone of voice can change the meaning of spoken words. For example, if a person says in a friendly tone of voice, "That is a great dress you have on," you know that you are being given a compliment. If someone says the same sentence in a sarcastic tone of voice, you know that you are being insulted.

As you read the poems in this selection, ask yourself:

1. What is the tone of each poem?
2. What does the tone tell about the speaker's attitudes?

WRITING CONNECTION

Read the following sentences silently. Then try reading each sentence aloud using various tones of voice. Write down how the meaning of each sentence is changed by the way it is spoken.

Where are you going?
The weather is supposed to be warm and sunny.
You are an hour early!
I am going out to take a walk.

READING FOCUS

Identify Cause and Effect A cause is something that brings about a certain result, or effect. Thinking about cause and effect when you read can help you understand why events happen or why characters feel as they do. For example, snow can cause roads to become slippery. A harsh remark can cause someone to feel sad. Sometimes several events in a row are linked by cause and effect. For example, snow can cause slippery roads, which can cause car accidents. Asking why as you read can help you discover which events are linked by cause and effect.

Whale Hunting

by Sally Nashookpuk

My daddy goes whaling in the Bering Sea
I'm just a girl, he can't take me
My brother joins the whaling group
They caught four this year
For muk-tuk soup.

Luther Leavitt

by Alfred Brower

Luther Leavitt is a whale hunter.
last year
they got a whale
we went
to the blanket toss
I never
got a chance to go
on the blanket
cause there were too many kids.

---

whaling (HWAYL ing) hunting whales
Bering Sea (BIR ing SEE) part of the north Pacific Ocean between Alaska and Siberia

Review the Selection

UNDERSTAND THE SELECTION

Recall

1. What is the setting of the first poem?

2. What is the setting of the second poem?

3. What occupation is discussed in both poems?

Infer

4. In the second poem, what tells you that catching a whale is an important event?

5. What can you infer from the first poem about the speaker's feelings about being a girl?

6. Why do you think the speaker feels this way?

7. Why is whaling important to the speaker in the first poem?

Apply

8. The second poem is entitled "Luther Leavitt," but who is the poem really about? Explain your answer.

9. In what way do the speakers in both poems have similar feelings?

10. How do you think the speaker in the first poem feels toward her brother?

Respond to Literature
What aspect of the theme of generations is illustrated by these two poems?

WRITE ABOUT THE SELECTION

In the poems, two children express their observations and feelings about events connected with whale hunting. You may never have lived in a place where people whale hunt, but you may have childhood memories that are similar to those of the speakers in other ways. For example, perhaps you had to stay behind as your brother or sister joined a parent or grandparent in doing something important. Perhaps you were the only child who did not win a prize at a party. Write a paragraph in which you compare a memory from your childhood with one in these poems.

Prewriting Take a few minutes to cluster incidents that you remember from childhood. Write down your ideas and any details that you can remember.

Writing Choose the incident that you remember most vividly or about which you feel most strongly. Then use your prewriting cluster to write a paragraph in which you compare and contrast this incident with the incident described in one of the poems.

Revising As you revise your paragraph, make sure that your feelings about the incident are clearly communicated. Often, adding adverbs can help to communicate feelings. Use parallel structure to make your comparison logical and organized.

Proofreading Check your paper for correct grammar, spelling, and punctuation. If you are writing in the past tense, make sure that you have used correct verb forms.

THINK ABOUT TONE

The **tone** of a poem indicates the speaker's attitude toward his or her subject. The tone can also indicate the speaker's or poet's attitude toward the reader. Some elements that contribute to the tone are the formality or informality of the poem's language, the rhythm, the choice of certain words, and the energy or pace of the poem. Sometimes, tone will change within a poem, especially if the poem is long.

1. What is the tone of "Whale Hunting"?

2. Which line in "Whale Hunting" displays the tone most clearly?

3. What is the tone of "Luther Leavitt"?

4. In which part of the poem is the tone most evident?

5. How might the tone of the poem be different if the speaker had been able to go on the blanket?

READING FOCUS

Identify Cause and Effect Identify one cause-and-effect relationship in each of the poems.

DEVELOP YOUR VOCABULARY

Antonyms are words that have opposite, or nearly opposite, meanings. *Short* and *tall* are antonyms, as are *thin* and *fat*. In the poem "Luther Leavitt," the speaker says that there were "too many kids." An antonym of the word *many* would be *few*. The phrase would have exactly the opposite meaning if the word *few* were substituted for the word *many*.

Two words in each group below are antonyms. Write the antonyms on a separate sheet of paper. Then write a sentence using the first antonym in each pair. Rewrite each sentence using the second antonym, and see how the meaning of the sentence changes.

1. knowledge, thoughtfulness, ignorance, consideration

2. tired, rude, polite, quick

3. difficult, hidden, confusing, easy

4. politely, hesitantly, eagerly, slowly

Write About Theme

All of the stories and poems in this unit are about generations. Suppose that four of the characters from this unit meet at a family reunion, and the conversation turns to family history and tradition. What might these characters say to one another? Write their conversation as a dialogue for a story.

Prewriting Choose the four characters that you feel you know best. You will have to decide how the four characters are related. Perhaps one character is the distant cousin of another character or one character has married into the family of another character. Maybe one character comes to the reunion as the boyfriend or girlfriend of another character. Freewrite their conversations, thinking of questions that they might ask one another and the answers that might be given.

Writing Use your freewriting as a basis for your dialogue. Be sure to describe each character's facial expressions and tone of voice. Introduce your dialogue by describing the setting of the reunion.

Revising Make sure that the personality of each character stands out clearly. Add details and descriptive words to make each characterization more vivid.

Proofreading Make sure that you have used quotation marks correctly. Remember that a new paragraph must begin each time the speaker changes.

Write About Genre

You have studied five important elements that can be used to analyze poetry: denotation and connotation, rhythm, sounds, form, and symbolism. Choose two poems from this unit about which you feel strongly. Compare and contrast the works according to the literary elements you have studied.

Prewriting Review the work that you did for the Think About sections for the poems in this unit. Then make a chart that has the name of the two poems that you have chosen at the top and the five literary elements on the side. Fill in the spaces on the chart with details about each element from the poems.

Writing Use your prewriting chart to write a comparison of the two poems. You might enjoy writing your paper as if you were a literary critic writing for a newspaper or magazine.

Revising Try to include in your paper both positive and negative statements about each poem. Add a sentence or two that states how well you think a particular poet uses such devices as symbolism, sounds, or connotation.

Proofreading Check your paper for correct punctuation. If you used colons or semicolons, make sure that they are used correctly. Also check to be certain that you used either a question mark or an exclamation mark at the end of a sentence in which a period would be inappropriate.

Vocabulary

A **prefix** is a letter or letters added to the beginning of a word or word root to change its meaning. A negative prefix acts like the word *not* and changes the meaning of the word from positive to negative. For example, the word *inconsiderate* is formed by adding the prefix *in-* to *considerate*. The word *inconsiderate* means "not considerate." In addition to *in-*, some commonly used negative prefixes include *un-*, *dis-*, *il-*, *ir-*, and *im-*.

Identify the negative prefix and root word for each italicized word below. Then write a definition for each word.

1. It would be *inappropriate* to wear sneakers to graduation.

2. She was wearing a very *unusual* hat.

3. The boy lost something that was *irreplaceable*.

4. Grandfather was *immobilized* by the injury.

5. It would be *impossible* for Roberto to go to school.

6. He *disregarded* his father's remarks and kept on walking.

7. It is *illogical* to wear mittens in the summer.

Grammar, Usage, and Mechanics

A **conjunction** is a part of speech that makes a direct connection between words or groups of words. Some common conjunctions are *and*, *or*, and *because*.

Two kinds of conjunctions are coordinating conjunctions and subordinating conjunctions. **Coordinating conjunctions** connect similar words or word groups. The following are examples:

It was a thoroughly happy *and* relaxed time for everybody.

Should she choose chocolate *or* vanilla?

Subordinating conjunctions connect two complete ideas by making one of the ideas less important than the other. Some subordinating conjunctions are *after*, *as*, *even though*, *since*, *unless*, and *wherever*. Here are some examples:

I cheered loudly for my team *even though* they were losing the game.

I will not go to college *unless* I have enough money to support myself.

Find five sentences from the selections that use conjunctions. Identify the conjunctions and state whether they are coordinating or subordinating. Then identify the words or word groups that the conjunctions connect. Use the five sentences as models to write five original sentences.

SPEAKING AND LISTENING

You have read about many interesting real people and some colorful imaginary characters in this unit. If you were asked to name the most notable real person in this unit, whom would it be and why? Also, if you were asked to name the character who seemed the most interesting to you, whom would it be and why? Think about these questions as you prepare to talk about literature.

1. Think about the people you have read about in this unit. Choose two, one real and one imaginary, who seem to stand out from all the others. Write their names on 3 × 5 index cards.

2. On each card, write as much as you can recall about the person or character whose name is on the card. Limit yourself to two minutes per card, but try to remember as many things as you can. Write without stopping if possible, and do not worry about complete sentences.

3. Try to fill up both sides of the card. In writing about the character, you will want to consider memorable qualities, personality, importance in the story, and whether he or she represented a stereotype or was an unusual character. In writing about the real person,

you probably will want to include such information as personal life, personality, and contributions to family or community.

4. After you have filled your cards, work with a group of your classmates. Decide whether you will discuss characters or real people, or a mix of both. Then take turns round-robin style to discuss the characters and real people you have chosen. Use your cards to help you. Limit your dialogue to about one minute.

5. If someone in your group has chosen the same person or character that you have, try not to repeat anything already said. Instead, add to his or her dialogue. You will be surprised how something another person says can jar your memory so that you recall something new about that person or character.

Now that you have read these five steps, go back to the beginning and prepare yourself to talk about characters from literature. Once you meet with your group, you will want to spend enough time together so that everyone has a chance to share ideas.

CRITICAL THINKING

Generalization A general conclusion drawn from particular details is called a **generalization**. For example, suppose that all the children on your block play a certain game. You might make the generalization that this game is popular among children.

Sometimes, when you read a piece of literature, you will be tempted to make a generalization based on what you have read. It is important that you recognize whether such a generalization is accurate or inaccurate. For example, after reading the short story "The Medicine Bag," you might come to the conclusion that the Sioux place a great deal of importance on passing traditions from generation to generation. This is an accurate generalization. However, suppose that after reading the story you come to the conclusion that all Sioux children fear that their grandparents might embarrass them. This is an inaccurate generalization.

Choose a selection from this unit that suggests several generalizations. Use the selection to answer the following questions:

1. What generalizations are suggested by this story or poem? What specific details support these generalizations?

2. What inaccurate generalizations might a reader make based on this selection? Why are these generalizations inaccurate?

EFFECTIVE STUDYING

Tests In a matching test, first read the instructions. Notice whether an item in either column can be used more than once. Also, note if some items in a column may not be used at all. Begin by matching the items that you are sure of. If each item is used only once, it is possible to match some of the remaining items by the process of elimination.

In a multiple-choice test, answer the question in your own mind before you look at the choices. Eliminate the choices that are obviously wrong. Then choose the remaining answer that seems best.

In true and false tests, do not mark a statement true unless it is totally true. If you know that a statement is true only in some cases, it is probably false. Be aware of limiting words such as *always*, *never*, or *only*. Also be aware if a statement has two parts joined by a word such as *because*. One or both parts might be true, but the relationship between the two parts might be false.

Test Preparation

On any type of test, it is a good idea to answer all the items you are sure of first. Keep track of the ones you skipped. Then take more time to work on them.

GLOSSARY

PRONUNCIATION KEY

Accent is the force or stress given to some words or syllables in speech. In this book, accent is indicated by the use of uppercase letters. One syllable words are always shown as accented. Thus, the pronunciation of *hand* is (HAND). In words of more than one syllable, the accented syllable is printed in uppercase letters. The other syllable or syllables are printed in lowercase letters. Thus, the pronunciation of *handbag* is (HAND bag).

Letter(s) in text words	Letter(s) used in respelling	Sample words	Phonetic respelling	Letter(s) in text words	Letter(s) used in respelling	Sample words	Phonetic respelling
a	a	bandit	(BAN dit)	i	uh	possible	(POS uh bul)
a	ay	makeup	(MAYK up)	o	o	bottle	(BOT ul)
a	air	daring	(DAIR ing)	o	u	gallon	(GAL un)
a	ah	dart	(DAHRT)	o	oh	open	(OH pun)
a	uh	about	(uh BOUT)	o	aw	horn	(HAWRN)
a	aw	ball	(BAWL)	oo	oo	move	(MOOV)
e	e	denim	(DEN im)	oo	uu	football	(FUUT bawl)
e	eh	ingest	(in JEHST)	oo	oo	pool	(POOL)
e	ih	delight	(dih LYT)	oi	oi	point	(POINT)
e	u	darken	(DAHR kun)	ou	ou	output	(OUT put)
e	ee	he	(HEE)	u	u	upshot	(UP shot)
i	i	mitten	(MIT un)	u	uh	support	(suh PAWRT)
i	ih	gravity	(GRAV ih tee)	u	oo	ruler	(ROO lur)
i	y	idle	(YD ul)	y	i	rhythm	(RITH um)
i	eye	idea	(eye DEE uh)	y	ee	lazy	(LAY zee)
i	ee	medium	(MEE dee um)	y	y	thyme	(TYM)

A

abhorred (ab HAWRD) hated, dreaded *p. 70*

absurd (ab SURD) unreasonable; ridiculous *p. 169*

acquainted (un KWAYN tid) known to one another *p. 38*

acrid (AK rid) bitter to the tongue *p. 324*

aloof (uh LOOF) at a distance, apart *p. 65*

amorous (AM uh rus) full of love *p. 70*

anatomy (uh NAT uh mee) here, body *p. 158*

apologetic (uh pol uh JET ik) filled with apology; suggesting that one is sorry *p. 120*

ardently (AR dent lee) with great eagerness *p. 13*

attorney (uh TUR nee) lawyer *p. 252*

authorities (uh THAWR uh teez) people with official power *p. 132*

automatically (aw tuh MAT ihk lee) happening in a regular way without planning *p. 43*

avarice (AV uh ris) greed *p. 101*

B

banter (BAN tur) good-natured teasing *p. 324*

barbaric (bahr BAR ik) wild and cruel; not yet civilized *p. 285*

bedlam (BED lum) confusion *p. 416*

belt (BELT) area; region *p. 383*

beseech (bih SEECH) ask earnestly *p. 62*

bifocals (BY foh kulz) eyeglasses with parts to correct both near and far vision *p. 44*

bilingual (by LING gwul) able to use two languages *p. 415*

blare (BLAIR) make a loud noise *p. 414*

blunt (BLUNT) having a rounded point *p. 277*

bogies (BOH geez) real or imaginary things that startle or frighten *p. 171*

bottoms (BAH tumz) low-lying land along a river *p. 37*

brawl (BRAWL) noisy fight *p. 228*

bustle (BUS ul) move about busily *p. 477*

C

caravans (KAR uh vanz) in Great Britain, camping trailers *p. 188*

carcass (KAHR kus) body of dead animal *p. 386*

catastrophe (kuh TAS truh fee) a sudden, horrible disaster *p. 435*

charred (CHAHRD) partly burned *p. 388*

civic (SIV ik) having to do with good citizenship *p. 140*

clarity (KLAR uh tee) clearness *p. 418*

client (KLY unt) person who pays for a duty performed *p. 138*

coincidence (koh IN suh duns) two or more related events accidentally happening at the same time *pp. 144, 173, 243*

companion (kum PAN yun) a friend *p. 274*

comprehension (kom prih HEN shun) understanding or knowledge of something *p. 266*

Confederate (kun FED uh raht) during the Civil War, a supporter of the South *p. 5*

confide (kun FYD) tell as a secret *p. 353*

consolations (KAHN suh LAY shunz) the acts of comforting in time of sorrow *p. 8*

contagion (kun TAY jun) spreading disease *p. 72*

corral (kuh RAL) a fenced-in area for keeping livestock *p. 531*

correspondence (kawr uh SPON duns) exchange of letters *p. 95*

covert (KOH vurt) hidden or disguised *p. 266*

creed (KREED) formal statement of belief *p. 453*

crocus (KROH kus) spring flower *p. 235*

croksack, variation of *croker sack* (KRO kur sak) a bag of rough cloth or burlap *p. 36*

cuddling (KUD ling) holding and petting *p. 381*

cupboard (KUB urd) a closet fitted with shelves for holding cups *p. 256*

D

deception (dih SEP shun) trickery; action intended to fool another person *pp. 97, 201*

deftly (DEFT lee) cleverly *p. 505*

deliberately (dah LIH bur ayt lee) in an unhurried, slow, and steady manner *p. 176*

demonstration (dem un STRAY shun) any happening that can be observed *p. 205*

denouement (day noo MAHN) the final outcome *p. 507*

despite (dih SPYT) in spite of *p. 349*

destination (des tuh NAY shun) a place to which one is going *p. 43*

dignitary (DIG nuh ter ee) important person *p. 414*

dismaying (dis MAY ing) losing courage or confidence *p. 340*

doff (DOF) take off or discard *p. 58*

douse (DOUS) soak with water *p. 388*

E

elimination (ih lim uh NAY shun) in a tournament, dropped out after one loss *p. 410*

emerged (ih MURJD) came out *p. 467*

endure (en DUUR) put up with *p. 92*

entitled (en TYT uld) have as a claim or right; empowered *p. 148*

evade (ee VAYD) to keep away from; avoid *p. 177*

eventually (ih VEN choo ul ee) in the end; at some time *p. 434*

exclusive (ik SKLOO siv) private and expensive *p. 148*

exhausting (eg ZAW sting) very tiring *p. 43*

explicitly (ik SPLIS it lee) very clearly *p. 140*

extreme (ik STREEM) very great *p. 433*

F

facetiously (fuh SEE shus lee) jokingly, especially at an inappropriate time *p. 269*

fanatical (fuh NAT ih kul) incredibly devoted, to the point of being unreasonable *p. 190*

fantasy (FAN tuh see) daydream; idea created by the imagination; something imagined *pp. 157*

faze (FAYZ) confuse; weaken *p. 92*

felon (FEL un) criminal *p. 68*

ferocious (fuh ROH shus) very fierce *pp. 44, 349*

fiancé (fee ahn SAY) husband-to-be *p. 226*

fitful (FIT ful) uneasy; very restless *p. 412*

fortnight (FAWRT nyt) two weeks *p. 192*

frustrations (frus TRAY shunz) unhappy feelings that come from not being able to reach one's goals *p. 453*

G

gables (GAY bulz) the triangular top part of an outer wall between the sides of a sloped roof *p. 169*

gaped (GAYPT) opened wide; yawned *p. 474*

gaudy (GAWD ee) showy; bright-colored *p. 321*

genial (JEEN yul) pleasant; good-natured *p. 285*

gopher (GOH fur) a rodent that digs into the ground *p. 274*

gory (GAWR ee) bloody *p. 71*

greed (GREED) a great desire for wealth or material things *p. 101*

guile (GYL) the use of cunning; slyness *p. 13*

H

habitation (hab ih TAY shun) a building to live in *p. 384*

hamlet (HAM lit) very small village *p. 454*

heritage (HER ih tij) what is handed down to a person from ancestors *p. 353*

homesteaded (HOHM sted id) occupied land as a home *p. 267*

hummocks (HUM uks) areas of fertile, wooded land, higher than the surrounding swamp *p. 277*

I

idle (YD ul) unused; not busy *p. 468*

illustrate (IL uh strayt) to make clear by giving an example *p. 45*

impeach (im PEECH) accuse *p. 75*

improvised (IM pruh vyzd) made up quickly, without planning *p. 414*

indolence (IN dul lens) laziness *p. 321*

inexorable (in EKS uh ruh bul) unable to change or control *p. 67*

insolent (IN suh lunt) deliberately rude or insulting *p. 16*

instinct (IN stingkt) a natural tendency; unconscious skill *p. 258*

invalid (IN vuh lid) sick person *p. 143*

K

knobby (NOB ee) lumpy *p. 129*

L

lagoon (luh GOON) a shallow body of water, usually connected to a larger one *p. 164*

lamentable (LAM un tuh bul) distressing, sorrowful *p. 71*

lest (LEST) for fear that *p. 53*

lust (LUST) powerful desire *p. 412*

M

malignant (muh LIHG nunt) evil *p. 177*

malnutrition (mal noo TRISH un) poor health condition caused by not having enough of the right kinds of food *p. 130*

marina (muh REE nuh) large area set up for docking boats *p. 356*

maw (MAW) stomach *p. 67*

medallion (muh DAL yun) large medal *p. 409*

mingle (MING gul) mix *p. 411*

mortgage (MAWR gij) loan given to purchase a house *p. 227*

motive (MOHT iv) reason to act *p. 237*

murky (MUR kee) clouded; unclear *p. 91*

musket (MUHS kut) an old type of firearm *p. 9*

mute (MYOOT) unable to talk; quiet *p. 418*

N

nimble (NIM bul) quick and accurate *p. 415*

O

oafs (OHFS) stupid, awkward persons *p. 474*

omelet (OM lut) eggs beaten up, fried, and folded in half when done *p. 358*

P

pallet (PAL it) bed *p. 70*

paramour (PAR uh muur) lover *p. 70*

pensively (PEN siv lee) thoughtfully *p. 411*

perpetual (pur PECH oo ul) never stopping; without pause *p. 412*

persevered (pur suh VIRD) kept going by not giving up *p. 467*

perturbed (pur TURBD) greatly disturbed or alarmed *p. 15*

perverse (pur VURS) here, stubbornly difficult or contrary; wrong, improper *pp. 60, 159*

plaited (PLAYT ihd) braided *p. 36*

pleasantries (PLEZ un treez) lively, agreeable talks *p. 266*

pneumonia (noo MOHN yuh) disease of the lungs caused by an infection *pp. 133, 253*

poltergeist (POHL tur gyst) a noisy ghost *p. 201*

portly (PAWRT lee) heavy, but dignified *p. 53*

potion (POH shun) a drink with special powers, such as medicine or poison *p. 75*

presence (PREZ uns) nearness; being there *p. 381*

prodigious (pruh DIJ us) great; huge *pp. 55, 454*

profane (proh FAYN) show disrespect for holy things *p. 53*

purge (PURJ) get rid of *p. 53*

Q

quilt (KWILT) a bed cover made by stitching a layer of cotton between two layers of fabric *p. 261*

R

raggedy (RAG ih dee) tattered or torn *p. 349*

reconnaissance (rih KON uh sens) quick survey of information *p. 189*

reeds (REEDZ) tall grass in a marsh *p. 467*

relent (ruh LEHNT) to become gentler or more compassionate *p. 11*

relentless (rih LENT lis) without pity; harsh and cruel *p. 288*

relic (REH lik) something that remains from what has disappeared or been destroyed *p. 174*

resignation (reh zig NAY shun) patient acceptance *p. 10*

restorative (rih STAWR uh tiv) something that brings back consciousness or health generally; a medicine *p. 72*

righteous (RY chus) morally right, virtuous *p. 70*

rigid (RIH jihd) stiff *p. 177*

ritual (RICH oo ul) ceremony; tradition; a set pattern *pp. 155, 353*

rival (RY vul) one who wants the same things as another person *p. 92*

S

sanctified (SANK tuh fyd) set apart as holy *p. 9*

sarcastic (sahr KAS tik) sneering or ironic, and meant to hurt feelings *p. 260*

scowled (SKOULD) frowned *p. 121*

scullery (SKUL er ee) a room for cleaning and storing dishes and pots *p. 156*

scythe (SYTH) a long, curved blade fixed at an angle to a long, bent handle and used to cut down grass or grain *p. 123*

self-centered (SELF SENT urd) selfish; concerned with oneself *p. 137*

self-conscious (SELF KON shus) very aware of oneself; embarrassed or shy *p. 434*

semblance (SEHM bluns) outward appearance *p. 7*

severity (suh VAIR uh tee) great strictness or harshness *p. 43*

shields (SHEELDZ) defends; protects *pp. 173, 490*

shrewdest (SHROOD ist) cleverest, often in a tricky way *pp. 354, 465*

sluggish (SLUG ish) lacking energy *p. 274*

snatches (SNACH iz) grabs suddenly *p. 269*

somber (SOM bur) gloomy and sad *p. 122*

spellbinding (SPEL bynd ing) fascinating *p. 391*

stammered (STAM urd) in speaking, repeated the same sound without meaning to *p. 15*

stout (STOUT) having a heavy-set body *p. 489*

strides (STRYDZ) long steps *p. 130*

stupor (STOO pur) dazed or dull state *p. 385*

suffused (suh FYOOSD) spread through or over, as with a color, liquid or light *p. 16*

superstitious (soo pur STISH us) too much fear of the unknown *p. 266*

surged (SURJD) rolled; swelled up *p. 182*

T

tarpaulin (tahr PAW lin) a waterproof sheet used to protect *p. 343*

technique (tek NEEK) a way of doing something *pp. 45, 190*

telephoto (TEL uh foht oh) a camera lens that is able to make faraway things appear large *p. 188*

tepee (TEE pee) a cone-shaped tent of animal skins, used by the Plains Indians *p. 511*

theory (THEE uh ree) guess based on reasoning *p. 234*

thrive (THRYV) grow healthy and strong *p. 387*

timid (TIM id) shy *p. 265*

traditional (truh DISH uh nul) following old customs *p. 354*

transmitter (trans MIT ur) radio device that sends out signals *p. 194*

tremor (TREH mur) a quick, constant shaking or trembling *p. 174*

trifles (TRY fulz) anything of little value or importance *p. 257*

turret (TUR it) tower on top of a building *p. 181*

twine (TWYN) a thin rope *p. 37*

U

unnerved (un NURVD) terrified *p. 142*

V

vague (VAYG) not clear, hazy *pp. 144, 226*

varmints (VAHR munts) animals regarded as troublesome *p. 273*

vegetation (vej uh TAY shun) plant life *p. 274*

vestal (VES tul) virtuous, pure *p. 56*

virtuous (VUR choo us) honorable *p. 53*

W

wainscot (WAYNS koht) a facing for the walls in a room, usually made of wood paneling *p. 171*

welterweight (WEL tur wayt) boxer in a weight division between light- and middleweight *p. 411*

woes (WOHZ) misery, sorrows *p. 73*

womb (WOOM) stomach or uterus; any place that holds or generates something else *p. 67*

wryly (RY lee) humorously *p. 504*

Z

zealously (ZEL us lee) eagerly; fanatically *p. 325*

INDEX OF TITLES AND AUTHORS

INDEX OF SKILLS

INDEX OF FINE ART

ACKNOWLEDGMENTS

Unit 1: *The Lucky Stone* by Lucille Clifton. © 1979 by Lucille Clifton. Used by permission in the World excluding the UK by Dell Publishing, a division of Random House. Used by permission in the UK by Curtis Brown Ltd. "First Person Demonstrative" from *Mindscape* by Phyllis Gotlieb edited by Richard Peck. © 1971, 1990 by Richard Peck. Published by Delacorte Press. "Where Have You Gone" from *I am a Black Woman,* published by Wm. Morrow & Co., 1970, used by permission of the author. "Here Hold My Hand" from *I am a Black Woman,* published by Wm. Morrow & Co., 1970, used by permission of the author. "Greyday" from *Oh Pray My Wings Are Gonna Fit Me Well* by Maya Angelou. Copyright © 1975 by Maya Angelou. Reprinted by permission of Random House. "Reflections" by Vanessa Howard from *Soulscript Afro-American Poetry* edited by June Jordan. Copyright © 1970 by June Meyer Jordan. Published by Zenith Books a division of Random House. "Love" from *3000 Years of Black Poetry.* Translated by Raoul Abdul from the Raoul Abdul Collection used by permission of the Buxton National Historic Site & Museum. "Troubled Island" by Langston Hughes and William Grant Still. Copyright © 1976 by Southern Music Publishing Co., Inc. International Copyright Secured. Used by permission. All Rights Reserved. "Housecleaning" from *The Selected Poems of Nikki Giovanni* by Nikki Giovanni compilation copyright © 1996 by Nikki Giovanni. Reprinted by permission of HarperCollins Publishers, Inc./William Morrow. Eight pages from Babyhood by Paul Reiser. Copyright © 1997 by Paul Reiser. Reprinted by permission of HarperCollins Publishers, Inc./William Morrow. "Spring" by Carole Gregory Clemmons from *The Poetry of Black America* edited by Arnold Adoff © 1973 by Arnold Adoff. "Where Are You Now, William Shakespeare?" from *ME, ME, ME, ME, ME: Not a Novel* by M. E. Kerr. Copyright © 1983 by M. E. Kerr. Published by Harper & Row. Reprinted by permission of McIntosh and Otis, Inc. "What Is Once Loved..." by Elizabeth Coatsworth from *Alice-All-By-Herself.* Reprinted with the permission of Simon & Schuster Books for Young Readers, an imprint of Simon & Schuster Children's Publishing Division. Copyright © 1937 Macmillan Publishing Company; copyright renewed © 1965 Elizabeth Coatsworth Beston. **Unit 2:** "hist, whist." Copyright 1923, 1951, © 1991 by the Trustees for the E. E. Cummings Trust. Copyright © 1976 by George James Firmage, from Complete Poems: 1904-1962 by E. E. Cummings, edited by George J. Firmage. Used by permission of Liveright Publishing Corporation. "Incident in a Rose Garden" from *New and Selected Poems* by Donald Justice. Copyright © 1995 by Donald Justice. Reprinted by permission of Alfred A. Knopf, a Division of Random House Inc. "The Listeners" from *The Collected Poems of Walter de la Mare* by Walter de la Mare. The Literary Trustees of Walter de la Mare, and the Society of Authors as their representatives. "Sorry, Wrong Number" from *Sorry, Wrong Number and the Hitch-hiker* by Lucille Fletcher. Copyright © 1948 by Lucille Fletcher. Reprinted by permission of William Morris Agency, Inc. on behalf of the author. "Overheard on a Saltmarsh" from Collected Poems by Harold Monro. Used by permission of Freda McGregor. "Thus I Refute Beelzy" from *The John Collier Reader* by John Collier. Copyright © 1951 by John Collier renewed 1979 by the Estate of John Collier. Permission granted by Harold Matson Co., Inc. on behalf of John George Stafford Collier. "Boy in the Shadows" from *House of Evil* by Margaret Ronan. Copyright © 1977 by Scholastic Inc. Reprinted by permission. "The Great Amherst Mystery by Walter Hubbell from *Tales of Mystery and the Unknown* by Robert Potter. © 1976 by Globe Book Company, Inc. **Unit 3:** Used as unit opener "The Admirals Ghost. . ." from *Collected Poems in One Volume* by Alfred Noyes. Published by J. B. Lippincott. "Trifles" from *Plays by Susan Glaspell.* Copyright 1920 by Dodd, Mead & Company, Inc. Copyright renewed 1948 by Susan Glaspell. "Displays of Skill: The Bat" (first published as "Being a Mammal" in *Nature and Love Poems*), copyright © 1969 by Ruth Hershberger, Eakins Press Foundation. Reproduced with permission. "Earth" by John Hall Wheelock from *Modern American Poetry* by Louis Untermeyer. Published by arrangement with the Estate of Louis Untermeyer, Norma Anchin Untermeyer c/o Professional Publishing Services Company. This permission is expressly granted by Laurence S. Untermeyer. "Bird of Night" from *The Bat-Poet* by Randall Jarrell. Reprinted by permission of Mary Jarrell. "The Getaway" by John Savage from *Saturday Evening Post 5/7/66.* "Ancient Enmity (retitled: The Rattlesnake Hunt from Cross Creek)" excerpted and reprinted with the permission of Scribner, a Division of Simon & Schuster from *Cross Creek* by Marjorie Kinnan Rawlings. Copyright 1942 by Marjorie Kinnan Rawlings; copyright renewed © 1970 by Norton Baskin and Charles Scribner's Sons. "Earth" from *The Gardener and Other Poems* by John Hall Wheelock. Reprinted with the permission of Scribner, a Division of Simon & Schuster. Copyright © 1961 by John Hall Wheelock, renewed 1989 by Sally Wheelock Brayton. "A Secret for Two" by Quentin Reynolds. Published in Collier's magazine. **Unit 4:** "Haiku (Crying Insects...)" by Issa from *An Anthology of Hàiku Ancient* and Modern translated and annotated by Asataro Miyamori. Published by Greenwood Publishing Group. "Haiku" (Waterfalls…) by Buson from *An Anthology of Haiku Ancient and Modern* translated and annotated by Asataro Miyamori. Published by Greenwood Publishing Group. "Chee's Daughter" by Juanita Platero and Siyowin Miller, from *Common Ground*, vol. VIII, no. 2 (Winter 1948), pp. 22–31. Reprinted from *Common Ground* with the permission of the Immigration and Refugee Services of America. Used as unit opener from *The Oxford Dictionary of Quotations*, Published by the Oxford University Press. Copyright © 1979, first edition 1941, second edition 1953, third edition 1979, reprinted with corrections 1980. "Hokku Poems" copyright by Richard Wright. "Haiku (Friends that open mouth…)" from *Japanese Haiku*. Copyright © 1955, 1956. Used by permission of Peter Pauper Press. "Starvation Wilderness" by Olive A. Fredrickson from *Outdoor Life*, Vol. 143, No. 6 (June 1969). "Dreams" from *Collected Poems* by Langston Hughes. Copyright © 1994 by the Estate of Langston Hughes. Reprinted by permission of Alfred A. Knopf, a Division of Random House Inc. Reprinted in the UK by permission of Harold Ober. "Ta-Na-E-Ka" by Mary Whitebird from *Scholastic Voice*, Vol. 55, No. 12 (Dec. 13, 1973). Copyright © 1973 Scholastic Inc. Reprinted by permission of Scholastic Inc. "A bee thumps …" from *Bunch Grass* by Robert Sund. Copyright © 1969 by Robert Sund. Reprinted by permission of the University of Washington Press. "Four Skinny Trees" from *The House on Mango Street* by Sandra Cisneros. Published by Vintage Books a division of Random House © 1989 by Sandra Cisneros. Reprinted by permission in the World excluding Britian by the Susan Bergholz Literary Services, New York Reprinted by permission of Bloomsbury Publishing in Britian. "Dead at Seventeen"used by permission of Solis Creative Services, Inc. "Thank you, M'am" from *Short Stories* by Langston Hughes. Copyright © 1996 by Romona Bass and Arnold Rampersad. Introduction copyright © 1996 by Arnold Rampersad. Compilation and editorial contribution copyright © 1996 by Akiba Sullivan Harper. Reprinted by permission of Hill & Wang, a division of Farrar, Straus and Giroux, LLC. Reprinted outside North America by permission of Harold Ober. "Sympathy" from *Black Writers of America* by Paul Dunbar. Prentice Hall Inc. **Unit 5:** "The Secret Life of Walter Mitty" from the book *My World—and Welcome To It* © 1942 by James Thurber. Copyright © renewed 1971 by Helen Thurber and Rosemary A. Thurber. Reprinted by arrangement with Rosemary A. Thurber and The Barbara Hogenson Agency. All rights reserved. "Song of Failure" "War Song" "Warrior Song I" "Warrior Song II" from *Literature of the American Indians* by Sanders © 1974. Reprinted by permission of Prentice Hall Inc., Upper Saddle River, NJ. . "Terror in the North" from *American Girl Magazine*, 3/66 used by permission of Girl Scouts of the USA. "Ulysses Meets the Cyclops" by Homer. Retold by Alice Delman. From Chapman's Homer © 1956 by Bolingen Foundation. Reprinted by permission of Princeton University Press. "Amigo Brothers" from *Stories from El Barrio* by Piri Thomas Copyright © 1978 by Piri Thomas. Used as unit opener from The Oxford Dictionary of Quotations, Published by the Oxford University Press. Copyright © 1979, first edition 1941, second edition 1953, third edition 1979, reprinted with corrections 1980. **Unit 6:** "Medicine" from *ONCE* by Alice Walker. Copyright © 1968 and renewed 1996. Reprinted by permission of Harcourt, Inc. Reprinted by permission of David Highman Assoc. in the UK. "Andre" from *Bronzeville Boys & Girls*. Copyright © 1956 by Gwendolyn Brooks Blakely. Used by permission of HarperCollins Publishers. "Otto" by Gwendolyn Brooks Blakely from *Bronzeville Boys & Girls*. Published by HarperCollins Publishers. "Bread" by Amado V. Hernandez from *Rice Grains* selected and translated by E. San Juan, Jr. Copyright © 1966 by International Publishers Co. Used by permission. "Family Album" from *Poetry by Diane Stevenson*. Copyright © 1987 by Modern Poetry Association. Reprinted by permission of the Editor of Poetry. "My People" by Bernice George from *Here I Am!* by Virginia Olsen Baron. Copyright © 1969 by Virginia Olsen Baron. Used by permission of Dutton Children's Books, a division of Penguin Putnam Inc. "Whale Hunting" by Sally Nashookpuk from *Here I Am!* by Virginia Olsen Baron. Copyright © 1969 by Virginia Olsen Baron. Used by permission of Dutton Children's Books, a division of Penguin Putnam Inc. "Luther Leavitt" by Alfred Brower from *Here I Am!* by Virginia Olsen Baron. Copyright © 1969 by Virginia Olsen Baron. Used by permission of Dutton Children's Books, a division of Penguin Putnam Inc. Used as unit opener "Lineage" from *For My People* by Margaret Walker. Copyright © 1942 by Yale University Press. "Christmas Morning i" copyright © 1968 by Carol Freeman Reprinted from *Black Fire* edited by LeRoi Jones and Larry Neal (William Morrow & Co) "Some People" reprinted with the permission of Simon & Schuster Books for Young Readers, an imprint of Simon & Schuster Children's Publishing Division from *Poems* by Rachel Field (Macmillan, NY, 1957).

Note: Every effort has been made to locate the copyright owner of material reprinted in this book. Omissions brought to our attention will be corrected in subsequent editions.

ART CREDITS

Illustrations

Unit 1: pp. 6, 9, 12, 14, 17: Dan Clifford; pp. 34, 35, 36–37, 38, 43, 45: Guy Porfirio; p. 82: Sterling Brown; p. 100: Guy Porfirio. **Unit 2:** p. 112: Guy Porfirio; p. 123: Marlies Merk-Najaka; p. 126: Guy Porfirio; p. 164: David Palladin; pp. 168, 170, 172, 175: Janet Hamlin; p. 183: Michael Bryant; pp. 186, 187, 191: Doug Schneider; pp. 200, 203: Alex Bloch, **Unit 3:** pp. 216, 220: Den Schofield; pp. 224, 227, 230, 235, 237, 240, 246: Bert Dodson/Bookmakers Ltd.; p. 280: Steven Hunt; **Unit 4:** p. 316: David Dircks; p. 332: Eva Auchincloss; pp. 336, 338, 341, 344: Rupert Baxter; pp. 348, 349, 368: Guy Porfirio; pp. 369, 373: Dick Smolinski; p. 376: Gary Underhill; p. 394: Michael Bryant; p. 396: Robert Pasternak; **Unit 5:** pp. 408, 413, 417, 419: Paul Lackner; pp. 442, 445, 447, 449: (tinting) Donna Day; p. 455: Merlies Merk-Najacka; pp. 464: William Hunter-Hicklin; **Unit 6:** p. 489: Robert Martin; p. 496: Jack Stockman; pp. 500, 503, 507: Yoshi Miyake; p. 524: Richard Leonard.

Photographs

Contents: p. v: *The Letter*, Mary Cassatt. Courtesy of the Library of Congress; p. vii: *Allegory*, Ben Shahn. Collection of the Modern Art Museum of Fort Worth. Estate of Ben Shahn/Licensed by VAGA, New York, NY; p. ix: *Tiger*, Edward J. Detmold. The Metropolitan Museum of Art, The Elisha Whittelsey Collection; p. xi: *Familia India*, Amado M. Pena, Jr. El Taller, Inc.; p. xiii: *Buffalo Hunter,* Unknown American. Gift of Harriett Cowles Hammett Grahm in Memory of Buell Hammett; **Unit 1:** p. 20: R. Andrew Odum/Peter Arnold, Inc.; p. 39: Courtesy of Michael Glaser; p. 42: Ed Bock/The Stock Market; pp. 48, 50, 54, 57, 61, 65, 69: The Museum of Modern Art/Film Stills Archive; p. 77: The Granger Collection; p. 83: AP/Wide World Photos; p. 91: Eve Arnold/Magnum; p. 96: Photofest; **Unit 2:** pp. 136, 141, 145: H. Armstrong Roberts; p. 151: Courtesy of Lucille Fletcher; p. 165: UPI/Corbis Bettmann; p. 180: Gregory K. Scott/Photo Researchers, Inc.; p. 195: London Daily Mail/Photo Researchers, Inc.; **Unit 3:** p. 272: Gary Retherford/Photo Researchers, Inc.; p. 276: Juan Manuel Rejifo/Animals Animals; pp. 290–291: A&L Sinibaldi/Stone; p. 294: Mark Boulton/Photo Researchers, Inc.; p. 300: Chris Jones/Photo Researchers, Inc.; p. 302: Eastcott/Momatiuk/Animals Animals; **Unit 4:** p. 397: The Granger Collection; **Unit 5:** p. 432: Will & Deni McIntyre/Photo Researchers Inc.; p. 452: Flip Schulke/Black Star; p. 453: Dennis Brack/Black Star; p. 455: American Stock/Archive Photos; p. 473: Topham/The Image Works; **Unit 6:** p. 488: Stone; p. 491: the Granger Collection; p. 521: Courtesy of Holiday House; p. 530: C.K. Lorenz/Photo Researchers, Inc.; p. 538: Chris Arend/Alaska Stock Images.

Note: Every effort has been made to locate the copyright owner of material reprinted in this book. Omissions brought to our attention will be corrected in subsequent editions.